The JUNIOR CLASSICS

VOLUME EIGHT · STORIES FROM HISTORY

Wilfred Jones

Slowly Kanana raised the lance. "I am Kanana, son of the Terror of the Desert."

[See page 82]

The JUNIOR CLASSICS

Edited by MABEL WILLIAMS and MARCIA DALPHIN.

With Introduction by WILLIAM ALLAN NEILSON, Former
President of Smith College; Introduction to First Edition by
CHARLES W. ELIOT, Former President of Harvard University

Popular Edition

ILLUSTRATED

VOLUME
EIGHT

STORIES
FROM
HISTORY

P. F. COLLIER & SON CORPORATION

CONTENTS

THE JUNIOR CLASSICS

(The sources of the stories in this volume will be found listed on page 380.)

LEONIDAS

By JENNIE HALL

AN army lay encamped on a little plain. At one side was the
sea. On the other rose a steep mountain, with its oaks and
pines. In front of the army the mountain came close to the water.
An oxcart could just go between sea and hill. Across this place was
a stone wall, with a gate. Behind the army was another narrow pass.
The place was called the pass of Thermopylæ. North of it lay part
of Greece. South of it lay the other part, where Athens and Sparta
were. Between these parts were steep mountains. Thermopylæ was
like a gate in that mountain-wall. It was the only good road from
north to south. This army was here now to guard it.

The Persians from across the sea were marching down toward
the south. This news fled ahead of them:

"The king himself is coming. His army drinks rivers dry. Whole
cities grow poor in feeding it. It stretches, glittering like the sea.
The Greeks bow down as the king comes near. He meets no foes.
The land is afraid. He comes to make us slaves."

The men of Southern Greece said:

"We must stop those Persians. Thermopylæ is the place. We must
send an army."

"There is no hurry," the Spartans said. "They are yet far off. It
is time for the great festival at Olympia. We must stay for that. But
we will send a few men as a promise. More will come later!"

So the Spartan king went with his guard of three hundred men.
That little army was fine to look at as it swung out of the city in
double line, with shining armor and red chitons and long bronze
shields and tall bronze helmets and dangling swords and stiff lances.
And the king who led this army was Leonidas; for his brother had
died and had left no sons.

These soldiers marched their long way through the country. People
came to look at them.

"Sparta surely makes fine warriors," they thought.

A few cities, seeing them, said,
"We will help."

So other soldiers joined Leonidas. From one city came eighty; from another, a thousand; from Thebes, four hundred; from Thespiæ, seven hundred. But, after all, it was only a little company.

Now this army was in camp at Thermopylæ. Tents were dotted over the little plain. Mules and horses were feeding in the grass. The rough carts were drawn into a circle. Some of the soldiers were at work. They were building up the old wall across the pass. Others were playing games—running, throwing the disc, dancing, wrestling. The red chitons of the Spartans showed bright in the crowd. One of these Spartans was saying to a Theban:

"War is our play. You think it a hardship. You feast in time of peace. We feast in time of war. You put on gay clothes for a visit. We wear rags in peace, and fine things for war. You curl your hair for a banquet. We go cut and uncombed to table. Our hair grows long for war, and we dress it for battle; for lions must have manes."

"Have you seen the army of the Great King?" asked the other man, pointing past the mountain.

"Yes," answered the Spartan. "Yesterday I was a scout. An hour's walk from our camp lie the Persians. Their tents are as many as the stars. The foolish king has had a great throne put up. There he sits and looks about."

"I suppose he is waiting to see us run away," said the Theban.

"Perhaps," laughed the Spartan. "Have you heard of the man who sat down to see a river turn and run uphill?"

"Meanwhile," said the Theban, "we play our games and have our drills and sharpen our swords."

So the armies sat for four days. But on the fifth morning a Greek scout came running into camp.

"At last the fish bites!" he cried. "They are coming, but only one company of them."

Then there was a rushing to arms.

"You Spartans look as though the best course of the banquet were being served," said a Theban.

"So it is," shouted a dozen Spartans.

The men fell into line at Leonidas' command. The gates were opened, and they marched out. They formed in a deep mass before the wall. They waited. Soon there was a glint of bronze from around a hill. Then sounded horses' hoofs. Still the Greeks waited. Leonidas stood in front of his Spartans. He was tall and straight. His head was high. His blue eyes blazed. His brown arms, rough with big muscles, held ready shield and spears.

The hoof-beats and the shining armor came nearer. Now the Persians were in full view—thousands of men on running horses. Brilliant cloths fluttered from their heads. A strange iron dress, like the scales of a fish, shone on their bodies. Wide scarlet trousers flapped in the wind. Every man leaned forward as he rode. At last they pulled their long bows and let fly their arrows. They yelled strange words. They came on like a whirlwind. The Greeks waited until the Persians were crowded together in the narrow pass just in front of them. Then they opened their mouths and shouted their good war cry and blew their shrill trumpets. They swung their swords and ran into that crowd of Persians. Then was the noise of a great fight—clashing of swords, whizzing of arrows, shouting of men. From morning to afternoon they fought. Greeks fell dead under Persian arrows, but more Persians under Greek swords. At last the enemies' arrows were gone, their spears were broken. They were bleeding with wounds and stiff with fighting. And still the Greeks stood like a wall of biting swords. So at last the Persians turned in fear and rode back to their camp.

The Greeks sat down in front of the wall to rest. They sat as they were in their armor, their spears in their hands. They knew that a million Persians waited back of the hills. They ate a quick meal. They carried their wounded behind the wall. The Spartans cleaned their armor and combed their long hair. But all the time the warriors kept their eyes on the pass ahead. At last they saw again the flash of bronze and heard the clatter of hoofs. In a moment the Greeks were on their feet and in line of battle. This time there swung into view ten thousand gay horsemen.

"They are the king's own guard," called out a Greek. "This is the flower of their army."

"The Great King flatters us," said a Spartan, smiling, as he felt the edge of his sword.

Again the Greeks and Persians met. The Greeks were tired from the other battle: the Persians were fresh. Yet the Greeks stood. But the Persians were doing brave deeds. Neither side could force the other back. They stood struggling for an hour. At length Leonidas gave a signal. Then his men turned their backs and all ran toward the wall. When the Persians saw them running away, they shouted and clapped their heels to their horses and rode after them. They laughed and waved their swords and forgot to be careful. That was what Leonidas wanted. At last he gave another signal, and the Greeks turned in a flash and marched back against the Persians and cut them down and made them flee to camp.

That was near night. Then the Greeks built fires before the walls and cooked their suppers and ate. Every man slept in his armor that night, with his spear by his hand.

All the next day there was fighting, but the Greeks stood their ground, and the Persians ran away.

Before supper that night, Leonidas said:

"Let us sacrifice to the gods for our good battle."

So they put meat and wine into the fire that burned on a sod altar. As the smoke went up, Leonidas raised his hands and cried:

"O great Zeus, and Ares, father of battles, and Athene of the bright shield, and all the gods who have fought with Greece today, receive our thanks!"

Then all the soldiers standing about raised a great song of thanksgiving. After that, Leonidas said to a man near him:

"Megistias, you are wise in reading the signs of what will happen. Come and look at the sacrifice and tell us of tomorrow."

Then Megistias came and studied the fire. He noticed the color of the flame and the direction of the smoke and many other things. Then he stepped upon a pile of sod. There was no joy in his face. He raised his hands over the camp.

"O ye Spartans and other Greeks, the gods will send you the good luck of dying in battle! Tomorrow your wives will be widows, your sons orphans. We shall lie here dead, and the Persians will march past us to Greece."

Leonidas leaped upon the sod.

"Then they will meet our brothers, more brave and of better luck. It is no mean thing to die here for Sparta and for Greece. Let us make ready for a noble death that men shall talk about."

As the Spartans sat about the camp fire after supper, one of them took his lyre in his hands and stood among his countrymen and sang:

> "A foe, a sword,
> Our land to guard,
> The gods to watch,
> A grave, a stone,
> A song of praise—
> Enough for me."

Then he gave the lyre to the man next him. This was his song:

> "They say that some men sit and feast
> And spend their nights in drink and song,
> And idly sleep their days away.
> Such men are laughter to the gods,
> A shame unto themselves and Greece.
> How do the Spartans spend their time?
> In drills and games and mess and hunts,
> To make them fit for death like this."

The singer passed on the lyre, and the next man sang:

> "For what do we fight, O Spartan men?
> O memories dear; O Spartan land;
> O heroes of old, in Sparta dead;
> O tombs of our kings, who Sparta loved;
> Lycurgus the wise, the Spartan seer;
> O shrines of the gods, who Sparta trod;
> O mothers and wives in Sparta now.
> For these things we die, O Spartan men."

So they passed an hour or more in song. Around the other camp fire different things were happening. At some, men sat silent, with white faces. Around others were grumbling and angry looks.

"These Spartan fools!" some men said. "Hear them boast! They would fight against the sea itself."

Two or three hours after dark a guard came to Leonidas, leading a man.

"This man came running to me now," he said. "He calls himself a Greek, a deserter from the Great King."

The stranger turned to the men and spoke.

"I am a Greek from across the sea," he said. "You know how the Great King has crushed us with his heavy hands. After that he said, 'You shall go with me to fight against your countrymen!'—But I did not come to tell you my story, but this news: The Persian army is moving. They are crossing the mountains at your left. A traitor told them of the path. They broke camp at lamp-lighting time. Part stayed behind. In the morning they will close around you from front and back and wipe you out. I swear by the gods that I speak the truth!"

"We believe you," said Leonidas quietly. "A prophet has already told us that we shall die tomorrow."

Just then another deserter was brought in. He told the same story.

"We put some men to guard that path," Leonidas said, "but they are few. The path is little known. We thought the Great King would not hear of it. Besides, it is narrow and steep. So he would rather face the mountain than the Spartans?" he laughed. "But we need sleep to make us ready for the fight. The gods give us sweet rest, comrades!"

So the Spartans slept calmly all night.

Before sunrise next morning the Greeks were at breakfast. As they ate, scouts came running down the mountain-side. They leaped, panting, among the men.

"They are crossing the mountain. They will shut us in from behind and in front."

Then there was murmuring among the Greeks. Leonidas heard it and said:

"Come close, all you men of Greece. Let us talk this matter over. It is my opinion that we ought to stay and fight. How many think with me?"

Every Spartan and Thespian hand shot up with a shout.

"It is folly," cried out a Theban. "Do you think you can stop a million men?"

"No," answered a Spartan. "Neither can we run away."

"Do you know how many there are?" called another man. "When they shoot their arrows, they will hide the sun."

"So much the better," laughed a Spartan. "We shall fight in the shade."

"Let the Spartans stay," called another Theban. "They are afraid to go back home. But we have mothers and wives who love us."

"And we Thespians will stay," shouted a man, "because we have mothers and wives whom we love."

At last Leonidas spoke.

"O men of Greece," he said, "we Spartans were sent here to guard this pass! There is nothing else for us to do. But your commands are not so strong. You have different laws. It is needless for you to stay. It means only death. The Persians are still on the mountain. The way to the south is clear. I send you to your homes. The Thespians stay with us from choice. The Thebans stay because I command it. We have heard whispers of what they wish to do—to join the Persians. To you others, farewell! May the gods keep you to fight against our enemies another day!"

Then Leonidas went to Megistias.

"No man will go alive from this field," he said. "You can give the messages of the gods to men. Go with these soldiers and save your life."

"No!" said Megistias. "I will not leave the company of the brave for the company of cowards."

So those others marched away south. Those who were left waited until about noon. They cleaned their armor and got their weapons ready and talked quietly of what was coming.

"Here are our graves," one said, looking about the little plain. "But, by Heracles! here are some Persian graves, too."

"We fight in the sight of our gods and by their holy altars," Leonidas said. "For see, yonder is a healing spring of Heracles, and his altar by it. I pray that we may not make him ashamed of his children."

At last there came the trampling of horses from the north. Then the Greeks marched out of the gate and on past the narrow place. They spread out into a thin line and went on to meet the Persians. Then the fight began. A god seemed to burn in every Greek. The Persians fell fast. Then they grew afraid and tried to turn back, but those behind pushed them ahead. And at the back the officers whipped their men into the fight. So some were trampled down, others were pushed into the sea. Soon all the Greek spears were broken or lost. The men fought only with their short swords. Then many of them died, and Leonidas was one. When he fell, the Persians gave a great shout and rushed to get his body. But the Greeks cried out, "Sparta and Leonidas!" and closed around him in a circle, with swords flashing death. So they stood for a long time fighting. But at last the word went about:

"The other Persians are coming from behind."

Then those Spartans and Thespians who were left took up Leonidas and carried him back to a little hill behind the wall, fighting all the way. But the Thebans ran to the Persians and held out their hands, crying, "We are friends of the Great King."

So the Persians passed them by and went on to the hill. On the top was that little ring of brave men, facing out to their foes on every side. But such a thing could not last long. That sea of Persians swept up the hill and left every Spartan and Thespian dead and went on into Greece.

After that there was a terrible war. But when it was over, and the Persians were driven out, the Greeks said,

"Our children's children must know what happened at Thermopylæ."

So they raised a great mound over the dead there and set up two columns. One was for all who fought on those first two days. There were carved on it these words:

"Four thousand Greeks here fought against a million Persians."

The other column was for the Spartans alone. On it were these words:

"Stranger, go tell Sparta that we lie here at her command."

But on that little hill where the Spartans made their last stand was another monument, a stone lion, with "Leonidas" carved upon it.

Sparta never forgot that battle or that hero. In her market place she built a covered walk, called the Persian Walk. Instead of columns to hold up the roof, were Persians carved in stone, and on the wall of the porch were paintings of the Persian battles. That porch seemed always to say:

"Remember the courage of the men who drove the Persians out of Greece."

Four years after the battle of Thermopylæ, the Spartans said:

"Our greatest hero lies in strange soil. Let us bring him home. It will do our sons good always to see his tomb."

So they brought the bones of Leonidas to Sparta, and buried them in a great stone tomb. And there they hung a bronze tablet, with the names of those three hundred Spartans on it, and these words:

"These are the men who looked the Persians in the face."

Every year at this tomb there were games and speeches. Only Spartans might play, and only Spartans might hear.

"Other heroes sleep in Spartan soil," those speakers said. "Here sleeps the lion of Thermopylæ. He was a king. He was a Spartan. Let Spartans see that they be worthy of this countryman and of this king."

THE GREEK SLAVE
AND THE LITTLE ROMAN BOY

By JENNIE HALL

ARISTON, the Greek slave, was busily painting. He stood in a little room with three smooth walls. The fourth side was open upon a court. A little fountain splashed there. Above stretched the brilliant sky of Italy. The August sun shone hotly down. It cut sharp shadows of the columns on the cement floor. This was the master's room. The artist was painting the walls. Two were already gay with pictures. They showed the mighty deeds of warlike Heracles. Here was Heracles strangling the lion, Heracles killing the hideous hydra, Heracles carrying the wild boar on his shoulders, Heracles training the mad horses. But now the boy was painting the best deed of all—Heracles saving Alcestis from death. He had made the hero big and beautiful. The strong muscles lay smooth in the great body. One hand trailed the club. On the other arm hung the famous lion skin. With that hand the god led Alcestis. He turned his head toward her and smiled. On the ground lay Death, bruised and bleeding. One batlike black wing hung broken. He scowled after the hero and the woman. In the sky above him stood Apollo, the lord of life, looking down. But the picture of the god was only half finished. The figure was sketched in outline. Ariston was rapidly laying on paint with his little brushes. His eyes glowed with Apollo's own fire. His lips were open, and his breath came through them pantingly.

"O god of beauty, god of Hellas, god of freedom, help me!" he half whispered while his brush worked.

For he had a great plan in his mind. Here he was, a slave in this rich Roman's house. Yet he was a free-born son of Athens, from a family of painters. Pirates had brought him here to Pompeii, and had sold him as a slave. His artist's skill had helped him, even in this cruel land. For his master, Tetreius, loved beauty. The Roman had soon found that his young Greek slave was a painter. He had said to his steward: "Let this boy work at the mill no longer. He shall paint the walls of my private room."

So he had talked to Ariston about what the pictures should be. The Greek had found that this solemn, frowning Roman was really a kind man. Then hope had sprung up in his breast and had sung of freedom.

"I will do my best to please him," he had thought. "When all the walls are beautiful, perhaps he will smile at my work. Then I will clasp his knees. I will tell him of my father, of Athens, of how I was stolen. Perhaps he will send me home."

Now the painting was almost done. As he worked, a thousand pictures were flashing through his mind. He saw his beloved old home in lovely Athens. He felt his father's hand on his, teaching him to paint. He gazed again at the Parthenon, more beautiful than a dream. Then he saw himself playing on the fishing boat on that terrible holiday. He saw the pirate ships sail swiftly from behind a rocky point and pounce upon them. He saw himself and his friends dragged aboard. He felt the tight rope on his wrists as they bound him and threw him under the deck. He saw himself standing here in the market place of Pompeii. He heard himself sold for a slave. At that thought he threw down his brush and groaned.

But soon he grew calmer. Perhaps the sweet drip of the fountain cooled his hot thoughts. Perhaps the soft touch of the sun soothed his heart. He took up his brushes again and set to work.

"The last figure shall be the most beautiful of all," he said to himself. "It is my own god, Apollo."

So he worked tenderly on the face. With a few little strokes he made the mouth smile kindly. He made the blue eyes deep and gentle. He lifted the golden curls with a little breeze from Olympos. The god's smile cheered him. The beautiful colors filled his mind. He forgot his sorrows. He forgot everything but his picture. Minute by minute it grew under his moving brush. He smiled into the god's eyes.

Meantime a great noise arose in the house. There were cries of fear. There was running of feet.

"A great cloud!" "Earthquake!" "Fire and hail!" "Smoke from hell!" "The end of the world!" "Run! Run!"

And men and women, all slaves, ran screaming through the house and out of the front door. But the painter only half heard the cries. His ears, his eyes, his thoughts were full of Apollo.

For a little the house was still. Only the fountain and the shadows and the artist's brush moved there. Then came a great noise as though the sky had split open. The low, sturdy house trembled. Ariston's brush was shaken and blotted Apollo's eye. Then there was a clattering on the cement floor as of a million arrows. Ariston ran into the court. From the heavens showered a hail of gray, soft little pebbles like beans. They burned his upturned face. They stung his bare arms. He gave a cry and ran back under the porch roof. Then he heard a shrill cry above all the clattering. It came from the fore end of the house. Ariston ran back into the private court. There lay Caius, his master's little sick son. His couch was under the open sky, and the gray hail was pelting down upon him. He was covering his head with his arms and wailing.

"Little master!" called Ariston. "What is it? What has happened to us?"

"Oh, take me!" cried the little boy.

"Where are the others?" asked Ariston.

"They ran away," answered Caius. "They were afraid. Look! O-o-h!"

He pointed to the sky and screamed with terror.

Ariston looked. Behind the city lay a beautiful hill, green with trees. But now from the flat top towered a huge, black cloud. It rose straight like a pine tree and then spread its black branches over the heavens. And from that cloud showered these hot, pelting pebbles of pumice stone.

"It is a volcano," cried Ariston.

He had seen one spouting fire as he had voyaged on the pirate ship.

"I want my father," wailed the little boy.

Then Ariston remembered that his master was away from home. He had gone in a ship to Rome to get a great physician for his sick boy. He had left Caius in the charge of his nurse, for the boy's mother was dead. But now every slave had turned coward and had run away and left the little master to die. Ariston pulled the couch into one of the rooms. Here the roof kept off the hail of stones.

"Your father is expected home today, master Caius," said the Greek. "He will come. He never breaks his word. We will wait for him here. The strange shower will soon be over."

So he sat on the edge of the couch, and the little Roman laid his head in his slave's lap and sobbed. Ariston watched the falling pebbles. They were light and full of little holes. Every now and then black rocks of the size of his head whizzed through the air. Sometimes one fell into the open cistern and the water hissed at its heat. The pebbles lay piled a foot deep all over the courtyard floor. And still they fell thick and fast. "Will it never stop?" thought Ariston.

Several times the ground swayed under him. It felt like the moving of a ship in a storm. Once there was thunder and a trembling of the house. Ariston was looking at a little bronze statue that stood on a tall, slender column. It tottered to and fro in the earthquake. Then it fell, crashing into the piled-up stones. In a few minutes the falling shower had covered it.

Ariston began to be more afraid. He thought of Death as he had painted him in his picture. He imagined that he saw him hiding behind a column. He thought he heard his cruel laugh. He tried to look up toward the mountain, but the stones pelted him down. He felt terribly alone. Was all the rest of the world dead? Or was every one else in some safe place?

"Come, Caius, we must get away," he cried. "We shall be buried here."

He snatched up one of the blankets from the couch. He threw the ends over his shoulders and let a loop hang at his back. He stood the sick boy in this and wound the ends around them both. Caius was tied to his slave's back. His heavy little head hung on Ariston's shoulder. Then the Greek tied a pillow over his own head. He snatched up a staff and ran from the house. He looked at his picture as he passed. He thought he saw Death half rise from the ground. But Apollo seemed to smile at his artist.

At the front door Ariston stumbled. He found the street piled deep with the gray, soft pebbles. He had to scramble up on his hands and knees. From the house opposite ran a man. He looked wild with fear. He was clutching a little statue of gold. Ariston called to him, "Which way to the gate?"

But the man did not hear. He rushed madly on. Ariston followed him. It cheered the boy a little to see that somebody else was still alive in the world. But he had a hard task. He could not run. The soft pebbles crunched under his feet and made him stumble. He leaned far forward under his heavy burden. The falling shower scorched his bare legs and arms. Once a heavy stone struck him on his cushioned head, and he fell. But he was up in an instant. He looked around bewildered. His head was ringing. The air was hot and choking. The sun was gone. The shower was blinding. Whose house was this? The door stood open. The court was empty. Where was the city gate? Would he never get out? He did not know this street. Here on the corner was a wine shop with its open sides. But no men stood there drinking. Winecups were tipped over and broken on the marble counter. Ariston stood in a daze and watched the wine spilling into the street.

Then a crowd came rushing past him. It was evidently a family fleeing for their lives. Their mouths were open as though they were crying. But Ariston could not hear their voices. His ears shook with the roar of the mountain. An old man was hugging a chest. Gold coins were spilling out as he ran. Another man was dragging a fainting woman. A young girl ran ahead of them with white face and streaming hair. Ariston stumbled on after this company. A great black slave came swiftly around a corner and ran into him and knocked him over, but fled on without looking back. As the Greek boy fell forward, the rough little pebbles scoured his face. He lay there moaning. Then he began to forget his troubles. His aching body began to rest. He thought he would sleep. He saw Apollo smiling. Then Caius struggled and cried out. He pulled at the blanket and tried to free himself. This roused Ariston, and he sat up. He felt the hot pebbles again. He heard the mountain roar. He dragged himself to his feet and started on. Suddenly the street led him out into a broad space. Ariston looked around him. All about stretched wide porches with their columns. Temple roofs rose above them. Statues stood high on their pedestals. He was in the forum. The great open square was crowded with hurrying people. Under one of the porches Ariston saw the money changers locking their boxes. From a wide doorway ran several men. They were carrying great bundles of woolen cloth, richly embroidered and dyed with precious purple. Down the great steps of Jupiter's temple ran a priest. Under his arms he clutched two large platters of gold. Men were running across the forum dragging bags behind them.

Everyone seemed trying to save his most precious things. And everyone was hurrying to the gate at the far end. Then that was the way out! Ariston picked up his heavy feet and ran. Suddenly the earth swayed under him. He heard horrible thunder. He thought the mountain was falling upon him. He looked behind. He saw the columns of the porch tottering. A man was running out from one of the buildings. But as he ran, the walls crashed down. The gallery above fell cracking. He was buried. Ariston saw it all and cried out in horror. Then he prayed:

"O Lord Poseidon, shaker of the earth, save me! I am a Greek!"

Then he came out of the forum. A steep street sloped down to a gate. A river of people was pouring out there. The air was full of cries. The great noise of the crowd made itself heard even in the noise of the volcano. The streets were full of lost treasures. Men pushed and fell and were trodden upon. But at last Ariston passed through the gateway and was out of the city. He looked about.

"It is no better," he sobbed to himself.

The air was thicker now. The shower had changed to hot dust as fine as ashes. It blurred his eyes. It stopped his nostrils. It choked his lungs. He tore his chiton from top to bottom and wrapped it about his mouth and nose. He looked back at Caius and pulled the blanket over his head. Behind him a huge cloud was reaching out long black arms from the mountain to catch him. Ahead, the sun was only a red wafer in the shower of ashes. Around him people were running off to hide under rocks or trees or in the country houses. Some were running, running anywhere to get away. Out of one courtyard dashed a chariot. The driver was lashing his horses. He pushed them ahead through the crowd. He knocked people over, but he did not stop to see what harm he had done. Curses flew after him. He drove on down the road.

Ariston remembered when he himself had been dragged up here two years ago from the pirate ship.

"This leads to the sea," he thought. "I will go there. Perhaps I shall meet my master, Tetreius. He will come by ship. Surely I shall find him. The gods will send him to me. O blessed gods!"

But what a sea! It roared and tossed and boiled. While Ariston looked, a ship was picked up and crushed and swallowed. The sea poured up the steep shore for hundreds of feet. Then it rushed back and left its strange fish gasping on the dry land. Great rocks fell from the sky, and steam rose up as they splashed into the water. The sun was growing fainter. The black cloud was coming on. Soon it would be dark. And then what? Ariston lay down where the last huge wave had cooled the ground.

"It is all over, Caius," he murmured. "I shall never see Athens again."

For a while there were no more earthquakes. The sea grew a little less wild. Then the half-fainting Ariston heard shouts. He lifted his head. A small boat had come ashore. The rowers had leaped out. They were dragging it up out of reach of the waves.

"How strange!" thought Ariston. "They are not running away. They must be brave. We are all cowards."

"Wait for me here!" cried a lordly voice to the rowers.

When he heard that voice Ariston struggled to his feet and called. "Marcus Tetreius! Master!"

He saw the man turn and run toward him. Then the boy toppled over and lay face down in the ashes.

When he came to himself he felt a great shower of water in his face. The burden was gone from his back. He was lying in a row boat, and the boat was falling to the bottom of the sea. Then it was flung up to the skies. Tetreius was shouting orders. The rowers were streaming with sweat and sea water.

In some way or other they all got up on the waiting ship. It always seemed to Ariston as though a wave had thrown him there. Or had Poseidon carried him? At any rate, the great oars of the galley were flying. He could hear every rower groan as he pulled at his oar. The sails, too, were spread. The master himself stood at the helm. His face was one great frown. The boat was flung up and down like a ball. Then fell darkness blacker than night.

"Who can steer without sun or stars?" thought the boy.

Then he remembered the look on his master's face as he stood at the tiller. Such a look Ariston had painted on Heracles' face as he strangled the lion.

"He will get us out," thought the slave.

For an hour the swift ship fought with the waves. The oarsmen were rowing for their lives. The master's arm was strong, and his heart was not for a minute afraid. The wind was helping. At last they reached calm waters.

"Thanks be to the gods!" cried Tetreius. "We are out of that boiling pot."

At his words fire shot out of the mountain. It glowed red in the dusty air. It flung great red arms across the sky after the ship. Every man and spar and oar on the vessel seemed burning in its light. Then the fire died, and thick darkness swallowed everything. Ariston's heart seemed smothered in his breast. He heard the slaves on the rowers' benches scream with fear. Then he heard their leader crying to them. He heard a whip whiz through the air and strike on bare shoulders. Then there was a crash as though the mountain had clapped its hands. A thick shower of ashes filled the air. But the rowers were at their oars again. The ship was flying.

So for two hours or more Tetreius and his men fought for safety. Then they came out into fresher air and calmer water. Tetreius left the rudder. "Let the men rest and thank the gods," he said to his overseer. "We have come up out of the grave."

When Ariston heard that, he remembered the Death he had left painted on his master's wall. By that time the picture was surely buried under stones and ashes. The boy covered his face with his ragged chiton and wept. He hardly knew what he was crying for—the slavery, the picture, the buried city, the fear of that horrid night, the sorrows of the people left back there, his father, his dear home in Athens. At last he fell asleep. The night was horrible with dreams— fire, earthquake, strangling ashes, cries, thunder, lightning. But his tired body held him asleep for several hours. Finally he awoke. He was lying on a soft mattress. A warm blanket covered him. Clean air filled his nostrils. The gentle light of dawn lay upon his eyes. A strange face bent over him. "It is only weariness," a kind voice was saying. "He needs food and rest more than medicine."

Then Ariston saw Tetreius, also, bending over him. The slave leaped to his feet. He was ashamed to be caught asleep in his master's presence. He feared a frown for his laziness.

"My picture is finished, master," he cried, still half asleep.

"And so is your slavery," said Tetreius, and his eyes shone. "It was not a slave who carried my son out of hell on his back. It was a hero." He turned around and called, "Come hither, my friends."

Three Roman gentlemen stepped up. They looked kindly upon Ariston. "This is the lad who saved my son," said Tetreius. "I call you to witness that he is no longer a slave. Ariston, I send you from my hand a free man."

He struck his hand lightly on the Greek's shoulder, as all Roman masters did when they freed a slave. Ariston cried aloud with joy. He sank to his knees weeping. But Tetreius went on.

"This kind physician says that Caius will live. But he needs good air and good nursing. He must go to some one of Æsculapius' holy places. He shall sleep in the temple and sit in the shady porches, and walk in the sacred groves. The wise priests will give him medicines. The god will send healing dreams. Do you know of any such place, Ariston?"

The Greek thought of the temple and garden of Æsculapius on the sunny side of the Acropolis at home in Athens. But he could not speak. He gazed hungrily into Tetreius' eyes. The Roman smiled.

"Ariston, this ship is bound for Athens! All my life I have loved her—her statues, her poems, her great deeds. I have wished that my son might learn from her wise men. The volcano has buried my home, Ariston. But my wealth and my friends and my son are aboard this ship. What do you say, my friend? Will you be our guide in Athens?"

Ariston leaped up from his knees. A fire of joy burned in his eyes. He stretched his hand to the sky.

"O blessed Heracles," he cried, "again thou hast conquered Death. Thou didst snatch us from the grave of Pompeii. Give health to this Roman boy. O fairest Athena, shed new beauty upon our violet-crowned Athens. For there is coming to visit her the best of men, my master Tetreius."

THE LANCE OF KANANA

By HARRY W. FRENCH

Illustrations by Wilfred Jones

I

THE COWARD OF THE BENI SADS

KANANA was an Arab—a Bedouin boy of many years ago, born upon the desert, of the seed of Ishmael, of the tribe of Beni Sad.

It seems well-nigh impossible that the Bedouin boy could have lived who was not accustomed to the use of the sword and lance, long before he reached the dignity of manhood.

The peculiar thing about Kanana was that he never held a lance in his hand but once; yet many a celebrated sheik and powerful chieftain of his day lies dead, buried, and forgotten long ago, while the name of Kanana is still a magic battle cry among the sons of Ishmael, and his lance is one of the most precious relics of Arabia.

The old mothers and the white-haired veterans love to tell the story of the lance of Kanana; their black eyes flash like coals of fire when they say of it that it rescued Arabia.

The Beni Sads were a powerful tribe of roving Bedouins. Kanana was the youngest son of the venerable chief; the sheik who in the days of his strength was known from the Euphrates to the sea as the "Terror of the Desert."

By a custom older than the Boyhood of King David it fell to the lot of the youngest son to tend his father's sheep. The occupation was not considered dignified. It was not to Kanana's liking and it need not have lasted long; for the Terror of the Desert thought more of making warriors than shepherds of his sons, but greatly to his father's disgust Kanana refused to exchange his shepherd's staff for a warrior's lance. It was not that he loved the staff, but that he objected to the lance.

The tribe called Kanana effeminate because he was thoughtful and quiet, where other boys were turbulent, and as he grew older and the boyish fancy became a decided conviction against the combats constantly going on between the different tribes, they even called him a coward and said that he did not dare to fight.

There is but one name more bitter than "coward" to the Arab. That name is "traitor," and after being called a coward almost all his life, the very last words which Kanana heard from the lips of his countrymen came in frantic yells, calling him a traitor.

Today, however, it is always with throbbing hearts and flashing eyes that they repeat the story of the Lance of Kanana that rescued Arabia.

Until he was five years old, Kanana rolled about in the sand and sunshine, like the other children, with nothing on him but a twisted leather cord, tied round his waist.

Then, for five years, according to the custom of his people, he helped the women of his father's tent; shaking the goatskin filled with cream till it turned into butter; watching the kedder upon the fire, drying the buttermilk to be ground into flour, and digging kemma, which grow like truffles, under the sand.

After he was ten, for three years he watched the sheep and goats and the she-camels. That was the regular course of education through which all Bedouin boys must pass.

When he reached the age at which Ishmael was sent away with Hagar by Abraham, he was supposed to drop all menial labor and take his place among men; making a position for himself according to the fighting qualities which he possessed.

Kanana's fighting qualities, however, were only exhibited in the warfare which now began between him and his father.

There were at that time very few occupations open to the Bedouin boy. The tribe was celebrated for its men of learning and boasted the most skillful physicians in all Arabia; but they had all won their first laurels with the lance, and none of them wanted Kanana.

Three times his father came to him with the question: "Are you ready to be a man?" and three times Kanana replied, "My father, I cannot lift a lance to take a life, unless it be for Allah and Arabia."

How he came by a notion so curious no Arab could tell. The lad well knew the old decree that the hand of the Ishmaelite should be against every man, and every man's hand against him. He knew that every Arab of the desert lived by a warfare that was simply murder and robbery. Was he not an Arab, and an Ishmaelite?

Alone, among the sheep and camels, he had thought out his own theory. Kanana said to himself, "I am taught that Allah created these animals, and cares for them, and that I cannot please him if I allow them to suffer; it must be surely that men are more precious to Allah than animals. Why should we kill one another, even if we are Arabs and Ishmaelites?"

The menial tasks still allotted to Kanana grew more and more irksome. His punishment was far more keen than the tribe supposed; no one dreamed of the sharp cringe of pain with which he heard even the children call him a coward.

There were some faculties which Kanana possessed that made the warriors all envy him. He had a remarkable power over animals. No other Beni Sad could ride a camel or a horse so fast as Kanana. The most refractory creature would obey Kanana. Then, too, Kanana was foremost in the games and races. No other shepherd's eye was nearly so quick as Kanana's to detect an enemy approaching the flocks at night. No other young Bedouin, watching the ripening grain, could throw a stone from his sling so far and so accurately at the robber birds.

These accomplishments, however, only made his father the more angry that Kanana would not turn his gifts to some more profitable end.

Every year for three months—from planting to harvest-time—the Beni Sads encamped upon a river bank, on the outskirts of the Great Desert. The encampment numbered nearly five hundred tents set in four rows as straight as an arrow flies. These tents, of black goat's-hair cloth, were seven feet high in the center and five feet high on the sides. Some of them were twenty feet broad, and each was divided by a beautiful hanging white Damascus carpet. The men occupied one side, and the women and children the other. The favorite mare and the most valuable of the camels always slept by the tent, and the master's lance stood thrust into the ground at the entrance.

Far as the eye could reach, up and down the sluggish river, a field of ripening grain filled the narrow space between the yellow water and the silver-gray of the desert sand.

Here and there, through the grainfield, rose curious perches— platforms, constructed upon poles driven into the ground. Upon these platforms watchers were stationed when the grain began to head, and there they remained night and day till it was harvested, frightening the birds away.

Once a day the women brought them food, consisting of butter-milk, dried and ground and mixed with melted butter and dates; these same women renewed the supply of stones to throw at the birds.

The watchers were old men, women who were not needed in the tents, and little children; but all alone, this year, upon the most distant perch, sat Kanana.

There was not one of the tribe but felt that he richly deserved this disgrace; and Kanana could see no way to earn their respect, no way to prove himself a brave fellow. He was glad that they had given him the most distant perch, for there he could bear his hard lot, away from jests and jeers.

The women who brought the food stopped for a long time at some of the perches reporting all the news, but they never troubled themselves to relieve Kanana's solitude. The perches were too far apart for conversation. Kanana had always time enough to think, and as the grain grew yellow this year, he came to two positive con-clusions. He firmly resolved that before the reapers entered that field he would do something to convince his people that he was not a coward; failing that, he would hang his head in shame, acknowledge that they were right, and fly forever from their taunts.

II

THE OLD SHEIK'S PROMISE

The sun was beating fiercely down upon Kanana's perch, but he had not noticed it. The stones piled beside him for his sling were almost hot enough to burn his hand, but he did not realize it, for he had not touched them for a long time. The wooden dish of paste and dates stood in the shadow of the perch. He had not tasted them.

The pile of stones grew hotter and hotter. The hungry birds ate and quarreled and ate, with no one to disturb them. The Bedouin boy sat cross-legged on his perch, heedless of everything, twisting and untwisting the leather cords of his sling, struggling to look into the mists that covered up his destiny.

"Hi, there! You slothful son of a brave father! Look at the birds about you. Are you dead, or only sleeping?" sounded the distant but shrill and painfully distinct voice of an old woman who, with two children much younger than Kanana, occupied the next perch.

Kanana roused himself and sent the stones flying from his sling till there was not a bird in sight. Then he sank into deep thought once more; with his head resting upon his hands he became oblivious to everything.

Suddenly he was roused by the sound of horses' hoofs upon the sandy soil, a sharp rustling in the drying grain. He looked up, as thoroughly startled as though he had been sleeping, to see approaching him the one person than whom he would rather that any or all of the tribe of Beni Sad should find him negligent at his post of duty.

It was his father.

"O Kanana! O Kanana!" cried the old man, angrily. "Thou son of my old age, why didst thou come into the world to curse me? When thou shakest the cream, the butter is spoiled. When thou tendest the sheep, they are stolen! When thou watchest the grain, it is eaten before thy face! What shall a father do with a son who will neither lift his hand among men nor bear a part with women? And now, when all the miseries of life have taken hold upon me and the floods cover me, thou sittest at thine ease to mock me!"

Kanana sprang down from his perch. Kneeling, he touched his forehead to the ground.

"My father, slay me and I will take it as a mercy from thy hand. Or, as I am fit for nothing here, bid me go, and among strangers I will beg. But thou shalt not, my father, speak of me as ungrateful, unfilial. I know of no flood of sorrow that has come down upon thee."

"Thou knowest not what they all know?" exclaimed the old man fiercely.

"I know of nothing, my father. Since I came into the field, three weeks ago, no one has spoken to me but to chide me."

"Then know now," replied the sheik reproachfully, "that of thy two brave brothers who went with the last caravan, one has returned, wounded and helpless, and the other, for an old cause of blood between our tribes, has been made a prisoner by Raschid Airikat. The whole caravan, with the white camel at its head, Raschid has taken, and he has turned with it toward Damascus."

"Thy part of the caravan was very small, my father," said Kanana. "Only four of the camels were thine, and but for the white camel they were all very old. Their burdens, too, saving my brothers, were only honey and clay dust, of little value."

This was the simple truth, and evinced at least a very practical side to Kanana's mind; but it was not the kind of sympathy which the sheik desired, and his anger burst out afresh against Kanana.

"Ay, thou tender of flocks and sleeper!" he cried. "Wouldst thou teach me the value of camels and merchandise to comfort me? And hast thou fixed the price of ransom which Airikat will demand, or slay thy brother? And hast thou reckoned up the value of the white camel which could not be bought for gold, as it brought to thy father and thy father's father all their abundance of good? Answer me, if thou art so wise. Oh, that I had a son remaining who could lift a lance against this Airikat as bravely as he hurls his empty words at an old father!"

"My father," said Kanana earnestly, "give me a horse, a sack of grain, a skin of water, and I will follow after Raschid Airikat. I will not slay him, but, by the help of Allah, I will bring back to thee thy white camel with my brother seated upon his back."

The old sheik made a gesture of derision: "Thou wisp of flax before a fire! Thou reed before a whirlwind! Get thee back to thy perch and thy birds, and see if thou canst keep awake till sundown. Harvesting will begin with the daylight tomorrow. See that thou workest then."

Kanana rose to his feet. Looking calmly into the old sheik's angry face, he replied:

"My father, I will watch the birds till sundown. Then let others do the reaping. Kanana, whom thou scornest, will be far away upon the desert, to seek and find his brother."

"Did I not say I would not trust a horse to thee?" exclaimed the old man, looking at him in astonishment.

"These feet of mine can do my bidding well enough," replied Kanana. "And by the beard of the Prophet they shall do it till they have returned to thee thy son and thy white camel. I would do something, O my father, that I, too, might have thy blessing and not thy curse. It is the voice of Allah bids me go. Now say to me that if I bring them back, then thou wilt bless me, too; ay, even though still I will not lift a lance, unless it be for Allah and Arabia."

The aged warrior looked down in a sort of scornful pity upon his boy, standing among the stalks of grain; half in jest, half in charity, he muttered, "Yes, *then* I will bless thee," and rode away.

The harvesting began, as the old sheik had said, with the next daylight, but Kanana was not among the reapers.

Few so much as missed him, even, and those who did miss him supposed that he had hidden himself to avoid their jests.

Only the sullen sheik, bowed under his affliction, thought often of Kanana as he rode up and down the line. He remembered his looks, his words. He wondered if he could have been mistaken in the boy. He wished he had given him the horse and that he had blessed him before he went away.

III

AT THE FOOT OF MOUNT HOR

The moment the sun sank into the billows of sand Kanana had left his perch.

From the loaded stalks about him he gathered a goat's-hair sack of grain and fastened it upon his back. There was no one to whom he need say farewell, and, armed only with his shepherd's staff, he started away upon the desert, setting his course to the north and west.

Before he had gone far he passed a lad of about his own age who had come from the encampment to hunt for desert rats. Had Kanana seen him he would have made a wide detour, but the boy lay so still upon the sand that the first Kanana knew of his presence was when a low sarcastic voice uttered his name.

"Kanana!" it exclaimed. "Thou here! Dost thou not fear that some rat may bite thee? Whither darest thou to go thus, all alone and after dark, upon the sand?"

Fire flashed from Kanana's eyes. His hand clutched his shepherd's staff and involuntarily he lifted it; but the better counsel of his curious notions checked the blow. It was so dark that the boy upon the sand did not notice the effect of his taunts and knew nothing of his narrow escape. He only heard the quiet voice of Kanana as presently it meekly replied to his question:

"I go to Mount Hor."

It was an answer so absurd that the boy gave it no second thought and by the time that the footsteps of Kanana had died away the rat-hunter had as utterly forgotten him as though he had never existed.

To Mount Hor?

Kanana had only the most imperfect information to guide him. He knew that the Beni Sad caravan had been for some days upon the road southward to Mecca, when it was captured by Raschid Airi-kat and turned at an angle, northward toward Damascus.

Seen from a great distance over the sea of sand, the solitary peak of old Mount Hor, where Aaron, the great high priest of Israel, was buried, forms a startling beacon. By day or night, it rises clear and sharp against the sky, guiding the caravans northward from Arabia to Jerusalem and Damascus, and southward from Syria to Medina and Mecca; while the fertile oasis about it is the universal resting-place.

Kanana was not at all sure that the caravan would not have passed Mount Hor long before he could reach it; but if so, it must in time return that way, and, in any case, of all Arabia Mount Hor was the one spot where he could be sure to gather further information from passing caravans.

He knew his path upon that shifting sand as well as an Indian knew his way through the trackless forests of New England. With the sun and stars above him, any Arab would have scorned the idea of being lost in Arabia, and through the long night with strong and steady strides Kanana pressed onward toward Mount Hor.

As the harvest moon rose above the desert behind him, the Bedouin boy was softly chanting from the second *sura* of Al Koran:

> "God, there is no God but him;
> The living! The Eternal!
> Slumber doth not overtake him,
> Neither Sleep.
> And upholding all things,
> To him is no burden.
> He is the Lofty and the Great."

His long black shadow fell over the silver sand, and, watching it, he chanted the Koran again:

> "God is God. Whatever of good betideth
> thee cometh from him.
> "Whatever of evil is thine own doing."

Suddenly a speck appeared upon the distant horizon. None but the keen eye of a shepherd would have seen it in the night, but Kanana watched it as it quivered and wavered, disappearing as it sank into a valley in the rolling sand, appearing again, like a dory on the ocean, each time a little nearer than before.

Kanana noted the direction the speck was taking, and he made a wide path for it; he crouched among the sand shrubs when it came too near.

First a small party of horsemen passed him, the advance guard of a moving tribe. Then came the main body of men upon camels and horses; but the only sounds were made by the feet of the animals and the clanking of the weapons.

The she-camels with their young followed; then the sheep and goats driven by a few men on foot; next, the camels laden with the tents and furniture; last of all, the women and children of the tribe accompanied by another armed escort.

From all that company there was not a sound but of the sand and the trappings. There was nothing but shadows, swinging, swaying shadows, moving like phantoms over the white sand, as the trailing train went gliding on in that mysterious land of shadows and silhouettes.

There was nothing in it that was weird to Kanana, however. He hid himself simply as a precaution. He had often been a part of such a caravan, and he knew from experience that if a solitary Arab were found upon the desert, he would very quickly be forced to help drive the sheep and goats, and kept at it until he could make his escape. Any Arab boy would have hidden himself.

Long before Kanana's next halt the sun was pouring down its furious heat. To his great good fortune he came upon a boulder rising out of the sand; there he quickly made a place for himself where the sun could not reach him and, lying down, slept until night.

Only one who has walked upon a desert hour after hour, parched with thirst and utterly exhausted in the fierce glare and heat, can properly appreciate the Bible picture of "the shadow of a great rock in a weary land."

Had he not found this rock, Kanana would simply have dug a hole in the sand and forced himself into it.

Here and there as he pressed on, Kanana saw grim skeletons of men and animals as they lay whitening among the sand shrubs, but he paid them little attention. Before the sun had set upon the second

day, he beheld the distant summit of Mount Hor cutting sharply
into the blue sky.

This sight renewed his strength. Hour after hour he pressed
onward, with his eyes fixed upon the tomb of Aaron, a white monument upon the summit of the mountain, flashing like snow as the
moon rose in the clear, blue-black sky.

Kanana did not pause again until he fell upon his knees beside
the stream which rises in a spring upon Mount Hor, to die in the
sand, not far from its base. He plunged into the water; then, dressing himself again, he lay down upon the bank to sleep. He awoke
with the first gray lighting in the east, when the air of a desert is
almost cold enough to freeze.

He had now nothing more to do till he could obtain some information from passing caravans. It would soon be sunrise, the hour
for morning prayer, and, to warm himself while he waited, he
walked along the banks of the stream. They were blue as the very
sky with masses of forget-me-nots.

Suddenly Kanana paused. He started back. His eyes dilated, and
his hand trembled till the shepherd's staff fell, unheeded, to the
ground. The next moment he dropped to the ground to examine
the place more carefully.

What was it? Only some marks upon the grass where a caravan
had camped. The herbage was matted here and there where the
camels lay, and cropped short in little circles about each spot where
they had eaten it as far as they could reach.

Caravans were continually resting for the day under the shadow
of Mount Hor. There was nothing remarkable in the fact that a
caravan had camped here and gone. They always move at night;
not so much because it is cooler as because a camel will not eat at
night, no matter how hungry he may be, and must be given the
daylight or he will deliberately starve.

A moment later Kanana was upon his feet again with a triumph
in his eyes which clearly indicated his satisfaction.

The grass about the spot was unevenly cropped; there were
straggling spears of green left standing in the center of each mouthful which the camel had taken. Upon one side the bees were clus-

tering on the matted grass. A multitude of ants appeared upon the other side. The imprint left by the forefoot of the camel showed that it had been extended in front of him, instead of being bent at the knee and folded beneath him.

All this meant to the young Arab that the camel was old, that it was lame in the left knee, that it had lost a front tooth, that its burden on one side was honey, on the other the dust of river clay to be used in the manufacture of stucco.

Had one of his father's camels stood before him, Kanana could not have been more sure. Nothing more was needed to assure him that Raschid Airikat, with the stolen camels, had left Mount Hor the night before, upon the trail leading southward into Arabia.

His eyes flashed with excitement. "My brother and the white camel are not ten hours from here, and they are on the road to Mecca or Medina," he exclaimed as his fingers tightened about the staff. His white teeth glistened in a smile, as he added, "They are mine, or I am a coward!"

He stood there motionless for a moment, his dark eyes instinctively turning southward. The magnitude of his task lay vividly before him. He recalled his father's words: "Thou wisp of flax before a fire! Thou reed before a whirlwind!" They served to strengthen him.

The first step which lay before him was enough to test the courage of a brave man, and yet it was only a step toward a grand destiny.

Suddenly starting from his reverie, Kanana exclaimed: "I will do it! Or I will consent to be known forever as the coward of the Beni Sads!" and turning he ran up the rocky sides of old Mount Hor, toward the white tomb of Aaron, whence he knew he could see far away over the great ocean of sand.

It might be there would yet appear a speck upon the distant horizon, to guide him toward the retreating caravan.

IV

THE PROMISE

Up the steep sides of Mount Hor Kanana climbed, without waiting to look for a path. He saw nothing, heard nothing. He was all eagerness to reach the summit, in the faint hope that it might not be too late to see the departing caravan of Raschid Airikat.

Unless a camel is fresh, unusually large and strong, or constantly urged, it rarely makes more than two miles an hour. It was not over ten hours since the robber sheik had left the oasis, and some of the camels were very old and exhausted. It was a foolish hope no doubt, and yet Kanana hoped that anything so large as a great caravan might still be distinguishable.

Up, up, up he climbed—as fast as hands and feet could carry him. He no longer felt the cool air of early morning. He no longer looked about him to see the new sights of a strange oasis.

He did not even pause to look away over the desert as he climbed. The highest point was none too high. He did not care how far he could see until he had gained the white tomb of Aaron, upon the very crest.

Had he not been too thoroughly occupied with what was above him to notice what transpired about him and down below, he would have seen five Arab horsemen reach the stream by which he slept, almost as he began to climb.

They were Mohammedan soldiers, thoroughly armed for war and had evidently come from the northern borders of Arabia, where the victorious Mussulmans were planting the banner of Islam.

They had been riding hard, and both men and horses were exhausted. They hurried to the water. The men hastily ate some food which they carried, and tethered their horses in Arab fashion, by a chain, one end of which is fastened about the forefoot of the animal and the other end about the master, to prevent their being stolen while the master sleeps. The moment this was accomplished, the five men rolled themselves in their mantles, covering their faces as well as their bodies, and lay down upon the grass to sleep.

They were skilled in the art of making long journeys in the shortest possible time, and were evidently upon important business; for an Arab is never in haste unless his mission is very important.

Before Kanana reached the temple the men were soundly sleeping, and the horses, lying down to rest themselves, were still eating the grass about them, as a camel eats.

Panting for breath, trembling in eager haste, Kanana reached the tomb of Aaron: an open porch, with white pillars supporting a roof of white, like a crown of eternal snow on the summit of Mount Hor.

Between the snowy pillars Kanana paused. One quick glance at the sky gave him the points of the compass, and, shading his eyes from the glowing east, he looked anxiously to the south and west.

Sand, sand, sand, in billows like great waves of an ocean, lay about him in every direction. Far away there were low hills, and a semblance of green which, to his practiced eye, meant a grove of date palms upon the banks of a stream. But nowhere, search as he would, was there the faintest speck to indicate the caravan.

He was still anxiously scanning those distant hills when the first rays of the rising sun shot from the eastern horizon, flashing a halo of glory upon the snow-white crown of old Mount Hor, before they touched the green oasis lying about its base.

Never, in all the ages, had the sun rising from the Arabian desert seen such a tableau as his first beams illumined at Aaron's tomb.

All absorbed in his eager search, Kanana stood upon the very edge of the white porch. One hand was extended, grasping his shepherd's staff, the other was lifted to shade his eyes. In his eagerness to reach forward, one foot was far before the other, and the knee was bent as though he were ready to leap down the steep declivity before him.

His turban, a large square piece of cloth, was bound about his head with a camel's-hair cord; one corner was thrown back over his forehead, and a corner fell over each shoulder like a cloak. His coat was sheepskins, stitched together. Summer and winter, rain and sunshine, the Bedouin shepherd wears that sheepskin coat, as the best protection against both sun and frost. His bare feet rested firmly upon the white platform, and the arm that held the shepherd's staff was knotted with muscles which a strong man might have envied him.

His beardless face was dark, but not so dark as to hide the eager flush which heightened the color in his cheeks, and his chest rose and fell in deep, quick motions from his rapid climb.

His lips were parted. His dark eyes flashed, while the hand which shaded them stood out from his forehead as though trying to carry the sight a little farther, that it might pierce the defiles of those distant hills and the shadows of the date groves.

The sun rose higher, and its full light fell across the young Ishmaelite. It was the signal for the morning call to prayer, and from the minaret of every mosque in the realm of Islam was sounding *La Illaha il Allah Mahamoud rousol il Allah.*

Kanana did not need to hear the call, however. He instantly forgot his mission, and, a humble and devout Mohammedan, laid aside his staff and reverently faced toward Mecca to repeat his morning prayer.

Standing erect, with his open hands beside his head, the palms turned forward, he solemnly began the *Nummee Allah voulhamda.* With his hands crossed upon his breast he continued. Then he placed his hands upon his knees, then sat upon the floor. Then with his open hands upon the floor he touched his forehead to the platform as he repeated the closing words of the prayer.

In this position he remained for some time, whispering a petition for strength and courage to carry out the task he had undertaken.

There was something so solemn and impressive in the deathlike stillness of the early morning, upon that solitary peak, that it almost seemed to Kanana that, if he listened, he should hear the voice of Allah, answering his prayer.

Suddenly the silence was broken by a sharp cry, and another and another in quick succession mingled with savage yells.

It was not the voice of Allah, for which he had been waiting, and Kanana sprang to his feet and looked anxiously about him.

The mountains of Arabia are not high. Among real mountains, Mount Hor would be but a rocky hill. Looking down for the first time, Kanana saw the stream below him in its border of blue forget-me-nots, and could clearly distinguish the five soldiers who had so quickly fallen asleep upon its banks.

Wilfred Jones

"*Water, water! In the name of Allah, give me water,*" he gasped.

[See page 35]

It was a fearful sight which met his eyes. The five men were still lying there, but they were no longer sleeping. They were dead or dying; slain by three Bedouin robbers who had crept upon them for the valuable prize of their horses, and who did not dare attempt to steal the animals while the masters were alive.

It was almost the first time that Kanana's eyes had rested upon a scene of blood, common as such scenes are among his countrymen, and he stood in the porch benumbed with horror, while the robbers tore from the bodies about them such garments as pleased them; then took their weapons, mounted three of the horses, and leading two rode quickly away to the north.

There was no assistance which Kanana could render the unfortunate men. The caravan was already a night's march ahead of him and every moment that he lost must be redeemed by hurrying so much the faster under the burning sun, over the scorching sand, when, at the best, it was doubtful if flesh and blood could stand what must be required of it.

With a shudder he turned from the terrible scene and began to descend the mountain. Soon he was upon the bank of the stream and passing close to the spot where the five bodies were lying. He would not run, but he hurried on with his eyes fixed on the ground.

A faint sound caught his ear. He started, clutched his staff, and turned sharply about, thinking that the robbers had seen him and returned. It was only one of the unfortunate soldiers who had been left for dead. He had raised himself upon his elbow, and was trying to attract Kanana's attention.

"Water! Water! In the name of Allah, give me water!" he gasped, and fell back unconscious.

For a moment Kanana was tempted to hurry on. He did not want to go there, any more than he wanted to delay his journey; but something whispered to him of the promises of the Koran to those who show mercy to the suffering: that Allah would reward even a cup of water given to the thirsty.

It required no little courage of the Bedouin boy, all alone under Mount Hor, but he resolutely turned back, filled with water the wooden cup which a shepherd always carries at his girdle, and poured it down the parched throat of the almost insensible man.

"Bless Allah for water!" he gasped. "More! Give me more!"

Kanana ran to the brook and filled the cup again, but the poor man shook his head. It was too late. He was dying.

Suddenly he roused himself. He made a desperate struggle to call back his failing senses, and, for a moment, threw off the hand of Death. He had almost given up, forgetting something of great importance. Steadying himself upon his elbow, he looked into Kanana's face and said:

"You are a beardless youth, but you are an Arab. Listen to me. The mighty Prince Constantine, son of the Emperor Heraclius, is soon to leave Constantinople, at the head of a vast army of Turks and Greeks and Romans, like the leaves of the forest and the sand of the desert. He is coming to sweep the Arab from the face of the earth and the light of the sun. We were bearing a letter to the Caliph Omar, who is now at Mecca, telling him of the danger and asking help. If the letter does not reach him, Arabia is lost and the Faithful are destroyed. Would you see that happen?"

Too frightened to speak and hardly comprehending the situation, Kanana simply shook his head.

The man made another effort to overcome the stupor that had almost mastered him. He succeeded in taking from his clothing a letter, sealed with the great seal, and gasped:

"In the name of Allah, will you fly with this to the great caliph?"

Hardly realizing what he said, Kanana solemnly repeated: "In the name of Allah, I will."

He took the letter and was hiding it in his bosom when the soldier grasped the cup of water, drank ravenously, and, with the last swallow, let the cup fall from lifeless fingers.

Minute after minute passed, but Kanana did not move a muscle. His hand still touched the letter which he had placed in his bosom. His eyes still rested upon the lips that would never speak again.

His sacred promise had been pledged to fly with that letter to the great caliph at Mecca. It had been made in the name of Allah. It had been given to the man now lying dead before him. There was no power that could retract it. It must be performed, and until it was, no other consideration could retard his steps or occupy his thoughts.

His lips parted and he muttered, angrily: "Is this my reward for having given a cup of water to the thirsty?" Then it suddenly occurred to him that the caravan which he longed most of all to follow was also upon its way southward, and that, for the present at least, for either mission the direction was the same, and the demand for haste was great.

He caught his staff from the ground and set his face toward Mecca, pondering upon the dying statement of the soldier till word for word it was fastened in his memory, and the thought that his mission was for Allah and Arabia urged him on.

It was an easy task to follow the trail of the caravan. The Bedouin would be a disgrace to the desert, who could not recognize in the sand the recent footprint of one of his own tribe or of a camel with which he was familiar, and who could not tell by a footprint whether the man or camel who made it carried a burden, often what that burden was, always whether he was fresh or exhausted, walking leisurely or hurrying.

So Kanana hurried on, daily reading the news of the caravan before him as he went, testing his strength to the utmost before he rested, and starting again as soon as he was able; over the sand and over the hills, through groves and villages and over sand again; always towards Mecca.

V

LED BY A WHITE CAMEL

In the world-famous city of Mecca, two men stood by the arch that leads to the immortal Caaba.

They were engaged in an earnest conversation, heedless of everything about them, when the distant cry of a camel driver sounded on the still air.

Both of the men started and looked at each other in surprise. One of them said:

"A caravan at the gate at this time of day!" for it was several hours past midday and a caravan, in the ordinary course of things, reaches a city gate during the night or very early in the morning.

Arabia was seeing troubled times, and every one was on the alert for anything out of the accepted rule.

The camel-driver's cry was repeated. The first speaker remarked:

"They have left the burdened camels at the Moabede gate and are entering the city."

With an anxious look upon his face the elder of the two replied, "Either they have been hard pressed by an enemy or it is important news which brings them over the desert in such haste, in this insufferable heat."

The two men were evidently of great importance in the holy city. They were surrounded by powerful black slaves, who had all that they could do to keep the passers-by from pressing too close upon the elder man, in a desire to touch the hem of his garment. Many, in passing, knelt and touched their foreheads to the ground. Thus they waited the coming caravan.

The first camel of an important caravan is led by a man who walks before it through the narrow streets of a city, and his cry is to warn the crowd to clear the way; there being no sidewalks, and, indeed, but very little street.

"There it comes," said the younger of the two, as the long line of drowsy camels appeared, swinging, swinging, swinging along the narrow street.

"Led by a white camel," added the elder, and they both looked down the street.

The lead-camel was larger than the rest—much larger, and very much lighter colored; a sort of dingy white, like a sheep before shearing. The chief of the caravan sat upon his back, as unmindful of everything as though he were still upon the trackless sand.

It is not impossible that the sheik was really sleeping, and unconsciously grasping his ugly lance, while his Damascus blade hung ready by his side.

He roused in a moment, however, for with many a grunt and groan the great, ungainly, and yet very stately, ships of the desert came slowly and drowsily to anchor in the court before the Caaba.

"*Haji,*" a naked little urchin muttered, looking up from his play; but he should have known better. *Haji* means pilgrims, and these were no pilgrims.

There are seasons when this city is one mass of humanity. Haji by hundreds and thousands throng the narrow streets, but these are Bedouins of the desert, bound upon some other mission than worshiping before the Caaba, kissing the Black Stone, or drinking the holy water of Zemzem.

The leader of the white camel gave a peculiar pull to the rope hanging over his shoulder, attached to the animal's bridle, and uttered a short, sharp word of command.

Slowly, very slowly, the dignified, dingy creature, towering high above him, acknowledged the receipt of the order, but he gave no evidence that he was making any arrangements to obey.

His response was simply a deliberate grunt and a weird and melancholy wail that came gurgling out of his long, twisting throat. He would not have hurried himself one atom, even for the sheik upon his back.

A white camel is to the Arab what a white buffalo is to the Indian and a white elephant to the Ceylonese, and he fully appreciates his importance.

He deliberately turned his wooly head quite about till his great brown eyes, with the drooping lids almost closed over them, could most conveniently look back along the line of lank, inferior camels and gaunt and weather-beaten dromedaries, which had patiently followed him, day after day, to the temple court of immortal Mecca.

He was so long about it that the leader repeated the command, and very slowly the camel brought his head back again, till his languid eyes looked drowsily down in a sort of scornful charity upon the insignificant mortal at the other end of his halter.

He had stood in the court of Mecca long before that man was born and would doubtless guide caravans to the same spot long after he was buried and forgotten.

"You may be in haste, but I am not," he seemed to say, and dreamily turned his eyes toward the black-curtained Caaba, as if to see how it had fared since his last visit.

That Caaba, the Holy of Holies of the Mussulman, is the most revered and possibly the most venerable of all the sacred buildings on the earth; but the gentle, wistful eyes of the white camel were more practically drawn toward two or three date-palm trees then growing beside it. When he had satisfied himself that the only green thing in sight was quite beyond his reach, he deliberately lowered his head, changed his position a little, and with another grunt and another melancholy wail sank upon his knees, then upon his haunches. With a deep sigh he lifted his head again still high above the head of his driver, and his drowsy eyes seemed saying to him:

"Poor man! I kept you waiting, didn't I?"

Then he quickly turned his head to the opposite side, deliberately poking his nose into the passing throng, till, with a grunt of recognition, it touched the garment of one who was hurrying on among the crowd.

It was evidently a Bedouin, but the wings of his turban were drawn together in front, so that no one could see his face. He responded to the greeting of the white camel, however, by laying his hand upon the creature's nose as he passed. It was a motion which no one noticed, and a moment later he was out of sight.

He was following a boy who had led him directly to the arch, where the boy paused, pointed to the elder of the two men standing there, briefly observing: "It is he."

The Bedouin paused for a moment, as if struggling to collect his thoughts, then hurrying forward was the next to prostrate himself before the venerable man. As he rose he handed him a package, simply observing:

"A message to the Caliph Omar."

The great caliph quickly broke the seal and read.

Then, turning to the bearer, he asked sharply, "Who art thou?"

"I am Kanana, son of the sheik of the Beni Sads," replied the Bedouin boy, letting the wings of his turban fall apart that Omar might see his face.

"A beardless youth!" exclaimed the caliph. "And dost thou know aught of the import of this letter?"

Kanana repeated the dying words of the Arab soldier, which had so often escaped his lips as he urged his weary feet toward Mecca.

" 'Tis even so," replied the caliph. "And how came living man to trust a boy like you to come alone through the streets of Mecca with such an errand?"

"I came alone with the letter from the oasis at Mount Hor," replied Kanana, straightening himself up with very pardonable pride before the astonished eyes of the great caliph.

Then he related, briefly, how the letter came into his keeping, and the dangers and escapes of the three long weeks during which he carried it in his bosom; each rising and setting sun finding it a little nearer to its destination.

"Thou art a brave youth," said the caliph, "a worthy son of the Terror of the Desert. Would to Allah that every Arab had thy heart, and Heraclius himself, with all the world behind him, could not move the Faithful from their desert sands. And they shall not be moved! No! By the beard of the Prophet, they shall not be moved. Hear me, my son; I will see more of thee. This is no place for conversation, where the wind bloweth into what ears it listeth. One of my slaves shall conduct you to my house. There I will meet you presently. Go, and Allah go with you."

Indicating the slave who should take Kanana in charge, the Caliph Omar turned abruptly away and showed the letter to the man with whom he had been conversing.

VI

KANANA AND THE CALIPH

Guided by the black slave, Kanana passed out again under the arch, and walked the streets of Mecca, caring less and thinking less concerning what transpired about him than anyone, before or since, who for the first time stood in the holy city.

He found the narrow streets densely crowded. Soldiers and mer-

chants, Bedouins and city Arabs mingled with an array of every
tribe Arabia could furnish. There were venders of all things per-
taining to the necessities or luxuries of life; water carriers with goat-
skins on their shoulders; fruit criers with wooden trays upon their
heads; donkeys laden with cumbersome baskets, beneath which they
were almost lost to sight; camels carrying packs of a thousand
pounds' weight upon their backs, as though they were bundles of
feathers; everything hustling and jostling, men and boys shouting
and pushing for the right of way.

They all turned out as best they could, however, for the savage
black slave of the great caliph, and by keeping close behind him
Kanana always found an open space where he could walk without
fighting for room.

It was almost the first experience of the Bedouin boy in real city
life, and the very first time that his bare feet had ever touched the
beaten sand of the unpaved streets of his most sacred Mecca.

He turned from the arch, however, without once glancing at the
black-curtained Caaba, the Beitullah, or House of God, toward
which three times a day he had turned his face in reverent devotion
ever since he had learned to pray.

He followed the black slave onward through the streets, without
so much as looking at the walls of the houses that crowded close on
either hand.

He had fulfilled his vow. The packet he had sacredly guarded
through many a hardship and danger and narrow escape was safely
delivered. Now he was free to carry on the work for which he left
the perch and the birds in the grain-field of the Beni Sad.

Sometimes he thought of the black slave before him, and wondered if, after all, he was quite free. And the thought troubled him.

It seemed as though long years had passed since the day when his
father met him with the news of Raschid Airikat's capture of his
brother. He had suffered privations enough for a lifetime since then.
More than once his life had hung by a slender thread. He could
hardly imagine himself again sitting up on the perch, frightening
the birds away, his life had so entirely changed; his determination
to keep the vow he made his father had grown stronger every

day; only he realized more the magnitude of the task he had undertaken; and he appreciated his father's words: "Thou wisp of straw
before a fire! Thou reed before a whirlwind!" Still he gathered
hope, because he was beginning to understand himself.

The dangers and hardships of one enterprise he had met and
overcome, and under the shadow of the Caaba the great caliph
of Mecca had called him brave.

Now he was eager for the next. There was no vital need of
another interview with the caliph, and Kanana thought that if he
could only escape from the black slave, by darting into a crowded
alley, he could go at once about his own important business.

For the first time Kanana looked about him. At the moment
there was no opportunity, and while he watched for one, the slave
turned suddenly into a great gate, crossed a court paved with lime-
stone, lifted a reed curtain, entered one of the most substantial stone
structures of Mecca, and indicated to Kanana the apartment in
which he was to wait for the caliph. It was too late to escape. With
all the patience and dogged submission to destiny so strongly developed in the Bedouin, Kanana sat down upon a rug. There were
luxurious ottomans about the room, and divans taken from the
palaces of Persian princes, but the Bedouin boy preferred the desert
seat. Much as though he were still upon the perch, he laid his staff
beside him and buried his face in his hands. The magnificence in
this chamber of Omar's official residence only disturbed his thoughts.

He became so deeply buried in his plans that he had entirely forgotten where he was, when the rattle of the reed curtain aroused him
and, starting from his dream, he found the great caliph entering.

Reverently touching his forehead to the floor, Kanana remained
prostrate until the caliph was seated. Then he rose and stood leaning
upon his staff while the old ruler silently surveyed him. It seemed
to Kanana that his very heart was being searched by those grave
and piercing eyes.

Upon the shoulders of the Caliph Omar rested the fate of Islam
for future ages; his word was law wherever Mohammed was revered.
He could have little time to waste upon a shepherd boy; yet he sat

for a long while, silently looking at Kanana. When he spoke, it was only to bid him to repeat, at greater length, the story of how he came by the letter and how he brought it to Mecca.

"My son," he said, when Kanana had finished, "thou hast done what many a brave man would not have ventured to attempt. Ask what reward thou wilt of me."

"I would have the blessing of the Caliph Omar," Kanana replied.

"That thou shall have, my son; and camels, or sheep, or gold. Ask what thou wilt."

"I have no use for anything. I ask thy blessing, my father, and thy word to bid me go."

"Thou art a strange lad," replied the caliph. "Thou art like, and yet unlike the Terror of the Desert. I command thee, my son, say what I can best do for thee."

"Give me thy blessing, then let me go, my father," repeated Kanana, kneeling. "More than that, if I took it, I should leave at thy gate."

Omar smiled gravely at the boy's obstinacy.

"If I can do nothing for thee, there is yet something which thou canst do for me. Kahled is the greatest general who fights for the Prophet. He will soon reach Bashra, with thirty thousand warriors. He will turn to enter Persia, but these letters must reach him, with my orders that he go again to Syria. Bashra is three weeks from here, and a company of soldiers will start tonight to carry the messages, while I send far and wide for the Faithful to join him. It would be well, my son, for thee to go with the soldiers, to give the story to Kahled by word of mouth."

"The way is hard. The sand is deep and dry between Mecca and Bashra," said Kanana. The caliph looked in some surprise upon the hardy Bedouin boy.

"Hardship should not be hard to thee; but thou shalt be carried as one whom the caliph would honor."

"The way is dangerous. Robbers and hostile tribes are like the sand about Bashra," added Kanana, who had often heard of the countries along the eastern borders of Arabia.

Surprise became astonishment. The caliph exclaimed:

"Thou! Son of the Terror of the Desert, speaking of danger?"

"My father, I spoke for thy soldiers," replied Kanana, quickly. "Before they reach the sands of Bashra they will be with the five who started with this letter. Dost thou believe that Kanana spoke in fear or cowardice? If so, give him the letters, and with thy blessing and the help of Allah, he will deliver them to the Kahled, though every river run with fire, and the half of Arabia stand to prevent him!"

"Beardless youth!" cried the caliph. "I am too old for mockery."

"My father, without a beard I brought that letter here, and He who guarded me will guard me still."

"Wouldst thou dare to go without an escort?"

"I would rather have a sword I could not lift than have an escort," replied Kanana.

"By the beard of the Prophet, my son, there is both foolishness and wisdom in thy words. Thou shalt take the messages by one route, and by another I will send the soldiers with copies. It may be that Allah guides thy tongue. When wilt thou start?"

"Now," replied Kanana.

"That was well spoken," said the caliph. "What camels and servants shall be provided?"

"My father," said Kanana, "as I came a little way with the caravan which arrived today, I noted the white camel that took the lead. I never saw so great power of speed and endurance in a camel of the plain. The man who led him knew him well and was easily obeyed. I would have the two, none other, and the swiftest dromedary in Mecca, with grain for fourteen days."

The caliph shook his head: "It will be twenty days and more."

"My father, the burden must be light that the sand lie loose beneath their feet, and small that it tempts no envious eye." Then, in the direct simplicity resulting from his lonely life, Kanana added, "If it is a three weeks' journey for others, in fourteen days thy messages shall be delivered."

The caliph summoned an officer, saying, "Go to the caravan at the Moabede Gate. Say that Omar requires the white camel and the man who leads it; none other. Bid Ebno'l Hassan prepare my black dromedary and food for the two for fourteen days. Have everything at the gate, ready to start, in half an hour." Then to a slave he added, "Give to the son of the Terror of the Desert the best that the house affords to eat and drink."

Without another word the caliph left the room to prepare the messages. The slave hurried to produce a sumptuous feast. The officer left the house to execute the orders of the man whose word was law.

Alone, Kanana sat down again upon the mat and buried his face in his hands, as though he were quietly preparing himself to sleep.

Only a whisper escaped his lips. The words were the same which he had angrily spoken under the shadow of Mount Hor, but the voice was very different: "This is my great reward for giving a cup of water to the thirsty. *La Illaha il Allah!*" The slave placed the food beside him, but he did not notice it. Not until the caliph entered again did he suddenly look up, exclaiming, "This shepherd's coat would not be fitting the dignity of the white camel. I must have an *abbe* to cover it, and a mantle to cover my face, that Mecca may not see a beardless youth going upon a mission for the great caliph."

They were quickly provided. The camel and its driver were at the gate, with the black dromedary. All was ready, and with the mantle drawn over his beardless face, and the *abbe* covering his sheepskin coat, Kanana knelt and received the blessing of the Caliph Omar.

As he rose from his knees, the caliph handed him first the letters, which Kanana placed in his bosom, and next a bag of gold which Kanana held in his hand for an instant; then, scornfully, he threw it upon the mat, remarking, "My father, I have already received a richer reward than all the gold of Mecca."

The caliph only smiled: "Let each one dance according to the music which he hears. My son, I see the future opening before thee. This is not thy last mission. I read it in thy destiny that thou wilt succeed, and succeed again, until the name of Kanana be written among the greatest of those who have lifted the lance for Allah and Arabia. Go now, and God go with thee."

VII

A PRIZE WORTH WINNING

There was a group of several people standing about the caliph's gate as Kanana emerged. They were apparently waiting in careless curiosity to see the white camel start, and learn what they could of what was going on in official departments.

The information they received was very meager, yet it proved sufficient for more than one. They saw the white camel rise, with the veiled messenger of Omar upon its back. As the driver looked up to receive his first command their necks were bent in a way that betrayed their eagerness to hear. Only a word was spoken, however. It was "Tayf," the name of a city a short distance to the east of Mecca.

The camel-driver's cry sounded again through the streets, but the twilight shadows were gathering. There were few abroad, and the cries were not so loud or so often repeated as in the afternoon. When they ceased altogether, Kanana had turned his back upon Mecca forever.

The night wind blew cool and refreshing from the surrounding hills as the little caravan moved out upon the plain, but Kanana was ill at ease.

It was still as death in the valley. Far as the eye could penetrate the darkness they were all alone, except for five horsemen who left the gate of Mecca not long after the white camel, and were now riding slowly toward Tayf, a short distance behind it.

Ever and again Kanana looked back at them. The faint shadows, silently moving onward through the gloom, were always there; never nearer; never out of sight.

Leaning forward he spoke in a low voice to the driver, "You walk as though you were weary. The dromedary was brought for you. Mount it, and follow me."

"Master," replied the driver, "the white camel is obstinate. He will only move for one whom he knows well."

"You speak to the wind," muttered Kanana. "Do as I bid thee.

Hear my words. Yonder black dromedary has the fleetest foot in Mecca. He is the pride of the Caliph Omar. Mount him, and if you can overtake me while I drive the white camel, you shall throw the dust of the desert in the face of Raschid Airikat, and have the white camel for your own."

The driver started back, and stood staring at the veiled messenger of Omar. The word, "Mount!" was sternly repeated. Then he quickly obeyed, evidently bewildered, but well satisfied that he would have an easy task before him, from the moment the white camel realized that a stranger was in command.

Kanana spoke, and the camel started. The dromedary moved forward close behind it without a word from the driver. The horsemen had approached no nearer while they waited, though Kanana had purposely given them time enough to pass had they not halted when he halted. They were still five silent shadows upon the distant sand.

"Faster," said Kanana, and the long legs of the white camel swung out a little farther over the sand and moved more rapidly in response.

The dromedary immediately quickened its pace without urging, and, a moment later, from far in the distance, the night wind brought the sound of horses' hoofs through the silent valley.

It was very faint, but distinct enough to indicate that the shadows behind them had broken into a canter.

The camel driver gave little heed to his surroundings. He was too thoroughly engrossed in the prospect of owning the white camel to care who might be coming or going in a way as safe as that from Tayf to Mecca. Kanana, however, who could walk through the streets of the holy city without so much as knowing what the houses were made of, would have heard the wings of a night moth passing him, or seen a sand bush move, a quarter of a mile away.

His life as a shepherd had, after all, not been wasted.

"Faster," said Kanana, touching the camel's neck with his shepherd's staff, and without even the usual grunt of objection, the animal obeyed. The sand began to fly from his great feet as they rested upon it for an instant, then left it far behind; the Bedouin boy sat with eyes fixed on the path before him, and his head bent so that he could catch the faintest sounds coming from behind. The mantle that had covered his face fell loosely over his shoulder.

The dromedary lost a little ground for a moment, but gathering himself together, easily made it up. The driver was too sure of the final result to urge him unduly at the start. Soon enough the white camel would rebel of his own accord, and till then it was quite sufficient to keep pace with him.

The sound of horses' hoofs became sharper and more distinct, and Omar's messenger knew that the five shadows were being pressed to greater speed, and were drawing nearer.

"Faster!" said Kanana, and the white camel broke into a run, swinging in rapid motions from side to side, as two feet upon one side, then two on the other were thrown far in front of him and, in an instant, left as far behind.

Still the dromedary made light work of keeping close upon his track, evidently realizing what was expected of him; but the driver saw with dismay how quickly the camel responded to the word of his rider, how easily the man sat upon the swaying back—how carefully he selected the best path for the animal, and how skillfully he guided him so that he could make the best speed with the least exertion.

Many a night Kanana had run unsaddled camels about the pastures of the Beni Sads, guarding the sleeping sheep and goats, little dreaming for what he was being educated.

The sound of horses' hoofs grew fainter. They were losing ground, but now and then the listening ear caught the sharp cry of an Arab horseman urging his animal to greater speed.

"They are in earnest," muttered the Bedouin boy, "but they will not win the race."

"Faster!" said Kanana; the camel's head dropped till his neck lost its graceful curve, and the great white ship of the desert seemed almost flying over the billowy sand.

For a moment the dromedary dropped behind. The driver had to use the prod and force him to the very best that was in him, before he was able to regain the lost ground.

The sound of hoofs could no longer be heard, and Kanana was obliged to listen with the utmost care to catch the faintest echo of a distant voice.

"They are doing their best and are beaten, but we can do still better," he said to himself with a deep sigh of relief, as he watched the desert shrubs fly past them in fleeting shadows, scudding over the silver-gray sand.

The music of the sand, as it flew from the camel's feet and fell like hail upon the dry leaves of the desert shrubs, was a delightful melody, and hour after hour they held the rapid pace; over low hills and sandy plains; past the mud village and the well that marks the resting place for caravans, a night's journey from Mecca, without a sign of halting; and on and on, the dromedary always just so far behind, always doing his best to come nearer.

If by urging he was brought a little closer to the camel, the driver heard that low word, "Faster!" and in spite of him the camel gained again. Would he never stop?

The sounds from behind had been long lost when, far in advance, appeared the regular caravan from Tayf. They approached it like the wind. Only the mystic salaam of the desert was solemnly exchanged, then, in a moment, the trailing train as it crept westward was left, disappearing in the darkness behind them.

When it was out of sight the white camel suddenly changed its course, turning sharply to the north of east and striking directly over the desert, away from the hills and the beaten track of Tayf which he had been following.

The driver could not imagine that such a man as sat upon the white camel had lost his way. He silently followed till they passed a well that marked the second night's journey from Mecca toward Persia. The driver and dromedary would very willingly have stopped here; but the camel glided onward before them through the changing shadows of the night, as though it were some phantom, and not a thing of flesh and blood.

By dint of urging, the driver brought the dromedary near enough to call: "Master, we are not upon the road to Tayf."

"No," said Kanana, but the camel still went on.

Driven to desperation, as the eastern sky was brightening the driver called again:

"Master, you will kill the camel!"

"Not in one night," said Kanana; "but if you value your own life, come on!"

Faster still and faster the white camel swept toward the glowing east, but the dromedary had done his best. He could not do better. More and more he fell behind, and in spite of every effort of the driver, the pride of the caliph was beaten.

Fainter and fainter grew the outline of the white camel against the morning sky, ever swinging, swinging, swinging, over the silver-gray sea of desert sand, with a motion as regular and firm as though it had started but an hour before.

As the red disc of the fiery sun rose out of the desert, however, the driver saw the camel pause, turn half about till his huge outline stood out in bold relief against the sky, and then lie down.

Quickly Kanana dismounted. He caressed the camel for a moment whispering, "We are two days and a half from Mecca! Thou hast done better than I hoped. Thou didst remember me yesterday in the temple court. Tonight thou hast cheerfully given every atom of thy strength to help me. Tomorrow we shall be far apart. Allah alone knows for what or for how long; but if we ever meet again thou wilt remember me. Yes, thou wilt greet thy Kanana."

The boy's eyes were bright with tears as he gave the camel the best of the food provided for him; then, with sand instead of water performing the morning ablution, he faced toward Mecca.

When the dromedary and his rider reached the spot, the veiled messenger of Omar was solemnly repeating his morning prayer.

VIII

TO SEEK THE BENI SADS

All in vain the camel driver sought to obtain one glimpse beneath the mantle, to see the face of the caliph's messenger or to learn anything of their destination. He prepared their very frugal breakfast without a fire, and, when it was eaten, in the humble, reproachful tone of one who felt himself unjustly suspected, he said:

"My master, why didst thou deceive me, saying we should go to Tayf? Didst thou think that I would not willingly and freely lead the white camel anywhere, to serve the great caliph?"

"There were other ears than yours to hear," replied Kanana.

"There were only beggars at the gate, my master. Dost thou believe I would be treacherous to a servant of Omar and the Prophet?"

"I believe that every child of Ishmael will serve himself," replied Kanana; "but that had nothing to do with what I said. Before we start tonight, I will lay out your path before you, to the very end. As for the beggars, where were your senses? For three days, in disguise, I journeyed with the caravan of Raschid Airikat, as it came to Mecca. I saw in him a treacherous man, and when he yielded to a command he must obey and gave me the white camel and his driver, I knew that he would take them back again by stealth and treachery, if he were able to. Have I no eyes, that I should spend three days with the caravan and then not recognize the servants of Airikat, though they were dressed as beggars and slunk away, with covered faces, into the shadows of the caliph's gate? They did not cover their feet, and by their feet I knew them, even when they deceived you, one of their own. To them I said, 'Go, tell your master that his white camel is on the way to Tayf.'"

"My master," said the driver, respectfully, "the sheik Airikat is as devout as he is treacherous and brave. He gave the sacred camel and thy servant willingly, at the command of Omar, for the service of Allah and Arabia. I do not think he would deal treacherously."

Kanana did not reply, for far away over the desert, to the east, there was a little speck of dark, like a faint shadow upon the sand. He sat in silence watching it through the folds of his mantle as it grew larger and larger, and a long caravan approached.

The camels were worn out from a long journey. Their heads hung down, and their feet dragged languidly over the sand. Their slow progress had belated them, and the sun would be several hours above the desert when they reached the oasis by the well, which the two had passed before daylight.

As they drew nearer it could be easily seen that the camels bore no burdens but necessary food, in sacks that were nearly empty, and that their riders were savage men from the eastern borders of Arabia.

"Master, do they see us?" muttered the driver.

"They have eyes," replied Kanana. They had. A fresh dromedary and a white camel alone upon the desert were a tempting prize.

They evidently determined to appropriate them; for, leaving the main body of the caravan standing in the path, twenty or more turned suddenly, and came directly toward them.

"Master, we must fly from them," whispered the driver.

"If they were behind us I would fly," replied Kanana, "for every step would be well taken; but my path lies yonder." He pointed directly toward the caravan. "And I would not turn from it though devils instead of men were in the way."

"It is the will of Allah. We are lost," muttered the camel driver, and his arms dropped sullenly upon his knees in the dogged resignation to fate so characteristic of the Bedouin.

Kanana made no reply, but, repeating from the Koran, " 'Whatever of good betideth thee cometh from Him,' " he rose and walked slowly to where the white camel was lying.

Upon the high saddle, which had not yet been removed, hung the usual lance and sword, placed there by the officer of the caliph.

Leaning back against the saddle to await the approach of the caravan, the Bedouin boy threw his right hand carelessly across the hilt of the Damascus blade, exposing, almost to the shoulder, the rounded muscles of the powerful arm of—a shepherd lad.

The caravan drew nearer and finally halted when the leader was less than ten paces from the white camel.

His envious eyes had been gloating over the tempting prize as he approached; but gradually they became fastened upon that hand and arm, while the fingers that were playing gently upon the polished hilt seemed to beckon him on to test the gleaming blade beneath.

He could not see the beardless face, protected by the mantle. How could he know that the hand had never drawn a sword?

The whole appearance indicated a man without one thought of fear, and the savage chief realized that before the white camel became his prize some one beside its present owner would doubtless pay a dear price for it. He was still determined to possess it, but the silent figure demanded and received respect from him.

Instead of the defiant words which were upon his tongue, he pronounced the desert greeting.

Kanana returned the salutation, and immediately asked, "Did the dust from Kahled's host blow over you when your foot was on the sand of Bashra?"

The sheik drew back a little. It was a slight but very suggestive motion, speaking volumes to the keen eye of the Bedouin boy. He had been leaning forward before, more than is natural even to one tired out with sitting upon a camel's back. It was as if in his eagerness he was reaching forward to grasp the prize. Now he seemed suddenly to have lost that eagerness.

Quickly, Kanana took advantage of the hint. He drew from his bosom the letter of the caliph, sealed with the great seal of Mohammed, which every Mussulman could recognize, and calmly holding it plainly in view, he continued:

"The beak of the vulture has whitened, instead of the bones he would have plucked. The tooth of the jackal is broken, and not the flesh he would have torn. Raschid Airikat is neither at Damascus nor Mecca. Tomorrow morning he will be at Tayf. He would have you meet him there. Say to him, 'The fool hath eaten his own folly. The veiled messenger of the Prophet, sitting upon the sacred camel, glides with the night wind into the rising sun; for the fire is lighted in Hejaz that at Bashra shall cause the camels' necks to shine.'"

A decided change came over the savage face of the Arab sheik. He sat in silence for a moment, then, without a word, drove the prod into his camel. There was a grunt and a gurgling wail, and the tired animal was moving on, followed by all the rest.

Kanana and the camel driver were left alone. When they were well out of hearing the driver prostrated himself before Kanana, touching his forehead to the ground, and asked:

"Master, who was that sheik with all his warriors, and who art thou that they should cower before thy word?"

"I am no one to receive your homage. Stand upon your feet!" almost shouted Kanana. "I never saw or heard of them until today."

He breathed a deep, quivering sigh, and leaned heavily upon the saddle; every muscle in his body shook and trembled as the result of what had seemed so calm and defiant. He tried to replace the letter in his bosom, but his hand trembled so that he was obliged to wait.

"Thou knewest that he was of the tribe of Raschid Airikat, and that he came from Bashra," said the driver.

"I knew nothing," replied Kanana, petulantly, in the intense re-action. "How long have you been a man, well taught in killing other men, not to see what any cowardly shepherd boy could read? Were not their lances made of the same peculiar wood; and their camel saddles, were they not the same, stained with the deep dye of Bashra? Who should come out of the rising sun, with his camel licking the desert sand, if he came not from Bashra? Who should be going toward Mecca at this season, without a burdened camel in his caravan, if he went not to meet his chief for war? Why did Airikat crowd his caravan, day and night, if he expected no one?"

"But, master, Airikat is at Mecca, not at Tayf," said the driver,

"Bedouin, where are your eyes and ears?" exclaimed Kanana, scornfully. "Your paltry beggars at the caliph's gate carried my mes-sage swiftly. We had not left the gate of Mecca out of sight when on the road behind us came Airikat and four followers. While you were struggling to reach the white camel they did their best to over-take us both, but we outstripped them. We kept upon the way till we had passed the nightly caravan. They would have to rest their horses at the well, and the caravan would halt there, too. They would inquire for us, and the caravan would answer, 'We passed the white camel running like the wind toward Tayf.' Enough. Airikat with his horsemen cannot reach there before the next sunrise, and when he learns the truth he will be five days behind us. From him and yonder caravan, by the help of Allah we are safe. If you would learn a lesson, by the way, let it be this: that man can conquer man without a sword or lance. Sleep on it."

Setting the example, Kanana removed the camel's saddle, fastened his hind foot to his haunch with the twisted rope so that he could not rise, and sank upon the sand beside him, laying his head upon the creature's neck. The last words he heard from his driver were: "Master, thou art mightier than Airikat and all his warriors."

The sun beat fiercely down all day upon his resting place; but Kanana's sleep was sweeter than if the cool starlight had been over him, or a black tent of the Beni Sads; because, for that one day at least, his head was pillowed upon the white camel's neck.

It was late in the afternoon before he woke, and the sun was setting when the little caravan was again prepared to start.

They were ready to mount when the driver came to the white camel. He laid his hand upon the dingy haunch, and said, in a voice that was strangely pleading for a fierce Bedouin:

"Master, do not crowd him overhard tonight. He obeys too willingly. He is tired from a long journey. It is four weeks since he has rested. I would rather you would kill me than the white camel."

Kanana thought for a moment, then taking his shepherd's staff from the saddle, he replied: "You can better tell than I how he should be driven. Mount him, and I will ride the dromedary."

To the driver this was only Arab sarcasm, and he hesitated till Kanana silently pointed his staff toward the saddle, and the driver was more afraid to refuse than to obey.

Kanana turned and mounted the dromedary.

As the camel rose to his feet, a strange temptation sent the blood tingling to the driver's finger tips. The dromedary was unarmed. The messenger of Omar had only a shepherd's staff. Almost unconsciously his hand clutched the hilt of the Damascus blade, betraying the fact that it was better used to holding such a thing than the rope that led the white camel through Mecca.

Quickly the driver looked back, to see Kanana quietly watching him. Instantly his hand dropped the hilt, but it was too late. Scornfully Kanana said:

"Lo! every child of Ishmael, from the devout Raschid to the faithful camel driver, will serve himself. Nay, keep the hand upon the sword. Perchance there will be better cause to use it than in defying me. From here our paths must separate. I promised that tonight I would lay out your course for you. It is northward without swerving, for ten nights at least."

"And whither goest thou, my master?"

"That only Allah can direct from day to day. *La Illaha il Allah!*"

"And what is my mission to be?" asked the driver, anxiously.

"It is to seek the Beni Sads; to find the aged chief, the Terror of the Desert; to say to him, 'Kanana hath fulfilled his vow. He hath not lifted the lance against Airikat; but thy white camel is returned to thee, bearing thy first-born upon his back.' Go, and God go with thee!"

"Who art thou?" cried the man upon the white camel, starting from his seat as the dromedary gave the usual grunt in answer to the prod, and moved away.

The Bedouin boy turned in the saddle, tore off the *abbe* and the mantle that covered him, and clad in the sheepskin coat and desert turban answered:

"I am thy brother Kanana, the coward of the Beni Sads!"

IX

FOR ALLAH AND ARABIA

"Kanana! Our Kanana!" cried the brother, striking the camel's neck. The dingy dignity of the great white camel was ruffled by the blow received, and he expressed his disapproval in a series of grunts before he made any attempt to start.

"Kanana! Kanana!" the brother called again, seeing the dromedary already merging into the shadows; but the only response he received was from the shepherd's staff, extended at arm's length pointing northward.

"My young brother shall not leave me in this way. He has no weapon of defense and only a little of the grain."

Again he struck the camel a sharp blow as the animal began very slowly to move forward. The black dromedary was hardly distinguishable from the night, and was rapidly sinking into the deepening shadows before the camel was fairly on the way.

"Go!" cried the rider savagely, striking him again, and the camel moved a little faster; but he made slow and lumbering work, for he was not at all pleased with his treatment.

The rider's eyes were fixed intently upon the dim outline sinking away from him. The last he saw of it was the hand and arm, still holding the extended shepherd's staff pointing to the north. Then all was lost.

He kept on in that direction for an hour, but it was evident that he had begun in the wrong way with the camel, and that he was not forcing him to anything like his speed of the night before.

It was beyond his power to overtake the dromedary, and doubly chagrined he gave up the race and turned northward.

The path before Kanana was the highway between Persia and Mecca. At some seasons it was almost hourly traversed, but at midsummer only absolute necessity drove the Arabs across the very heart of the desert.

In the height of the rainy season there were even occasional pools of water in the hollows, here and there. Later there was coarse, tough grass growing, sometimes for miles along the way.

Little by little, however, they disappeared. Then the green of each oasis shrank toward the center, about the spring or well; and often before midsummer was over, they too had dried away.

The prospect of loneliness, however, was not at all disheartening to Kanana. He had no desire to meet with anyone, least of all with such parties as would be apt to cross the desert at this season.

If a moving shadow appeared in the distance, he turned well to one side and had the dromedary lie down upon the sand till it passed.

The black dromedary was fresh, and the Bedouin boy knew well how to make the most of his strength while it lasted; but it was for Allah and Arabia that they crossed the desert, and Kanana felt that neither his own life nor that of the dromedary could be accounted of value compared with the demand for haste.

He paid no heed to the usual camping grounds for caravans, except to be sure that he passed two of them every night until the dromedary's strength began to fail.

Each morning the sun was well upon its way before he halted for the day, and long before it set again he was following his shadow upon the sand.

More and more the dromedary felt the strain. When twelve nights had passed, the pride of the caliph was anything but a tempting prize, and Kanana would hardly have troubled himself to turn out for a caravan even if he had thought it a band of robbers.

The Bedouin boy, too, was thoroughly worn and exhausted. For days they had been without water, checking their thirst by chewing the prickly leaves of the little desert vine that is the last sign of life upon the drying sand. No dew fell at this season, and Kanana realized that it was only a matter of hours as to how much longer they could hold out.

Morning came without a sign of water or of life, as far as the eye could reach.

The sun rose higher, and Kanana longed for the sight of a human being as intensely as at first he had dreaded it.

Nothing but the ghastly bones of men and animals bleaching among the sand shrubs showed him that he was still upon the highway to Bashra.

Out of the glaring silver-gray, the fiery sun sailed into the lusterless blue of the dry, hot sky leaving the two separated by the eternal belt of leaden clouds that never rise above a desert horizon and never disperse in rain.

Kanana halted only for his morning prayer, and, when it was finished, the petition that he added for himself was simply. "Water! Water! O Allah! give us water."

Each day the heat had become more intense, and today it seemed almost to burn the very sand. As Kanana mounted again and started on, his tired eyes sought anxiously the glaring billows for some sign of life; but not a living thing, no shadow even, broke the fearful monotony.

There were gorgeous promises, but they did not deceive the eyes that had looked so often along the sand. There were great cities rising upon the distant horizon, with stately domes and graceful minarets such as were never known throughout the length and breadth of Arabia. And when the bells ceased tolling in Kanana's ears, he could hear the muezzin's call to prayer. Then the bells would toll again and he would mutter, "Water! Water! O Allah! give us water."

He had no longer any heart to urge the tired dromedary to a faster pace. He knew that it would only be to see him fall the sooner upon the sand. The tired creature's head hung down till his nose touched the earth as he plodded slowly onward.

The sun rose higher. It was past the hour when they always stopped, but neither thought of stopping. Waiting would not bring the water to them, and the Bedouin boy knew well that to lie on the desert sand that day meant to lie there forever.

The dromedary knew it as well as his master, and without a word to urge him, he kept his feet slowly moving onward, like an automaton, with his nose thrust forward just above the sand, as though he too were pleading: "Water! Water! O Allah! give us water!"

His eyes were closed. His feet dragged along the sand. Kanana did not attempt to guide him, though he swayed from side to side, sometimes reeling and almost falling over low hillocks which he made no effort to avoid.

Kanana could scarcely keep his own eyes open. The glare of the desert was blinding; but their last hope lay in his watchfulness.

He struggled hard to keep back the treacherous drowsiness, but his head would drop upon one shoulder, then upon the other. He could have fallen from the saddle and stretched himself upon the sand to die without a struggle, had it not been for the caliph's letter in his bosom. Again and again he pressed his hand upon it to rouse himself, and muttered, "By the help of Allah, I will deliver it."

Each time that this roused him he shaded his eyes and sought again the sand before him; but glaring and gray it stretched away to the horizon, without one shadow save that of the forest of low and brittle sand shrubs.

The burning sky grew black above him, and the desert became a fiery red. The dromedary did not seem like a living thing. He thought he was sitting upon his perch in the harvest field. The sun seemed cold as its rays beat upon his head. He shivered and unconsciously drew the wings of his turban over his face. No wonder it was cold. It was the early morning under Mount Hor. Yes, there were all the blue forget-me-nots. How the stream rippled and gurgled among them!

He started. What was that shock that roused him? Was it the robbers coming down upon him? He shook himself fiercely. Was he sleeping? He struggled to spring to his feet, but they were tangled in something.

At last his bloodshot eyes slowly opened and consciousness returned. The dromedary had fallen to the ground, beside—an empty well.

Kanana struggled to his feet and looked down among the rocks. The bottom was as dry as the sand upon which he was standing.

He looked back at the dromedary. Its eyes were shut. Its neck was stretched straight out before it on the sand, its head rested upon the rocks of the well.

"Thou hast given thy life for Allah and Arabia," Kanana said, "and when the Prophet returns in his glory, he will remember thee."

He took the sack of camel's food from the saddle and emptied the whole of it where the dromedary could reach it. Then he cut the saddle-straps and dragged the saddle to one side. It was all that he could do for the dumb beast that had served him.

Suddenly he noticed that the sun was setting. All the long day he must have slept, while the poor dromedary had crept onward toward the well. It had not been a healthful sleep, but it refreshed him, and combined with the excitement of waking and working for the dromedary, he found his tongue less parched than before. Quickly he took a handful of wheat and began to chew it vigorously; a secret which has saved the life of many a Bedouin upon the great sea of sand.

For a moment he leaned upon the empty saddle chewing the wheat, watching the sun sink into the sand and thinking.

"Thirteen days," he muttered. "I said fourteen when I started, but we have done better than three days in two. If we did not turn from the way today, this well is but one night from Bashra. *O Allah! Mahamoud rousol il Allah!* give thy servant life for this one night."

The dromedary had not moved to touch the food beside him, and there was no hope of further help from the faithful animal. Kanana stood beside it for a moment, laid his hand gratefully upon the motionless head, then took up his shepherd's staff and started on.

Sometimes waking, sometimes sleeping as he walked, sometimes thinking himself far away from the sands of Bashra, sometimes urging himself on with a realization that he must be near his journey's end, he pressed steadily on and on, hour after hour.

Sometimes he felt fresh enough to start and run. Sometimes he wondered if he had the strength to lift his foot and put it forward another time. Sometimes he felt sure that he was moving faster than a caravan, and that he should reach Bashra before morning. Sometimes it seemed as though the willing spirit must leave the lagging flesh behind as he had left the dromedary, and go on alone to Bashra.

Then he would press the sacred letter hard against his bosom and repeat, "By the help of Allah I will deliver it!" And all the time, though he did not realize it, he was moving forward with swift and steady strides, almost as though he were inspired with superhuman strength.

Far away to the east a little spark of light appeared. It grew and rose, until above the clouds there hung a thin white crescent; the narrowest line of moonlight.

Kanana gave a cry of joy, for it was an omen which no Arab could fail to understand.

Then the air grew cold. The darkest hour before the dawn approached, and the narrow moon served only to make the earth invisible.

The dread of meeting anyone had long ago left Kanana's mind. First he had feared it. Then he had longed for it. Now he was totally indifferent. He looked at the sky above him to keep his course. He looked at the sand beneath his feet; but he did not once search the desert before him.

Suddenly he was roused from his lethargy. There were shadows just ahead. He paused, shading his eyes from the sky, and looked forward long and earnestly.

"It is not sand shrubs," he muttered. "It is too high. It is not

Bashra. It is too low. It is not a caravan. It does not move. It has no beginning and no end," he added, as he looked to right and left.

"It is tents," he said a moment later, and a frown of anxiety gathered over his forehead. "Have I missed the way? No tribe so large as that would be tented near Bashra. If I turn back I shall die. If I go on—*La Illaha il Allah!*" he murmured, and resolutely advanced.

As he drew nearer, the indistinguishable noises of the night in a vast encampment became plainly audible, but he did not hesitate.

Following the Arab custom for every stranger in approaching a Bedouin camp, he paused at the first tent he reached, and standing before the open front repeated the Mussulman salutation.

Someone within roused quickly, and out of the darkness a deep voice sounded in reply.

Then Kanana repeated:

"I am a wanderer upon the desert. I am far from my people."
And the voice replied:

"If you can lift the lance for Allah and Arabia, you are welcome in the camp of Kahled the Invincible."

"*La Illaha il Allah!*" cried Kanana. "Guide me quickly to the tent of Kahled. I am a messenger to him from the great Caliph Omar."

The earth reeled beneath the feet of Kanana as the soldier led the way.

The general was roused without the formality of modern military tactics or even Mohammedan courtesies. A torch was quickly lighted. Kanana prostrated himself; then rising, he handed the precious packet to the greatest general who ever led the hosts of Mohammed.

Kahled the Invincible broke the seal, but before he had read a single word, the Bedouin boy fell unconscious upon the carpet of the tent. As the soldiers lifted him, Kanana roused for an instant and murmured:

"By the dry well, one night to the southwest, my black dromedary is dying of thirst. In Allah's name, send him water! He brought the message from Mecca in thirteen days!" Then the torchlight faded before his eyes and Kanana's lips were sealed in unconsciousness.

X

KANANA'S THIRD MISSION

A vast Mohammedan army, with its almost innumerable follow-ers, was marching toward Syria to meet the hosts of the Emperor Heraclius.

Like a pillar of cloud the dust rose above the mighty throng.

Armed horsemen, ten thousand strong, rode in advance.

A veteran guard of scarred and savage men came next, mounted upon huge camels, surrounding Kahled the Invincible and his chief officers, who rode upon the strongest and most beautiful of Persian horses.

A little distance behind were thousands of fierce warriors mounted on camels and dromedaries. Then came another vast detachment of camels bearing the tents, furniture, and provisions of the army; these were followed by a motley throng, comprising the families of many of the tribes represented in the front, while still another powerful guard brought up the rear.

Behind the bodyguard of Kahled and before the war camels rode a smaller guard, in the center of which were two camels bearing a litter between them.

Upon this litter lay Kanana, shielded from the sun by a goat's-hair awning; for almost of necessity the army moved by daylight. It started an hour after sunrise, resting two hours at noon, and halting an hour before sunset. It moved more rapidly than a caravan, how-ever, and averaged twenty-five miles a day.

Close behind Kanana's litter walked a riderless dromedary. At the start it was haggard and worn. Its dark hair was burned to a dingy brown by the fierce heat of the desert; but even Kahled received less careful attention, and every day it gathered strength and held its head a little higher.

The black dromedary was not allowed to carry any burden, but was literally covered with gay-colored cloths; decorating the pride of Omar the Great, that had brought the good news from Mecca to Bashra in less than thirteen days.

Nothing pleasanter could have been announced to that terrible army of veterans surrounding the valiant Kahled, than that it was to face the mightiest host which the Emperor Heraclius could gather in all the north.

There was not one in all that throng who doubted, for an instant, that Kahled could conquer the whole world if he chose, in the name of Allah and the Prophet.

Many of the soldiers had followed him since the day years before when he made his first grand plunge into Persia. They had seen him made the supreme dictator of Babylonia. They had seen him send that remarkable message to the great monarch of Persia:

"Profess the faith of Allah and his Prophet, or pay tribute to their servants. If you refuse, I will come upon you with a host that loves death as much as you love life."

Once before had they seen him summoned from his triumphs in Persia, because all of the Mohammedan generals and soldiers in Syria were not able to cope with the power of Heraclius. They had seen him invested with the supreme power by the Caliph Abu-Bekr, Omar's predecessor, and watched while, single-handed, he fought and conquered the great warrior, Romanus.

Most of them had been with him before the walls of Damascus, when he besieged that magnificently fortified city upon one side, and fought and conquered an army of a hundred thousand men upon the other side, sent from Antioch by Heraclius for the relief of the great city. Then they witnessed the fall of Damascus, and followed Kahled as he attacked and put to flight an army outnumbering his by two to one, and equipped and drilled in the most modern methods of Roman warfare.

They had fought with him in the fiercest battles ever recorded of those desert lands, and they knew him only as Kahled the Invincible.

After Abu-Bekr had died and Omar the Great had taken his place, the proud soldiers saw their general unjustly deposed and given such minor work as tenting about the besieged cities, while others did the fighting, until he left Syria in disgust.

No wonder they were glad to see him recalled to take his proper place. They jested without end about the cowards who were frightened because Heraclius had threatened to annihilate the Mussulmans. And the march was one grand holiday in spite of heat and hardships.

As Kanana lay in his litter and listened to these bursts of eloquence in praise of the general, he was often stirred with ardent patriotism and almost persuaded to cast his lot among the soldiers; but the same old theories which before had prevented his taking up a lance restrained him still.

On the fourth day he left the litter and took his seat upon the black dromedary. Kahled directed that costly garments and a sword and lance be furnished him, but Kanana prostrated himself before the general and pleaded: "My father, I never held a lance, and Allah knows me best in this sheepskin coat."

Kahled frowned, but Kanana sat upon the decorated dromedary precisely as he left the perch in the harvest field. He expected to take his place with the camp followers in the rear, but found that he was still to ride in state, surrounded by the veteran guard. Indeed, he became a figure so celebrated and conspicuous that many a warrior in passing, after prostrating himself before the general, touched his forehead to the ground before Kanana and the black dromedary.

It might have made a pleasant dream while sitting upon the perch in the harvest field, but the reality disturbed him, and again he began to plan some means of escape.

He carefully computed the position of the Beni Sad encampment, and determined the day when the army would pass but a few miles to the east of it.

One who has not lived upon the desert and seen it illustrated again and again, can scarcely credit the accuracy with which a wandering Bedouin can locate the direction and distance to any point with which he is familiar; but even then Kanana was at a loss as to how to accomplish his purpose, when the whole matter was arranged for him and he was supplied with a work which he could perform for Allah and Arabia, still holding his shepherd's staff and wearing his sheepskin coat.

The army halted for the night upon the eve of the day when it would pass the encampment of the Beni Sads. The tent which Kanana occupied was pitched next that of Kahled.

He sat upon the ground eating his supper. All about him was the clatter and commotion of the mighty host preparing for the night, when he heard an officer reporting to the general that in three days the supply of grain would be exhausted.

"My father," he exclaimed, prostrating himself before the general, "thy servant's people, the Beni Sads, must be less than a night's journey to the north and west. They were harvesting six weeks ago, and must have five hundred camel loads of grain to sell. Bid me go to them tonight, and with the help of Allah, by the sunrise after tomorrow it shall be delivered to thy hand."

Kahled had formed a very good opinion of the Bedouin boy. He had noticed his uneasiness, and suspecting that he would make an endeavor to escape, he had been searching for some occupation that should prevent it by rendering him more content to remain. He felt that a time might come when Kanana, with his sheepskin coat and shepherd's staff, might be of greater value to him than many a veteran with costly *abbe* and gleaming sword.

The result was an order that one hour after sunset Kanana should start, at the head of a hundred horsemen, with ten camels laden with treasure for the purchase of the grain, with twenty camels bearing grain-sacks and one with gifts from Kahled to the Terror of the Desert, in acknowledgement of the service rendered by his son.

When he had purchased what grain the Beni Sad would sell, he was to continue in advance of the army, securing supplies to the very border of Syria.

Kanana was no prodigy of meekness that he should not appreciate this distinction. A prouder boy has never lived in Occident or Orient than the Bedouin shepherd who sat upon the black dromedary and publicly received the general's blessing and command of the caravan.

In any other land there might have been rebellion among a hundred veteran horsemen, when placed under the command of a boy in a sheepskin coat, armed only with a shepherd's staff, but there was no man of them who had not heard wonderful tales of Kanana's courage; and the shepherd who had left the harvest field six weeks before, known only as the coward of the Beni Sads, set his face toward home that night, followed by a hundred savage warriors who obeyed him as one of the bravest of all the Bedouins.

As the caravan moved rapidly over the plain, bearing its costly burden, it is hardly surprising that the beardless chief recalled his last interview with an angry father, when that veteran sheik refused to trust him with a single horse to start upon his mission; but he was none the less anxious to reach his father's tent and receive his father's blessing.

XI

THE SACRED GIRDLE

Shortly after midnight five horsemen who rode in advance returned to report a large encampment, far away upon the left. Then Kanana took the lead as a brave Bedouin chieftain should, and, followed by the caravan, approached the smoldering fires which betrayed the location of the camp.

He rode directly toward the tent of the sheik, which always stands in the outer line, farthest from a river or upon the side from which the guests of the tribe will be most likely to approach.

As he approached, a shadow rose silently out of the shadows. It sniffed the air. Then there was a faint grunt of satisfaction and the shadow sank down into the shadows again.

Kanana slipped from the back of the dromedary without waiting for him to lie down, and running forward to the white camel, whispered, "I knew that thou wouldst know me."

The Terror of the Desert appeared at the tent door with a hand raised in blessing.

Kanana ran to his father with a cry of joy, and the white-haired sheik threw his arms about the neck of his son and kissed him, saying:

"Forgive me, Kanana, my brave Kanana! I said that thou hadst come to curse me with thy cowardice, and lo! thou hast done grander, braver deeds than I in all my years! Verily, thou hast put me to shame, but it is with courage, not with cowardice."

Kanana tried to speak, but tears choked him. All alone he could calmly face a score of savage robbers armed to the teeth, but suddenly he discovered that he was only a boy after all. He had almost forgotten it. And in helpless silence he clung to his father's neck.

The old sheik roused himself.

"Kanana," he exclaimed, "why am I silent? The whole tribe waits to welcome thee. Ho! every one who sleepeth!" he called aloud, "Awake! Awake! Kanana is returned to us!"

Far and near the cry was repeated, and a moment later the people came hurrying to greet the hero of the Beni Sads.

Not only had the brother returned with the white camel and a glowing account of his rescue by the veiled messenger of the caliph, but a special officer had come by a passing caravan, bearing to the Terror of the Desert a bag of gold and the congratulations of Omar the Great, that he was the father of such a son.

Now the gifts from Kahled the Invincible arrived, and the hundred horsemen obeying the voice of Kanana. The Beni Sads could scarcely believe their eyes and ears.

Torches were lighted. Fires were rekindled and before sunrise the grandest of all grand Bedouin feasts was in full glory.

Vainly, however, did the old sheik bring out the best robe to put it on him; with a ring for his hand and shoes for his feet; in a custom for celebrating a son's return which was old when the story of the Prodigal was told.

Kanana only shook his head and answered, "My father, Allah knows me best barefooted and in this sheepskin coat."

The Bedouin seldom tastes of meat except upon the occasion of some feast. When a common guest arrives, unleavened bread is baked and served with *ayesh,* a paste of sour camel's milk and flour. But Kanana was not a common guest.

For one of higher rank, coffee and melted butter are prepared, but these were not enough for a welcome to Kanana.

For one still higher, a kid or lamb is boiled in camel's milk and placed in a great wooden dish, covered with melted fat and surrounded by a paste of wheat that had been boiled and dried and ground and boiled again with butter.

Twenty lambs and kids were thus prepared, but the people were not satisfied. Nothing was left but the greatest and grandest dish which a Bedouin tribe can add to a feast in an endeavor to do honor to its noblest guest. Two she-camels were killed and the meat quickly distributed to be boiled and roasted. All for the boy who had left them, six weeks before, with no word of farewell but the parting taunt of a rat-catcher.

While the men were eating the meat and drinking camel's milk and coffee, the women sang patriotic songs, often substituting Kanana's name for that of some great hero; and when the men had finished and the women gathered in the maharems to feast upon what was left, the Terror of the Desert, roused to the highest pitch of patriotism, declared his intention to join the army of Kahled, and nearly two hundred of the Beni Sads resolved to follow him.

It was nearly noon when Kanana and those who were with him went to sleep in the goat's-hair tents, leaving the whole tribe at work, packing the grain sacks, loading the camels, and cleaning their weapons for war.

Kanana performed his mission faithfully, little dreaming that Kahled's one design in placing it in his hands was to keep him with the army for services of much greater importance.

The time which the general anticipated came when the hosts of Kahled, joined by the Mohammedan armies of Syria and Arabia, were finally encamped at Yermonk upon the borders of Palestine.

Kanana was summoned to the general's tent and, trembling like the veriest coward in all the world, he fell upon his face before the man to whom was entrusted the almost hopeless task of rescuing Arabia. To Kahled alone all eyes were turned, and Kanana trembled, not because he was frightened, but because he was alone in the tent with one who seemed to him but little less than God himself.

Kahled's words were always few and quickly spoken.

"Son of the Terror of the Desert," said he, "many conflicting rumors reach me concerning the approaching enemy. I want the truth. I want it quickly. What dost thou require to aid thee in performing this duty?"

Kanana's forehead still touched the ground. Overwhelmed by this sudden order, an attempt to obey which meant death without mercy, without one chance in a hundred to escape, he altogether forgot to rise.

Kahled sat in silence, understanding human nature too well to disturb the boy, and for five minutes neither moved. Then Kanana rose slowly and his voice trembled a little as he replied, "My father, I would have thy fleetest horse, thy blessing, and thy girdle."

Kahled the Invincible wore a girdle that was known to every soldier and camp follower of the army. It was of camel's-skin, soft-tanned and colored with a brilliant Persian dye which as far away as it could be seen at all no one could mistake.

It was part of a magnificent curtain which once hung in the royal palace of Babylon. It pleased the fancy of the fierce warrior, and he wore it as a girdle till it became his only insignia. There was not a color like it within hundreds of miles at least, and when the people saw it they knew that it was Kahled.

"Take what horse thou wilt," replied the general. "I give thee, now, my blessing." Then he hesitated for a moment. Had Kanana asked a hundred camels or a thousand horsemen he would have added, "Take them." As it was, he said a little doubtfully, "What wouldst thou with my girdle?"

In all the direct simplicity which clung to him in spite of everything, Kanana replied: "I would hide it under my coat; I would that it be proclaimed throughout the army that someone has fled to the enemy with the sacred girdle, and that a great reward be offered to him who shall return to Kahled any fragment of it he may find."

Without another word, the general unwound the sacred girdle, and Kanana, reverently touching it to his forehead, bound it about him under his sheepskin coat.

Kneeling, he received the blessing, and leaving the tent, he selected the best of Kahled's horses and disappeared in the darkness alone.

The next morning an oppressive sense of inaction hung about the headquarters.

The only order issued accompanied an announcement of the loss of the sacred girdle.

Every soldier was commanded to be on the watch for it, to seize and to return at once to Kahled even the smallest fragment which might be found. For this the fortunate man was promised as many gold coins as, lying flat, could be made to touch the piece which he returned.

XII

KANANA'S MESSENGERS

Far and wide the impatient soldiers asked, "Why is the army inactive?"

"Is not the motto of Kahled 'Waiting does not win'?"

"Has he not taught us that action is the soul and secret of success?"

"Does he not realize that the hosts of Heraclius are bearing down upon us, that he leaves us sitting idly in our tents?"

"Is Kahled the Invincible afraid?"

Such were the questions which they put to their officers, but no one dared to carry them to the general, who sat in his tent without speaking from sunrise to sunset the first day after the girdle disappeared. "Is it the loss of his girdle?" "Did he not conquer Babylonia without it?" "Does he not fight in the name of Allah and the Prophet? Could a bright-colored girdle give him strength?"

Thus the second day went by.

Kahled the Invincible was silent and sullen, and the impression grew and grew that in some way the safety and success of the whole army depended upon the recovery of that girdle.

So intense was this sentiment, that when at midnight after the third day it was reported that a fragment of the girdle had been captured by some scouts, and was then being taken to the general's tent the whole army roused itself and prepared for action.

Not an order had been issued, yet every soldier felt instinctively that the coming morning would find him on the march.

It was midnight. For a day Kahled had not even tasted food. He sat alone in his tent upon a Persian ottoman. A bronze vessel from Babylonia, filled with oil, stood near the center of the tent. Fragments of burning wick floating in the oil filled the tent with a mellow, amber light.

There was excitement without, but Kahled did not heed it till a soldier unceremoniously entered, bearing in his hand a part of the curtain from the palace of Babylon.

With a sudden ejaculation Kahled caught it from the soldier's hand, but ashamed of having betrayed an emotion, he threw it carelessly upon the rug at his feet, handing the soldier a bag of gold, and bidding him see how many pieces, lying flat, could touch it.

The soldier worked slowly, carefully planning the position as he laid the pieces down, and Kahled watched him as indifferently as though he were only moving men upon the Arab's favorite checkerboard.

When every piece that could was touching the camel skin, the soldier returned the bag, half-emptied, and began to gather up his share.

Kahled deliberately emptied the bag, bidding him take the whole and go.

He was leaving the tent when the general called him back. He had picked up the skin and was carelessly turning it over in his hand. It was neatly cut from the girdle, in the shape of a shield a little over a foot in width.

"How did you come by it?" Kahled asked indifferently.

"We were searching the plain, a day's journey to the north," the soldier answered. "We were looking for travelers who might bring tidings of the enemy. We saw four strangers, Syrians, riding slowly, and a shepherd who seemed to be their guide. Upon his horse's front, hung like a breastplate where every eye could see, was yonder piece of the sacred girdle. We dashed upon them, and the cowards ran. The shepherd was the last to turn. I was ahead, but not near enough to reach him, so I threw my lance. He fell from his horse and—"

"You killed him?" shrieked the general, springing to his feet and dropping the camel skin.

"No! No!" gasped the frightened soldier. "I only tried to. He wore a coat of sheepskin. It was too thick for my lance. He sprang to his feet, tore the lance from his coat, and ran after the rest faster even than they could ride, leaving his horse behind."

" 'Tis well," muttered the general, and he devoutly added. "Allah be praised for that sheepskin coat!"

The soldier left the tent, and going nearer to the light, Kahled examined the fragment of the sacred girdle. It was double. Two pieces had been cut and the edges joined together.

He carefully separated them, and upon the inner side found what he evidently expected.

These words had been scratched upon the leather, and traced with blood: "Sixty thousand from Antioch and Aleppo, under Jababal the traitor, encamp two days from Yermonk, north, waiting for Manuel with eighty thousand Greeks and Syrians, now six days away. Still another army is yet behind. Thy servant goes in search of Manuel when this is sent."

"Allah be praised for that sheepskin coat!" Kahled repeated, placing the fragment in his belt and walking slowly up and down.

"Jababal is two days to the north," he added presently. "A day ago Manuel was six days behind him. He will be still three days behind when I reach Jababal, and while he is yet two days away, the sixty thousand in advance will be destroyed."

An order was given for ten thousand horsemen and fifteen thousand camel riders to start for the north at once. The soldiers expected it, and were ready even before the general.

Four days and a night went by, and they were again encamped at Yermonk; but Jababal's army of sixty thousand men was a thing of the past.

Again a strip of the girdle was discovered. This time it hung upon the neck of a camel leading into the camp a long caravan laden with grain and fruit.

The camel driver reported that one had met them while they were upon the way to supply the army of Manuel. He had warned them that Manuel would simply confiscate the whole and make them prisoners, and had promised that if they turned southward instead, to the camp of Kahled, with the talisman which he hung about the camel's neck, they should be well received and fairly treated.

From this talisman Kahled learned that the army of Manuel was almost destitute of provisions, and that a detachment with supplies was another five or six days behind. The general smiled as he thought how the Bedouin boy had shrewdly deprived the hungry enemy of a hundred and fifty camel loads of food, while he secured for himself an excellent messenger to his friends.

During the night Manuel's magnificent army arrived, and en. camped just north of the Mohammedans. Manuel chose for his citadel a high cliff that rose abruptly out of the plain between the two armies, and ended in a precipitous ledge toward Arabia.

Standing upon the brow of this cliff, a little distance from the tent of Manuel, one could look far down the valley over the entire Mohammedan encampment.

When morning dawned, the prince sent for the leading Mohammedan generals to confer with him concerning terms of peace. He offered to allow the entire army to retire unmolested, if hostages were given that the Arabs should never again enter Syria.

The Mohammedan generals, who had been thoroughly dismayed at the sight of the Grecian phalanx, thanked Allah for such a merciful deliverance, and instantly voted to accept. The real authority, however, rested with Kahled, who replied, "Remember Jababal!"

With so many in favor of peace, Manuel hoped for an acceptance of his terms, and proposed that they consider the matter for a day.

Kahled, with his hand upon the camel skin in his belt, replied again: "Remember Jababal!"

He realized that his only hope of victory lay in striking a tired and hungry enemy, and that each hour's delay was dangerous. Less than half an hour later he was riding along the line of battle shouting the battle cry: "Paradise is before you! Fight for it!"

The soldiers were ready, and there began the most desperate struggle that was ever waged upon the plains of Syria.

All day long the furious conflict raged. Three times the Bedouins were driven back. Three times the cries and entreaties of their women and children in the rear urged them to renew the fight, and again they plunged furiously upon the solid Grecian phalanx.

Night came, and neither army had gained or lost, but among the Bedouin captives taken by the Greeks were several who recognized Kanana. They saw him moving freely about the enemy's camp. They learned that he was supposed to be a servant who had fled with other camp followers at the time of the slaughter of Jababal's army. They could see in it nothing but cowardly desertion. They said:

"He was afraid that we should be conquered and instead of standing by us to fight for Arabia, he ran to the enemy to hide himself"; and in their anger they betrayed him. They reported to the Greeks that he was a Bedouin of the army of Kahled, not a Syrian servant of Jababal.

Kanana was quickly seized, bound and dragged into the presence of the prince. Manuel had suspected that some one had betrayed both Jababal and himself to Kahled, and, chagrined at the result of the first day's battle, he fiercely accused Kanana.

Calmly the Bedouin boy admitted that it was he who had given the information, and he waited without flinching as Manuel drew his sword.

"Boy, dost thou not fear to die?" he exclaimed, as he brandished his sword before Kanana.

"I fear nothing!" replied Kanana proudly.

"Take him away and guard him carefully," muttered the prince. "Dying is too easy for such as he. He must be tortured first."

The second day and the third were like the first. The army of the Prophet fought with a desperation that never has been equalled. The Ishmaelite counted his life as nothing so that he saw a Greek fall with him. It was the fate of Allah and Arabia for which they fought, and they stood as though rooted to the ground, knowing of no retreat but death.

Again and again their general's voice rang loud above the clashing arms: "Paradise is before you if you fight! Hell waits for him who runs!" And they fought and fought and fought, and not a man dared turn his back.

Again and again the Grecian phalanx advanced, but they found a wall before them as solid as the cliff behind them.

When a Bedouin lay dead he ceased to fight, but not before; and the moment he fell, another sprang forward from behind to take his place.

XIII

THE LANCE OF KANANA

The army of the Prophet had not retreated one foot from its original position, when night brought the third day's battle to a close.

Kahled sank upon the ground among his soldiers, while the women from the rear brought what refreshments they could to the tired warriors.

All night he lay awake beside his gray battle horse, looking at the stars and thinking.

Flight or death would surely be the result of the coming day. Even Kahled the Invincible had given up all hope of victory.

He was too brave a man to fly, but he was also too brave to force others to stand and be slaughtered for his pride.

It was a bitter night for him, but as the eastern sky was tinged with gray, he at last resolved to make the sacrifice himself, and save such of his people as he could.

The women and children, with the wounded who could be moved, must leave at once, taking all that they could carry with them, and scatter themselves in every direction.

When they were well away, he, with such as preferred to stand and die with him, would hold the foe in check while the rest of the army retreated with orders to march at once to Mecca and Medina, and hold those two sacred cities as long as a man remained alive.

He breathed a deep sigh when the plan was completed, and rising, mounted his tired charger, to see that it was properly executed.

It was the first time in his career that Kahled the Invincible had ordered a retreat, and his only consolation was that he was neither to lead nor join in it.

In the camp of Manuel the same dread of the coming day clouded every brow. Food was entirely exhausted. Horses and camels had been devoured. They had neither the means with which to move away nor the strength to stand their ground.

Their solid phalanx was only what the enemy saw along the front. Rank after rank had been supplied from the rear till there was nothing left to call upon.

All that remained of the eighty thousand iron-hearted fighters— the pride of the Emperor Heraclius—as they gathered about the low campfires confessed that they were overmatched by the sharper steel of Mohammedan zeal and Bedouin patriotism.

Manuel and his officers knew that for at least three days no relief could reach them; they knew, too, that they could not endure another day of fighting.

"If we could make them think that their men are deserting and joining us, we might frighten them," suggested an officer.

"Send for the spy," said Manuel quickly, "and let it be proclaimed to the other prisoners that all who will join us shall be set free, and that those who refuse shall be slaughtered without mercy."

Haggard and worn Kanana stood before him. For fifty hours he had lain bound in a cave at the foot of a cliff, without a drop of water or a morsel of food.

"I am about to torture thee," said the prince. "Thou hast wronged me more than thy sufferings can atone, but I shall make them as bitter as I can. Hast thou anything to say before the work begins?"

Kanana thought for a moment, then, hesitating as though still doubtful, he replied:

"When the tempest rages on the desert, doth not the camel lay him down, and the young camel say to the drifting sand, 'Cover me; kill me, I am helpless'? But among the captives taken by the prince, I saw an old man pass my cave. He is full of years, and for him I would part my lips. I hear that the prince will have the prisoners slain, but it is not the custom of my people to make the women, the old men, and the children suffer with the rest. May it please the prince to double every torture he has prepared for me and in exchange to set that old man free?"

"Who is he?" asked the prince.

"The one with a long white beard. There are not two," replied Kanana.

"And what is he to you?"

Kanana hesitated.

"He shall die unless you tell me," said the prince, and Kanana's cold lips trembled as he whispered:

"He is my father,"

"'Tis well," said Manuel. "Let him be brought."

The old man entered, but paused at the opposite side of the tent, looking reproachfully at his son. He had heard from the other captives how they had discovered Kanana, a deserter in the hour of danger, living in the tents of the enemy. Even he had believed the tale, and he was enough of a patriot to be glad that they betrayed his son.

"Is this thy father?" asked the prince. "He does not look it in his eyes."

Kanana simply bowed his head.

That look was piercing his heart far deeper than the threats of torture; but Manuel continued:

"You have offered to suffer every torture I can devise if I will set him free. But you have not compassed your debt to me. You gave to Kahled the information by which he conquered Jababal. You gave him information which prevented his making terms of peace with me. But for you, I should be on my way to Mecca and Medina to sweep them from the earth. But I like courage, and you have shown more of it than Kahled himself. It is a pity to throw a heart like yours under a clod of earth, and I will give you an opportunity to save both yourself and your father. Stand upon the brow of the cliff yonder, as the sun comes up. There, according to the custom of your people, wave this lance above your head. Shout your own name, and your father's, so that all of your people can hear, and tell them that in one hour thirty thousand Arabs will draw the sword for the cause of Heraclius. Then throw the lance, and if your aim be good, and you do kill an Arab, that moment I will set thy father free and thou shalt be made a prince among my people. Do not refuse me, or, after

I have tortured thee, with red-hot irons I will burn out thy father's eyes, lest he should look savagely upon thy corpse!"

He had scarcely ceased speaking when the old sheik exclaimed:

"My son! My Kanana! I have wronged thee! Forgive me if thou canst, but let him burn out my eyes! Oh! not for all the eyes that watch the stars would I have a son of mine a traitor. Thou wouldst not lift a lance before. I charge thee now, by Allah, lift it not for any price that can be offered thee by this dog of an infidel!"

Kanana did not look at his father. His eyes were fixed on Manuel, and when all was still, he asked: "Will the prince allow his captive to sit alone till sunrise and consider his offer?"

"Take him out on the cliff and let him sit alone," said Manuel; "but have the irons heated for his father's eyes."

Kanana chose a spot whence he could overlook the valley, and whatever his first intentions may have been, he changed them instantly with his first glance. He started, strained his eyes, and looked as far as his keen sight could pierce the gray light of early morning.

Then his head sank lower and lower over his hands, lying in his lap, until the wings of his turban completely covered them. He did not move or look again.

In that one glance he had recognized the result of Kahled's last resolve. In the gray distance he saw that laden camels were moving to the south. He saw the dark spots, most distant in the valley, suddenly disappear. They were folding their tents! They were moving away! Kahled the Invincible had ordered a retreat.

Kanana knew that to retreat at that moment meant death to Arabia, but he did not move again till an officer touched him on the shoulder and warned him that in a moment more the sun would rise.

With a startled shudder he rose and entered Manuel's tent.

"Is the word of the prince unchanged?" he asked. "If I speak the words and throw the lance and kill an Arab, that moment will he set my father free?"

"I swear it by all the powers of earth and heaven!" replied the prince.

"Give me the lance," said Kanana.

His father crouched against the tent, muttering: "For such an act, Kanana, when I am set free I will find first a fire with which to heat an iron, and burn my own eyes out."

Kanana did not heed him. He took the lance, tested it, and threw it scornfully upon the ground.

"Give me a heavier one!" he exclaimed. "Do you think me like your Greek boys, made of wax? Give me a lance that, when it strikes, will kill."

They gave him a heavier lance.

"The hand rest is too small for a Bedouin," he muttered, grasping it; "but wait! I can remedy that myself. Come. Let us have it over with."

As he spoke he tore a strip from beneath his coat, and, turning sharply about, walked before them to the brink of the cliff, winding the strip firmly about the hand rest of the lance.

Upon the very edge he stood erect and waited.

The sun rose out of the plain, and flashed with blinding force upon the Bedouin boy clad in his sheepskin coat and desert turban, precisely as it had found him in the porch of Aaron's tomb upon the summit of Mount Hor.

His hand no longer held a shepherd's staff, but firmly grasped a Grecian lance that gleamed and flashed as fiercely as the sun.

Upon Mount Hor he was bending forward, eagerly shading his eyes, anxiously looking away into the dim distance, searching the path of his destiny.

Now there was no eagerness. Calmly he stood there. Vainly the sun flashed in his clear, wide-open eyes. He did not even know that it was shining.

Not a muscle moved. Why was he waiting?

"Are you afraid?" muttered the prince, who had come as near as possible without being too plainly seen from below, "Remember your old father's eyes."

Kanana did not turn his head, but calmly answered:

"Do you see yonder a man upon a gray horse, moving slowly among the soldiers? He is coming nearer, nearer. That man is Kahled the Invincible. If he should come within range of the lance of Kanana, I suppose that Manuel would be well pleased to wait?"

"Good boy! Brave boy!" replied the prince. "When thou hast made thy mind to do a thing, thou doest it admirably. Kill him, and thou shalt be loaded down with gold till the day when thou diest of old age."

Kanana made no reply, but standing in bold relief upon the cliff, watched calmly and waited, till at last Kahled the Invincible left the line of soldiers, and alone rode nearer to the cliff.

"Now is your chance! Now! Now!" exclaimed the prince.

Slowly Kanana raised the lance. Three times he waved it above his head. Three times he shouted:

"I am Kanana, son of the Terror of the Desert!" in the manner of the Bedouin who challenges an enemy to fight, or meets a foe upon the plain.

For a moment, then, he hesitated. The next sentence was hard to speak. He knew too well what the result would be. It needed now no straining of the eyes to see his destiny.

All the vast army down below was looking up at him. Thousands would hear his words. Tens of thousands would see what followed.

"Go on! Go on!" the prince ejaculated fiercely. Kanana drew a deep breath and shouted:

"In one hour thirty thousand Arabs will draw the sword in the army of Heraclius!"

Then gathering all his strength, he hurled the lance directly at the great Mohammedan general, who had not moved since he began to speak.

Throughout those two great armies one might have heard a sparrow chirp, as the gleaming flashing blade fell like a meteor from the cliff.

The aim was accurate. The Bedouin boy cringed, and one might have imagined that it was even more accurate than he meant. It pierced the gray charger. The war horse of Kahled plunged forward and fell dead upon the plain.

A fierce howl rose from the ranks of the Ishmaelites. Men and women shrieked and yelled.

"Kanana the traitor! A curse upon the traitor Kanana!" rent the very air.

Such was the confusion which followed that, had the Greeks been ready to advance, a thousand might have put a hundred thousand Bedouins to flight. But they were not ready.

Kanana stood motionless upon the cliff. He heard the yells of "Traitor!" but he knew that they would come, and did not heed them.

Calmly he watched till Kahled gained his feet, dragged the lance from his dying horse, and with it in his hand, hurried toward the soldiers. Only once he turned, and for an instant looked up at the solitary figure upon the cliff. He lifted his empty hand, as though it were a blessing and not a malediction he bestowed upon the Bedouin boy; then he disappeared.

With a deep, shivering sigh, Kanana pressed one hand beneath his sheepskin coat. A sharp contortion passed over him, but he turned about and stood calmly, face to face with Manuel.

"You did well," said the prince, "but you did not kill an Arab. It was for that I made my promise."

"'And if you kill an Arab,'" gasped Kanana, "'that moment I will set your father free!' Those were the prince's words! That was his promise, bound by all the powers of earth and heaven! He will keep it! He will not dare defy those powers, for I have killed an Arab!"

Clutching the sheepskin coat, Kanana tore it open, and, above a brilliant girdle, they saw a dagger buried in his bleeding breast. He tottered, reeled, stepped backward, and fell over the brink of the cliff. "You may as well go free," said Manuel, turning to the sheik. "A monstrous sacrifice has just been made to purchase your liberty."

Turning abruptly he entered his tent to consider, with his officers, the next result.

"I think they are flying," an officer reported, coming from the cliff. "The horsemen and camels are hurrying into the hills. Only foot soldiers seem remaining in the front."

"Let every soldier face them who has strength to stand!" commanded the prince. "Put everything to the front, and if they fly give them every possible encouragement."

The order was obeyed, and the fourth day of the battle began; but it was spiritless and slow.

The Bedouins, with their constantly thinning ranks, stood with grim determination where their feet rested, but they made no effort to advance.

The wearied out and starving Grecian phalanx simply held its ground. The prince was not there to urge his soldiers on. The voice of Kahled did not sound among the Mussulmans.

An hour went by.

Suddenly there was an uproar in the rear of the army of Heraclius. There was a wild shout, a clash of arms, and the watchword of Islam rang above the tumult, in every direction.

Ten thousand horse and twenty thousand war camels poured in upon that defenseless rear, and even as Kanana had declared, in just one hour there were thirty thousand Arabs wielding their savage swords in the army of Heraclius.

Another hour went by. The battle cry of Kahled ceased. The shout of victory rang from the throats of the Mussulmans. Manuel and all his officers were slain. The magnificent army of Heraclius was literally obliterated.

Treasure without limit glutted the conquered camp. Arabia was saved.

Quickly the soldiers erected a gorgeous throne and summoned Kahled to sit upon it, while they feasted about him and did him honor as their victorious and invincible leader.

The veteran warrior responded to their call, but he came from his tent with his head bowed down, bearing in his arms a heavy burden. Slowly he mounted the platform, and upon the sumptuous throne he laid his burden down.

It was the bruised and lifeless body of Kanana.

With trembling hand the grim chief drew back the sheepskin coat, and all men then beheld, bound about the Bedouin boy, the sacred girdle!

"I gave it to him," said Kahled solemnly; "and upon the fragments you have returned to me, he wrote the information by which we conquered Jababal and Manuel. You saw him throw this lance at me; you called him 'traitor!' but about the hand rest there was wound this strip. See! In blood — in his blood — these words are written here: 'Do not retreat. The infidels are starving and dying. Strike them in the rear.' It was his only means of reaching me. It was not the act of a traitor. No! It was the Lance of Kanana that rescued *Arabia*."

THE BOY VIKING
OLAF II OF NORWAY

By ELBRIDGE S. BROOKS

OLD RANE, the helmsman, whose fierce mustaches and shaggy shoulder mantle made him look like some grim old northern wolf, held high in air the great bison horn filled with foaming mead.

"Skoal to the Viking! Hael! Was-hael!"[1] rose his exultant shout. From a hundred sturdy throats the cry reëchoed till the vaulted hall of the Swedemen's conquered castle rang again.

"Skoal to the Viking! Hael! Was-hael!" and in the center of that throng of mail-clad men and tossing spears, standing firm and fearless upon the interlocked and uplifted shields of three stalwart fighting men, a stout-limbed lad of scarce thirteen, with flowing light-brown hair and flushed and eager face, brandished his sword vigorously in acknowledgment of the jubilant shout that rang once again through the dark and smoke-stained hall: "Was-hael to the sea wolf's son! Skoal to Olaf the King!"

Then above the din and clash of shouting and of steel rose the voice of Sigvat the saga-man, or songman of the young viking, singing loud and sturdily:

> "Olaf the King is on his cruise,
>> His blue steel staining,
>> Rich booty gaining,
> And all men trembling at the news.
> Up, war wolf's brood! our young fir's name
> O'ertops the forest trees in fame,
> Our stout young Olaf knows no fear.
>> Though fell the fray,
>> He's blithe and gay,
> And warriors fall beneath his spear.
> Who can't defend the wealth they have
> Must die or share with the rover brave!"

---

[1] "Hail and health to the Viking!"

A fierce and warlike song, boys and girls, to raise in honor of so young a lad. But those were fierce and warlike days when men were stirred by the recital of bold and daring deeds—those old, old days, nine hundred years ago, when Olaf, the boy viking, the pirate chief of a hundred mail-clad men, stood upon the uplifted shields of his exultant fighting men in the grim and smoke-stained hall of the gray castle of captured Sigtun, oldest of Swedish cities.

Take your atlas and, turning to the map of Sweden, place your finger on the city of Stockholm. Do you notice that it lies at the easterly end of a large lake? That is the Maelar, beautiful with winding channels, pine-covered islands, and rocky shores. It is peaceful and quiet now, and palace and villa and quaint northern farmhouse stand unmolested on its picturesque borders. But channels, and islands, and rocky shores have echoed and reëchoed with the war shouts of many a fierce sea rover since those far-off days when Olaf, the boy viking, and his Norwegian ships of war ploughed through the narrow sea-strait and ravaged the fair shores of the Maelar with fire and sword.

Stockholm, the "Venice of the North," as it is called, was not then in existence; and little now remains of old Sigtun save ruined walls. But travelers may still see the three tall towers of the ancient town, and the great stone heap, alongside which young Olaf drew his ships of war, and over which his pirate crew swarmed into Sigtun town, and planted the victorious banner of the golden serpent upon the conquered walls.

For this fair young Olaf came of hardy Norse stock. His father, Harald Graenske, or "Graymantle," one of the tributary kings of Norway, had fallen a victim to the tortures of the haughty Spanish queen; and now his son, a boy of scarce thirteen, but a warrior already by training and from desire, came to avenge his father's death. His mother, the Queen Aasta, equipped a large dragon-ship or war vessel for her adventurous son, and with the lad, as helmsman and guardian, was sent old Rane, whom men called "the far-traveled," because he had sailed westward as far as England and southward to Nörvasund (by which name men then knew the Straits of Gibraltar). Boys toughened quickly in those stirring days, and this lad, who, because he was commander of the dragon-ship, was called Olaf the King—though he had no land to rule—was of viking blood, and quickly learned the trade of war. Already, among the rocks and sands of Sodermann, upon the Swedish coast, he had won his first battle over a superior force of Danish war vessels.

Other ships of war joined him; the name of Olaf the Brave was given him by right of daring deeds, and "Skoal to the Viking!" rang from the sturdy throats of his followers as the little sea king of thirteen was lifted in triumph upon the battle-dented shields.

But a swift runner bursts into the gray hall of Sigtun. "To your ships, O king, to your ships!" he cries. "Olaf, the Swedish king, men say, is planting a forest of spears along the sea strait, and, except ye push out now, ye may not get out at all!"

The nimble young chief sprang from the upraised shields.

"To your ships, vikings, all!" he shouted. "Show your teeth, war-wolves! Up with the serpent banner, and death to Olaf the Swede!"

Straight across the lake to the sea strait, near where Stockholm now stands, the vikings sailed, young Olaf's dragon-ship taking the lead. But all too late; for, across the narrow strait, the Swedish king had stretched great chains, and had filled up the channel with stocks and stones. Olaf and his Norsemen were fairly trapped; the Swedish spears waved in wild and joyful triumph, and King Olaf, the Swede, said with grim satisfaction to his lords: "See, jarls and lendermen, the Fat Boy is caged at last!" For he never spoke of his stout young Norwegian namesake and rival save as "Olaf Tjocke" —Olaf the Thick, or Fat.

The boy viking stood by his dragon-headed prow, and shook his clenched fist at the obstructed sea strait and the Swedish spears.

"Shall we, then, land, Rane, and fight our way through?" he asked.

"Fight our way through?" said old Rane, who had been in many another tight place in his years of sea roving, but none so close as this. "Why, king, they be a hundred to one!"

"And if they be, what then?" said impetuous Olaf. "Better fall as a viking breaking Swedish spears than die a straw death[1] as Olaf of Sweden's bonderman. May we not cut through these chains?"

"As soon think of cutting the solid earth, king," said the helmsman.

"So; and why not, then?" young Olaf exclaimed, struck with a brilliant idea. "Ho, Sigvat," he said, turning to his saga-man, "what was that lowland under the cliff where thou didst say the pagan Upsal king was hanged in his own golden chains by his Finnish queen?"

"'Tis called the fen of Agnefit, O king," replied the saga-man, pointing toward where it lay.

"Why, then, my Rane," asked the boy, "may we not cut our way out through that lowland fen to the open sea and liberty?"

"'Tis Odin's own device," cried the delighted helmsman, catching at his young chief's great plan. "Ho, war wolves all, bite ye your way through the Swedish fens! Up with the serpent banner, and farewell to Olaf the Swede!"

It seemed a narrow chance, but it was the only one. Fortune favored the boy viking. Heavy rains had flooded the lands that slope down to the Maelar Lake; in the dead of night the Swedish captives and stout Norse oarsmen were set to work, and before daybreak an open cut had been made in the lowlands beneath Agnefit, or the "Rock of King Agne," where, by the town of Södertelje, the viking's canal is still shown to travelers; the waters of the lake came rushing through the cut, and an open sea strait awaited young Olaf's fleet.

"Unship the rudder; hoist the sail aloft!" commanded Rane the helmsman. "Sound war horns all! Skoal to the Viking; skoal to the wise young Olaf!"

A strong breeze blew astern; the Norse rowers steered the rudderless ships with their long oars, and with a mighty rush, through the new canal and over all the shallows, out into the great Norrström, or North Stream, as the Baltic Sea was called, the fleet passed in safety while the loud war horns blew the notes of triumph.

So the boy viking escaped from the trap of his Swedish foes, and,

---

[1] So contemptuously did those fierce old sea kings regard a peaceful life that they said of one who died quietly on his bed at home: "His was but a straw death."

standing by the "grim, gaping dragon's head" that crested the prow of his warship, he bade the helmsman steer for Gotland Isle, while Sigvat, the saga-man, sang with the ring of triumph:

"Down the fiord sweep wind and rain;
  Our sails and tackle sway and strain;
    Wet to the skin
    We're sound within.
  Our sea steed through the foam goes prancing,
  While shields and spears and helms are glancing.
    From fiord to sea,
    Our ships ride free,
  And down the wind with swelling sail
  We scud before the gathering gale."

What a breezy, rollicking old saga that is! Can't you almost catch the spray and sea swell in its dashing measures, boys?

Now, turn to your atlases again and look for the large island of Gotland off the southeastern coast of Sweden, in the midst of the Baltic Sea. In the time of Olaf it was a thickly peopled and wealthy district, and the principal town, Wisby, at the northern end, was one of the busiest places in all Europe. To this attractive island the boy viking sailed with all his ships, looking for rich booty, but the Gotlanders met him with fair words and offered him so great a "scatt," or tribute, that he agreed not to molest them, and rested at the island, an unwelcome guest, through all the long winter. Early in the spring he sailed eastward to the Gulf of Riga and spread fear and terror along the coast of Finland. And the old saga tells how the Finlanders "conjured up in the night, by their witchcraft, a dreadful storm and bad weather; but the king ordered all the anchors to be weighed and sail hoisted, and beat off all night to the outside of the land. So the king's luck prevailed more than the Finlanders' witchcraft."

Then away "through the wild sea" to Denmark sailed the young pirate king, and here he met a brother viking, one Thorkell the Tall. The two chiefs struck up a sort of partnership; and coasting southward along the western shores of Denmark, they won a sea fight in the Ringkiorbing Fiord, among the "sand hills of Jutland."

And so business continued brisk with this curiously matched pirate firm—a giant and a boy—until, under the cliffs of Kinlimma, in Friesland, hasty word came to the boy viking that the English king, Ethelred, "the Unready," was calling for the help of all sturdy fighters to win back his heritage and crown from young King Cnut, or Canute the Dane, whose father had seized the throne of England. Quick to respond to an appeal that promised plenty of hard knocks, and the possibility of unlimited booty, Olaf, the ever ready, hoisted his blue and crimson sails and steered his warships over the sea to help King Ethelred, the never ready. Up the Thames and straight for London town he rowed.

"Hail to the serpent banner! Hail to Olaf the Brave!" said King Ethelred, as the war horns sounded a welcome; and on the low shores of the Isle of Dogs, just below the old city, the keels of the Norse warships grounded swiftly, and the boy viking and his followers leaped ashore. "Thou dost come in right good time with thy trusty dragon-ships, young king," said King Ethelred; "for the Danish robbers are full well entrenched in London town and in my father Edgar's castle."

And then he told Olaf how, "in the great trading place which is called Southwark," the Danes had raised "a great work and dug large ditches, and within had builded a bulwark of stone, timber, and turf, where they had stationed a large army."

"And we would fain have taken this bulwark," added the king, "and did in sooth bear down upon it with a great assault; but indeed we could make naught of it."

"And why so?" asked the young viking.

"Because," said King Ethelred, "upon the bridge betwixt the castle and Southwark have the ravaging Danes raised towers and parapets, breast high, and thence they did cast down stones and weapons upon us so that we could not prevail. And now, sea king, what dost thou counsel? How may we avenge ourselves of our enemies and win the town?"

Impetuous as ever, and impatient of obstacles, the young viking said: "How? Why, pull thou down this bridge, king, and then may ye have free river-way to thy castle."

"Break down great London Bridge, young hero?" cried the amazed king. "How may that be? Have we a Duke Samson among us to do so great a feat?"

"Lay me thy ships alongside mine, King, close to this barricaded bridge," said the valorous boy, "and I will vow to break it down, or ye may call me caitiff and coward."

"Be it so," said Ethelred, the English king; and all the war-chiefs echoed: "Be it so!" So Olaf and his trusty Rane made ready the war-forces for the destruction of the bridge.

Old London Bridge was not what we should now call an imposing structure, but our ancestors of nine centuries back esteemed it quite a bridge. The chronicler says that it was "so broad that two wagons could pass each other upon it," and "under the bridge were piles driven into the bottom of the river."

So young Olaf and old Rane put their heads together, and decided to wreck the bridge by a bold viking stroke. And this is how it is told in the "Heimskringla," or Saga of King Olaf the Saint:

"King Olaf ordered great platforms of floating wood to be tied together with hazel bands, and for this he took down old houses; and with these, as a roof, he covered over his ships so widely that it reached over the ships' sides. Under this screen he set pillars, so high and stout that there both was room for swinging their swords, and the roofs were strong enough to withstand the stones cast down upon them.

"Now, out oars and pull for the bridge," young Olaf commanded; and the roofed-over warships were rowed close up to London Bridge.

And as they came near the bridge, the chronicle says: "There were cast upon them, by the Danes upon the bridge, so many stones and missile weapons, such as arrows and spears, that neither helmet nor shield could hold out against it; and the ships themselves were so greatly damaged that many retreated out of it."

But the boy viking and his Norsemen were there for a purpose, and were not to be driven back by stones or spears or arrows. Straight ahead they rowed, "quite up under the bridge."

"Out cables, all, and lay them around the piles," the young sea-king shouted; and the half-naked rowers, unshipping their oars,

reached out under the roofs and passed the stout cables twice around
the wooden supports of the bridge. The loose end was made fast at
the stern of each vessel, and then, turning and heading down stream,
King Olaf's twenty stout warships waited his word:

"Out oars!" he cried, "pull war-birds! Pull all, as if ye were for
Norway!"

Forward and backward swayed the stout Norse rowers; tighter
and tighter pulled the cables; fast down upon the straining warships
rained the Danish spears and stones; but the wooden piles under the
great bridge were loosened by the steady tug of the cables, and soon
with a sudden spurt the Norse warships darted down the river, while
the slackened cables towed astern the captured piles of London
Bridge. A great shout went up from the besiegers, and "now," says
the chronicle, "as the armed troops stood thick upon the bridge, and
there were likewise many heaps of stones and other weapons upon
it, the bridge gave way; and a great part of the men upon it fell
into the river, and all the others fled—some into the castle, some
into Southwark." And before King Ethelred, "the Unready," could
pull his ships to the attack, young Olaf's fighting men had sprung
ashore, and, storming the Southwark earthworks, carried all before
them, and the battle of London Bridge was won.

And the young Olaf's saga-man sang triumphantly:

> "London Bridge is broken down—
> Gold is won and bright renown.
> Shields resounding,
> War horns sounding,
> Hildar shouting in the din!
> Arrows singing,
> Mail coats ringing,
> Odin makes our Olaf win!"

And perhaps, who knows, this wrecking of London Bridge so
many hundred years ago by Olaf, the boy viking of fifteen, may
have been the origin of the old song-game dear to so many generations of children:

> "London Bridge is fallen down, fallen down, fallen down—
> London Bridge is fallen down, my fair lady!"

So King Ethelred won back his kingdom, and the boy viking was honored above all others. To him was given the chief command in perilous expeditions against the Danes, and the whole defense of all the coast of England. North and south along the coast he sailed with all his warships, and the Danes and Englishmen long remembered the dashing but dubious ways of this young sea rover, who swept the English coast and claimed his dues from friend and foe alike. For those were days of insecurity for merchant and trader and farmer, and no man's wealth or life was safe except as he paid ready tribute to the fierce Norse allies of King Ethelred. But soon after this, King Ethelred died, and young Olaf, thirsting for new adventures, sailed away to the south and fought his way all along the French coast as far as the mouth of the River Garonne. Many castles he captured; many rival vikings subdued; much spoil he gathered; until at last his dragon-ships lay moored under the walls of old Bordeaux, waiting for fair winds to take him around to the Straits of Gibraltar, and so on "to the land of Jerusalem."

One day, in the booty-filled "forehold" of his dragon-ship, the young sea king lay asleep; and suddenly, says the old record, "he dreamed a wondrous dream."

"Olaf, great stem of kings, attend!" he heard a deep voice call; and, looking up, the dreamer seemed to see before him "a great and important man, but of a terrible appearance withal."

"If that thou art Olaf the Brave, as men do call thee," said the vision, "turn thyself to nobler deeds than vikings' ravaging and this wandering cruise. Turn back, turn back from thy purposeless journey to the land of Jerusalem, where neither honor nor fame awaits thee. Son of King Harald, return thee to thy heritage; for thou shalt be king over all Norway." Then the vision vanished and the young rover awoke to find himself alone, save for the sleeping footboy across the cabin doorway. So he quickly summoned old Rane, the helmsman, and told his dream.

" 'Twas for thy awakening, king," said his stout old follower. " 'Twas the great Olaf, thine uncle, Olaf Tryggvesson, the King, that did call thee. Win Norway, King, for the portent is that thou and thine shall rule thy fatherland."

And the warships' prows were all turned northward again, as the boy viking, following the promise of his dream, steered homeward for Norway and a throne.

Now in Norway Earl Eric was dead. For thirteen years he had usurped the throne that should have been filled by one of the great King Olaf's line; and, at his death, his handsome young son, Earl Hakon the Fair, ruled in his father's stead. And when young King Olaf heard this news, he shouted for joy and cried to Rane:

"Now, home in haste, for Norway shall be either Hakon's heritage or mine!"

" 'Tis a fair match of youth 'gainst youth," said the trusty helmsman; "and if but fair luck go with thee, Norway shall be thine!"

So from "a place called Furovald," somewhere between the mouths of Humber and of Tees, on the English coast, King Olaf, with but two stout warships and two hundred and twenty "well-armed and chosen persons," shook out his purple sails to the North Sea blasts, and steered straight for Norway.

As if in league against this bold young viking the storm winds came rushing down from the mountains of Norway and the cold belt of the Arctic Circle and caught the two warships tossing in a raging sea.

The storm burst upon them with terrific force, and the danger of shipwreck was great. "But," says the old record, "as they had a chosen company and the king's luck with them all went on well."

"Thou able chief!"

sings the faithful saga-man,

"With thy fearless crew
Thou meetest with skill and courage true
    The wild sea's wrath
    On thy ocean path.
Though waves mast-high were breaking round,
Thou findest the middle of Norway's ground,
    With helm in hand
    On Saelö's strand."

Now *Sael* was Norse for "lucky" and Saelö's Island means the lucky island.

"I'll be a lucky king for landing thus upon the Lucky Isle," said rash young Olaf, with the only attempt at a joke we find recorded of him, as, with a mighty leap, he sprang ashore where the sliding keel of his warship plowed the shore of Saelö's Isle.

"True, 'tis a good omen, King," said old Rane the helmsman, following close behind.

But the soil of the "Lucky Isle" was largely of clay, moist and slippery, and as the eager young viking climbed the bank his right foot slipped, and he would have fallen had not he struck his left foot firmly in the clay and thus saved himself. But to slip at all was a bad sign in those old, half-pagan and superstitious times, and he said, ruefully: "An omen; an omen, Rane! The king falls!"

"Nay, 'tis the king's luck," says ready and wise old Rane. "Thou didst not fall, King. See; thou didst but set fast foot in this thy native soil of Norway."

"Thou art a rare diviner, Rane," laughed the young king, much relieved, and then he added solemnly: "It may be so if God doth will it so."

And now news comes that Earl Hakon, with a single warship, is steering north from Sogne Fiord; and Olaf, pressing on, lays his two ships on either side of a narrow strait, or channel, in Sandunga Sound. Here he stripped his ships of all their war gear, and stretched a great cable deep in the water, across the narrow strait. Then he wound the cable ends around the capstans, ordered all his fighting men out of sight, and waited for his rival. Soon Earl Hakon's warship, crowded with rowers and fighting men, entered the strait. Seeing, as he supposed, but two harmless merchant vessels lying on either side of the channel, the young earl bade his rowers pull between the two. Suddenly there is a stir on the quiet merchant vessels. The capstan bars are manned; the sunken cable is drawn taut. Up goes the stern of Earl Hakon's entrapped warship; down plunges her prow into the waves, and the water pours into the doomed boat. A loud shout is heard; the quiet merchant vessels swarm with mail-clad men, and the air is filled with a shower of

stones, and spears, and arrows. The surprise is complete. Tighter
draws the cable; over topples Earl Hakon's vessel, and he and all his
men are among the billows struggling for life. "So," says the record,
"King Olaf took Earl Hakon and all his men whom they could get
hold of out of the water and made them prisoners; but some were
killed and some were drowned."

Into the "forehold" of the king's ship the captive earl was led a
prisoner, and there the young rivals for Norway's crown faced each
other. The two lads were of nearly the same age—between sixteen
and seventeen—and young Earl Hakon was considered the hand-
somest youth in all Norway. His helmet was gone, his sword was
lost, his ring-steel suit was sadly disarranged, and his long hair, "fine
as silk," was "bound about his head with a gold ornament." Fully
expecting the fate of all captives in those cruel days—instant death
—the young earl nevertheless faced his boy conqueror proudly, resolved to meet his fate like a man.

"They speak truth who say of the house of Eric that ye be handsome men," said the King, studying his prisoner's face. "But now,
Earl, even though thou be fair to look upon, thy luck hath failed
thee at last."

"Fortune changes," said the young earl. "We both be boys; and
thou, King, art perchance the shrewder youth. Yet, had we looked
for such a trick as thou hast played upon us, we had not thus been
tripped upon thy sunken cables. Better luck next time."

"Next time!" echoed the King; "dost thou not know, Earl, that
as thou standest there, a prisoner, there may be no 'next time' for
thee?"

The young captive understood full well the meaning of the words.
"Yes, King," he said; "it must be only as thou mayst determine.
Man can die but once. Speak on; I am ready!" But Olaf said:
"What wilt thou give me, Earl, if at this time I do let thee go, whole
and unhurt?"

"'Tis not what I may give, but what thou mayst take, King,"
the earl made answer. "I am thy prisoner; what wilt thou take to
free me?"

"Nothing," said the generous young viking, advancing nearer to his handsome rival. "As thou didst say, we both be boys, and life is all before us. Earl, I give thee thy life, do thou but take oath before me to leave this my realm of Norway, to give up thy kingdom, and never to do battle against me hereafter."

The conquered earl bent his fair young head.

"Thou art a generous chief, King Olaf," he said. "I take my life as thou dost give it, and all shall be as thou wilt."

So Earl Hakon took the oath, and King Olaf righted his rival's capsized warship, refitted it from his own stores of booty, and thus the two lads parted: the young earl sailing off to his uncle, King Canute, in England, and the boy viking hastening eastward to Vigen, where lived his mother, the Queen Aasta, whom he had not seen for full five years.

It is harvest time in the year 1014. Without and within the long, low house of Sigurd Syr, at Vigen, all is excitement; for word has come that Olaf the sea king has returned to his native land, and is even now on his way to this his mother's house. Gay stuffs decorate the dull walls of the great-room, clean straw covers the earth floor, and upon the long, four-cornered tables is spread a mighty feast of mead and ale and coarse but hearty food, such as the old Norse heroes drew their strength and muscle from. At the doorway stands the Queen Aasta with her maidens, while before the entrance, with thirty "well-clothed men," waits young Olaf's stepfather, wise Sigurd Syr, gorgeous in a jeweled suit, a scarlet cloak, and a glittering golden helmet. The watchers on the housetops hear a distant shout, now another and nearer one, and soon, down the highway, they catch the gleam of steel and the waving of many banners; and now they can distinguish the stalwart forms of Olaf's chosen hundred men, their shining coats of ring mail, their foreign helmets, and their crossleted shields flashing in the sun. In the very front rides old Rane, the helmsman, bearing the great white banner blazoned with the golden serpent, and behind him, cased in golden armor, his long brown hair flowing over his sturdy shoulders, rides the boy viking, Olaf of Norway.

It was a brave home-coming; and as the stout young hero, leaping from his horse, knelt to receive his mother's welcoming kiss, the people shouted for joy, the banners waved, the war horns played their loudest; and thus, after five years of wandering, the boy comes back in triumph to the home he left when but a wild and adventurous little fellow of twelve. The hero of nine great sea fights, and of many smaller ones, before he was seventeen, young Olaf Haraldson was a remarkable boy, even in the days when all boys aimed to be battle-tried heroes. Toughened in frame and fiber by his five years of sea roving, he had become strong and self-reliant, a man in action though but a boy in years.

"I am come," he said to his mother and his stepfather, "to take the heritage of my forefathers. But not from Danish nor from Swedish kings will I supplicate that which is mine by right. I intend rather to seek my patrimony with battle-ax and sword, and I will so lay hand to the work that one of two things shall happen: Either I shall bring all this kingdom of Norway under my rule, or I shall fall here upon my inheritance in the land of my fathers."

These were bold words for a boy of seventeen. But they were not idle boastings. Before a year had passed, young Olaf's pluck and courage had won the day, and in harvest time, in the year 1015, being then but little more than eighteen years old, he was crowned King of Norway in the Drontheim, or "Throne-home," of Nidaros, the royal city, now called on your atlas the city of Drontheim. For fifteen years King Olaf the Second ruled his realm of Norway. The old record says that he was "a good and very gentle man"; but history shows his goodness and gentleness to have been of a rough and savage kind. The wild and stern experiences of his viking days lived again even in his attempts to reform and benefit his land. When he who had been himself a pirate tried to put down piracy, and he who had been a wild young robber sought to force all Norway to become Christian, he did these things in so fierce and cruel a way that at last his subjects rebelled, and King Canute came over with a great army to wrest his throne from him. On the bloody field of Stiklestad, July 29, 1030, the stern king fell, says Sigvat, his saga-man,

> "beneath the blows
> By his own thoughtless people given."

So King Canute conquered Norway; but after his death, Olaf's son, Magnus the Good, regained his father's throne. The people, sorrowful at their rebellion against King Olaf, forgot his stern and cruel ways, and magnified all his good deeds so mightily that he was at last declared a saint, and the shrine of Saint Olaf is still one of the glories of the old cathedral in Drontheim. And, after King Magnus died, his descendants ruled Norway for nearly four hundred years; and thus was brought to pass the promise of the dream that, in the "forehold" of the great dragon-ship, under the walls of old Bordeaux, came so many years before to the daring and sturdy young Olaf of Norway, the boy viking.

KNIGHTED BY KING HENRY IV

By *HOWARD PYLE*

Illustration by Albrecht Dürer

IN Myles Falworth's day one of the greatest ceremonies of courtly life was that of the bestowal of knighthood by the King, with the honors of the Bath. By far the greater number of knights were at that time created by other knights, or by nobles, or by officers of the crown. To be knighted by the King in person distinguished the recipient for life. It was this signal honor that the Earl of Mackworth, for his own purposes, wished Myles to enjoy, and for this end he had laid not a few plans.

The accolade was the term used for the creation of a knight upon the field of battle. It was a reward of valor or of meritorious service, and was generally bestowed in a more or less offhand way; but the ceremony of the Bath was an occasion of the greatest courtly moment, and it was thus that Myles Falworth was to be knighted in addition to the honor of a royal belting.

A quaint old book treating of knighthood and chivalry gives a full and detailed account of all the circumstances of the ceremony of a creation of a Knight of the Bath. It tells us that the candidate was first placed under the care of two squires of honor, "grave and well seen in courtship and nurture, and also in feats of chivalry," which same were likewise to be governors in all things relating to the coming honors.

First of all, the barber shaved him, and cut his hair in a certain peculiar fashion ordained for the occasion, the squires of honor supervising the operation. This being concluded, the candidate was solemnly conducted to the chamber where the bath of tepid water was prepared, "hung within and without with linen, and likewise covered with rich cloths and embroidered linen." While in the bath two "ancient, grave, and reverend knights" attended the bachelor, giving him "meet instructions in the order and feats of chivalry." The candidate was then examined as to his knowledge and acquirements, and then, all questions being answered to the satisfaction of his examiners, the elder of the two dipped a handful of water out from the bath, and poured it upon his head, at the same time signing his left shoulder with the sign of the cross.

As soon as this ceremony was concluded, the two squires of honor helped their charge from the bath, and conducted him to a plain bed without hangings, where they let him rest until his body was warm and dry. Then they clad him in a white linen shirt, and over it a plain robe of russet, "girdled about the loins with a rope, and having a hood like unto a hermit."

As soon as the candidate had arisen, the two "ancient knights" returned, and all being in readiness he was escorted to the chapel, the two walking, one upon either side of him, his squires of honor marching before, and the whole party preceded by "sundry minstrels making a loud noise of music."

When they came to the chapel, the two knights who escorted him took leave of the candidate, each saluting him with a kiss upon the cheek. No one remained with him but his squires of honor, the priest, and the chandler.

In the meantime the novitiate's armor, sword, lance and helmet had been laid in readiness before the altar. These he watched and guarded while the others slept, keeping vigil until sunrise, during which time "he shall," says the ancient authority, "pass the night in orisons, prayers, and meditation." At daylight he confessed to the priest, heard matins, and communicated in Mass, and then presented a lighted candle at the altar, with a piece of money stuck in it as close to the flame as could be done, the candle being offered to the honor of God, and the money to the honor of that person who was to make him a knight.

So concluded the sacred ceremony, which being ended his squires conducted the candidate to his chamber, and there made him comfortable, and left him to repose for a while before the second and final part of the ordinance.

Such is a shortened account of the preparatory stages of the ceremonies through which Myles Falworth passed.

Matters had come upon him so suddenly one after the other,

and had come with such bewildering rapidity that all that week was to him like some strange, wonderful, mysterious vision. He went through it all like one in a dream. Lord George Beaumont was one of his squires of honor; the other, by way of a fitting compliment to the courage of the chivalrous lad, was the Sieur de la Montaigne, his opponent soon to be. They were well versed in everything relating to knightcraft, and Myles followed all their directions with passive obedience. Then Sir James Lee and the Comte de Vermoise administered the ceremony of the Bath, the old knight examining him in the laws of chivalry.

It occurs perhaps once or twice in one's lifetime that one passes through great happenings—sometimes of joy, sometimes of dreadful bitterness——in just such a dazed state as Myles passed through this. It is only afterwards that all comes back to one so sharply and keenly that the heart thrills almost in agony in living it over again. But perhaps of all the memory of that time, when it afterwards came back piece by piece, none was so clear to Myles's back-turned vision as the long night spent in the chapel, watching his armor, thinking such wonderful thoughts, and dreaming such wonderful wide-eyed dreams. At such times Myles saw again the dark mystery of the castle chapel; he saw again the half-moon gleaming white and silvery through the tall, narrow window and throwing a broad form of still whiteness across stone floor, empty seats, and still, motionless figures of stone effigies. At such times he stood again in front of the twinkling tapers that lit the altar where his armor lay piled in a heap, heard again the deep breathing of his companions of the watch sleeping in some empty stall, wrapped each in his cloak, and saw the old chandler bestir himself, and rise and come forward to snuff the candles. At such times he saw again the day growing clearer and clearer through the tall glazed windows, saw it change to a rosy pink, and then to a broad, ruddy glow that threw a halo of light around Father Thomas's bald head bowed in sleep, and lit up the banners and trophies hanging motionless against the stony face of the west wall; heard again the stirring of life without and the sound of his companions arousing themselves; saw them come forward and heard them wish him joy that his long watch was ended.

It was nearly noon when Myles was awakened from a fitful sleep by Gascoyne bringing in his dinner, but, as might be supposed, he had but little hunger, and ate sparingly. He had hardly ended his frugal meal before his two squires of honor came in, followed by a servant carrying the garments for the coming ceremony. He saluted them gravely, and then arising, washed his face and hands in a basin which Gascoyne held; then kneeled in prayer, the others standing silent at a little distance. As he arose, Lord George came forward.

"The King and the company come presently to the Great Hall, Myles," said he; "it is needful for thee to make all the haste that thou art able."

Perhaps never had Devlen Castle seen a more brilliant and goodly company gathered in the great hall than that which came to witness King Henry create Myles Falworth a knight bachelor.

At the upper edge of the hall was a raised dais, upon which stood a throne covered with crimson satin and embroidered with lions and flower-de-luces; it was the King's seat. He and his personal attendants had not yet come, but the rest of the company were gathered. The day being warm and sultry, the balcony was all a-flutter with the feather fans of the ladies of the family and their attendants, who from this high place looked down upon the hall below. Up the center of the hall was laid a carpet of arras, and the passage was protected by wooden railings. Upon the one side were tiers of seats for the castle gentlefolks and the guests. Upon the other stood the burghers from the town, clad in sober dun and russet, and yeomanry in green and brown. The whole of the great vaulted hall was full of the dull hum of many people waiting, and a ceaseless restlessness stirred the crowded throng. But at last a whisper went around that the King was coming. A momentary hush fell, and through it was heard the noisy clatter of horses' feet coming nearer and nearer, and then stopping before the door. The sudden blare of trumpets broke through the hush; another pause, and then in through the great doorway of the hall came the royal procession.

First of all marched, in the order of their rank, and to the number of a score or more, certain gentlemen, esquires and knights, chosen mostly from the King's attendants. Behind these came two

Albrecht Dürer

Knights in Combat.

[See page 101]

pursuivants-at-arms in tabards, and following them a party of a dozen more bannerets and barons. Behind these again, a little space intervening, came two heralds, also in tabards, a group of the greater nobles attendant upon the King following in the order of their rank. Next came the King-at-arms and, at a little distance and walking with sober slowness, the King himself, with the Earl and Count directly attendant upon him—the one marching upon the right hand and the other upon the left. A breathless silence filled the whole space as the royal procession advanced slowly up the hall. Through the stillness could be heard the muffled sound of the footsteps on the carpet, the dry rustling of silk and satin garments, and the clear clink and jingle of chains and jeweled ornaments, but not the sound of a single voice.

After the moment or two of bustle and confusion of the King taking his place had passed, another little space of expectant silence fell. At last there suddenly came the noise of acclamation of those who stood without the door—cheering and the clapping of hands—sounds heralding the immediate advent of Myles and his attendants. The next moment the little party entered the hall.

First of all, Gascoyne, bearing Myles's sword in both hands, the hilt resting against his breast, the point elevated at an angle of forty-five degrees. It was sheathed in a crimson scabbard, and the belt of Spanish leather studded with silver bosses was wound crosswise around it. From the hilt of the sword dangled the gilt spurs of his coming knighthood. At a little distance behind his squire followed Myles, the center of all observation. He was clad in a novitiate dress, arranged under Lord George's personal supervision. It had been made somewhat differently from the fashion usual at such times, and was intended to indicate in a manner the candidate's extreme youthfulness and virginity in arms. The outer garment was a tabard robe of white wool, embroidered at the hem with fine lines of silver, and gathered loosely at the waist with a belt of lavender leather stitched with thread of silver. Beneath he was clad in armor (a present from the Earl), new and polished till it shone with dazzling brightness, the breastplate covered with a jupon of white satin, embroidered with silver. Behind Myles, and upon either hand, came his squires of honor, sponsors, and friends—a little company of some half-dozen in all. As they advanced slowly up the great, dim, high-vaulted room, the whole multitude broke forth into a humming buzz of applause. Then a sudden clapping of hands began near the doorway, ran down through the length of the room, and was taken up by all with noisy clatter.

"Saw I never youth so comely," whispered one of the Lady Anne's attendant gentlewomen. "Sure he looketh as Sir Galahad looked when he came first to King Arthur's court."

Myles knew that he was very pale; he felt rather than saw the restless crowd of faces upon either side, for his eyes were fixed directly before him, upon the dais whereon sat the King, with the Earl of Mackworth standing at his right hand, the Comte de Vermoise upon the left, and the others ranged around and behind the throne. It was with the same tense feeling of dreamy unreality that Myles walked slowly up the length of the hall, measuring his steps by those of Gascoyne. Suddenly he felt Lord George Beaumont touch him lightly upon the arm, and almost instinctively he stopped short—he was standing just before the covered steps of the throne.

He saw Gascoyne mount to the third step, stop short, kneel, and offer the sword and the spurs he carried to the King, who took the weapon and laid it across his knees. Then the squire bowed low, and walking backward withdrew to one side, leaving Myles standing alone facing the throne. The King unlocked the spur chains from the sword-hilt, and then, holding the gilt spurs in his hand for a moment, he looked Myles straight in the eyes and smiled. Then he turned, and gave one of the spurs to the Earl of Mackworth.

The Earl took it with a low bow, turned, and came slowly down the steps to where Myles stood. Kneeling upon one knee, and placing Myles's foot upon the other, Lord Mackworth set the spur in its place and latched the chain over the instep. He drew the sign of the cross upon Myles's bended knee, set the foot back upon the ground, rose with slow dignity, and bowing to the King, drew a little to one side.

As soon as the Earl had fulfilled his office the King gave the second spur to the Comte de Vermoise, who set it to Myles's other

foot with the same ceremony that the Earl had observed, withdrawing as he had done to one side.

An instant pause of motionless silence followed, and then the
King slowly arose, and began deliberately to unwind the belt from
around the scabbard of the sword he held. As soon as he stood,
the Earl and the Count advanced, and taking Myles by either hand,
led him forward and up the steps of the dais to the platform above.
As they drew a little to one side, the King stooped and buckled the
sword-belt around Myles's waist then, rising again, lifted his hand
and struck him on the shoulder, crying, in a loud voice,

"Be thou a good knight!"

Instantly a loud sound of applause and the clapping of hands
filled the whole hall, in the midst of which the King laid both
hands upon Myles's shoulders and kissed him upon the right cheek.
So the ceremony ended: Myles was no longer Myles Falworth, but
Sir Myles Falworth, Knight by Order of the Bath and by grace of
the King!

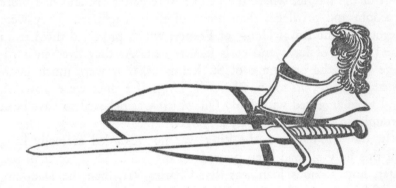

JOAN THE MAID

By *ANDREW LANG*

FOUR hundred and seventy years ago, the children of Domremy, a little village near the Meuse, on the borders of France and Lorraine, used to meet and dance and sing beneath a beautiful beech-tree, "lovely as a lily." They called it "The Fairy Tree," or "The Good Ladies' Lodge," meaning the fairies by the words "Good Ladies." Among these children was one named Jeanne (born 1412), the daughter of an honest farmer, Jacques d'Arc. Jeanne sang more than she danced, and though she carried garlands like the other boys and girls, and hung them on the boughs of the Fairies' Tree, she liked better to take the flowers into the parish church, and lay them on the altars of St. Margaret and St. Catherine. Joan's parents were not indigent; they had lands and cattle, and a little money laid by in case of need. Her father was, at one time, *doyen* or headman, of Domremy. Their house was hard by the church, and was in the part of the hamlet where the people were better off, and had more freedom and privileges than many of their neighbors. They were devoted to the Royal House of France, which protected them from the tyranny of lords and earls farther east. As they lived in a village under the patronage of St. Remigius, they were much interested in Reims, his town, where the kings of France were crowned, and were anointed with Holy Oil which was believed to have been brought in a sacred bottle by an angel.

In the Middle Ages, the king was not regarded as really king till this holy oil had been poured on his head. Thus we shall see, later, how anxious Joan was that Charles VII, then the Dauphin, should be crowned and anointed in Reims, though it was still in the possession of the English. It is also necessary to remember that Joan had once an elder sister named Catherine, whom she loved dearly. Catherine died, and perhaps affection for her made Joan more fond of bringing flowers to the altar of her namesake, St. Catherine, and of praying often to that saint.

Joan was brought up by her parents, as she told her judges, to be industrious, to sew and spin. She did not fear to match herself at spinning and sewing, she said, against any woman in Rouen. When very young she sometimes went to the fields to watch the cattle, like the goose-girl in the fairy tale. As she grew older, she worked in the house, she did not any longer watch sheep and cattle. But the times were dangerous, and, when there was an alarm of soldiers or robbers in the neighborhood, she sometimes helped to drive the flock into a fortified island, or peninsula, for which her father was responsible, in the river near her home. She learned her creed, she said, from her mother. Twenty years after her death, her neighbors, who remembered her, described her as she was when a child. Jean Morin said she was a good industrious girl, but that she would often be praying in church when her father and mother did not know it. Beatrix Estellin, an old widow of eighty, said Joan was a good girl. When Domremy was burned, Joan would go to church at Greux, "and there was not a better girl in the two towns." A priest, who had known her, called her "a good, simple, well-behaved girl." Jean Waterin, when he was a boy, had seen Joan in the fields, "and when they were all playing together, she would go apart, and pray to God, as he thought, and he and the others used to laugh at her. She was good and simple, and often in churches and holy places. And when she heard the church bell ring, she would kneel down in the fields." She used to bribe the sexton to ring the bells (a duty which he rather neglected) with presents of knitted wool.

All those who had seen Joan told the same tale: she was always kind, simple, industrious, pious, and yet merry and fond of playing with the others round the Fairy Tree. They say that the singing birds came to her, and nestled in her breast.

Thus, as far as anyone could tell, Joan was a child like other children, but more serious and more religious. One of her friends, a girl called Mengette, whose cottage was next to that of Joan's father, said: "Joan was so pious that we other children told her she was too good."

In peaceful times Joan would have lived and married and died

and been forgotten. But the times were evil. The two parties of
Burgundy and Armagnac divided town from town and village from
village. It was as in the days of the Douglas wars in Scotland, when
the very children took sides for Queen Mary and King James, and
fought each other in the streets. Domremy was for the Armagnacs
—that is, against the English and for the Dauphin, the son of the
mad Charles VI. But at Maxey, on the Meuse, a village near Domremy, the people were all for Burgundy and the English. The boys
of Domremy would go out and fight the Maxey boys with fists and
sticks and stones. Joan did not remember having taken part in those
battles, but she had often seen her brothers and the Domremy boys
come home all bruised and bleeding.

Once Joan saw more of war than these schoolboy bickers. It was
in 1425, when she was a girl of thirteen. There was a kind of robber
chief on the English side, a man named Henri d'Orly, from Savoy,
who dwelt in the castle of Doulevant. There he and his band of
armed men lived and drank and plundered far and near. One day
there galloped into Domremy a squadron of spearmen, who rode
through the fields driving together the cattle of the villagers, among
them the cows of Joan's father. The country people could make no
resistance; they were glad enough if their houses were not burned.
So off rode Henri d'Orly's men, driving the cattle with their spear-
points along the track to the castle of Doulevant. But cows are not
fast travelers, and when the robbers had reached a little village
called Dommartin le Franc they rested, and went to the tavern to
make merry. But by this time a lady, Madame d'Ogévillier, had
sent in all haste to the Count de Vaudemont to tell him how the
villagers of Domremy had been ruined. So he called his squire,
Barthélemy de Clefmont, and bade him summon his spears and
mount and ride. It reminds us of the old Scottish ballad, where
Jamie Telfer of the Fair Dodhead has seen all his cattle driven out
of his stalls by the English; and he runs to Branxholme and warns
the water, and they with Harden pursue the English, defeat them,
and recover Telfer's kye, with a great spoil out of England. Just so
Barthélemy de Clefmont, with seven or eight lances, galloped down
the path to Dommartin le Franc. There they found the cattle, and

d'Orly's men fled like cowards. So Barthélemy with his comrades was returning very joyously, when Henri d'Orly rode up with a troop of horse and followed hard after Barthélemy. He was wounded by a lance, but he cut his way through d'Orly's men, and also brought the cattle back safely—a very gallant deed of arms. We may fancy the delight of the villagers when "the kye cam' hame." It may have been now that an event happened, of which Joan does not tell us herself, but which was reported by the king's seneschal, in June 1429, when Joan had just begun her wonderful career. The children of the village, says the seneschal, were running races and leaping in wild joy about the fields; possibly their gladness was caused by the unexpected rescue of their cattle. Joan ran so much more fleetly than the rest, and leaped so far, that the children believed she actually *flew,* and they told her so! Tired and breathless, "out of herself," says the seneschal, she paused, and in that moment she heard a Voice, but saw no man; the Voice bade her go home, because her mother had need of her. And when she came home the Voice said many things to her about the great deeds which God bade her do for France. We shall hear later Joan's own account of how her visions and Voices first came to her.

Three years later there was an alarm, and the Domremy people fled to Neufchâteau, Joan going with her parents. Afterwards her enemies tried to prove that she had been a servant at an inn in Neufchâteau, had lived roughly with grooms and soldiers, and had learned to ride. But this was absolutely untrue. An ordinary child would have thought little of war and of the sorrows of her country in the flowery fields of Domremy and Vaucouleurs; but Joan always thought of the miseries of *France la bele,* fair France, and prayed for her country and her king. A great road, on the lines of an old Roman way, passed near Domremy, so Joan would hear all the miserable news from travelers. Probably she showed what was in her mind, for her father dreamed that she "had gone off with soldiers," and this dream struck him so much, that he told his sons that he, or they, must drown Joan if she so disgraced herself. For many girls of bad character, lazy and rude, followed the soldiers, as they always have done and always will. Joan's father thought that his dream meant that Joan would be like these women. It would be interesting to know whether he was in the habit of dreaming true dreams. For Joan, his child, dreamed when wide awake, dreamed dreams immortal, which brought her to her glory and her doom.

When Joan was between twelve and thirteen, a wonderful thing befell her. We have already heard one account of it, written when Joan was in the first flower of her triumph, by the seneschal of the King of France. A Voice spoke to her and prophesied of what she was to do. But about these marvelous things it is more safe to attend to what Joan always said herself. She told the same story both to friends and foes; to the learned men who, by her king's desire, examined her at Poictiers before she went to war (April 1429); and to her deadly foes at Rouen. No man can read her answers to them and doubt that she spoke what she believed. And she died for this belief. Unluckily the book that was kept of what she said at Poictiers is lost. Before her enemies at Rouen there were many things which she did not think it right to say. On one point, after for long refusing to speak, she told her foes a kind of parable, which we must not take as part of her real story.

When Joan was between twelve and thirteen (1424), so she swore, *"a Voice came to her from God for her guidance,* but when first it came, she was in great fear. And it came, that Voice, about noonday, in the summer season, she being in her father's garden. And Joan had not fasted the day before that, but was fasting when the Voice came. And she heard the Voice on her right side, toward the church, and rarely did she hear it but she also saw a great light." These are her very words. They asked her if she heard these Voices there, in the hall of judgment, and she answered, "If I were in a wood, I should well hear these Voices coming to me." The Voices at first only told her "to be a good girl, and go to church." She thought it was a holy Voice, and that it came from God; and the third time she heard it she knew it was the voice of an angel. The Voice told her of "the great pity there was in France," and that one day she must go into France and help the country. She had visions with the Voices; visions first of St. Michael, and then of

St. Catherine and St. Margaret. She hated telling her hypocritical judges anything about these heavenly visions, but it seems that she really believed in their appearance, believed that she had embraced the knees of St. Margaret and St. Catherine, and she did reverence to them when they came to her. "I saw them with my bodily eyes, as I see you," she said to her judges, "and when they departed from me I wept, and well I wished that they had taken me with them."

It was in 1424 that the Voices first came to Joan the Maid. The years went on, bringing more and more sorrow to France. In 1428 only a very few small towns in the east still held out for the Dauphin, and these were surrounded on every side by enemies. Meanwhile the Voices came more frequently, urging Joan to go into France and help her country. She asked how she, a girl, who could not ride or use sword and lance, could be of any help? Rather would she stay at home and spin beside her dear mother. At the same time she was encouraged by one of the vague old prophecies which were as common in France as in Scotland. A legend ran "that France was to be saved by a maiden from the Oak Wood," and there was an Oak Wood, *le bois chénu,* near Domremy. Some such prophecy had an influence on Joan, and probably helped people to believe in her. The Voices, moreover, instantly and often commanded her to go to Vaucouleurs, a neighboring town which was loyal, and there meet Robert de Baudricourt, who was a captain of the French garrison. Now, Robert de Baudricourt was not what is called a romantic person. Though little over thirty, he had already married, one after the other, two rich widows. He was a gallant soldier, but a plain practical man, very careful of his own interest, and cunning enough to hold his own among his many enemies, English, Burgundian, and Lorrainers. It was to him that Joan must go, a country girl to a great noble, and tell him that she, and she alone, could save France! Joan knew what manner of man Robert de Baudricourt was, for her father had been obliged to visit him and speak for the people of Domremy when they were oppressed. She could hardly hope that he would listen to her, and it was with a heavy heart that she found a good reason for leaving home to visit Vaucouleurs. Joan had a cousin, a niece of her mother's, who was married to one Durand Lassois, at Burey en Vaux, a village near Vaucouleurs. This cousin invited Joan to visit her for a week. At the end of that time she spoke to her cousin's husband. There was an old saying, as we saw, that France would be rescued by a Maid, and she, as she told Lassois, was that Maid. Lassois listened, and, whatever he may have thought of her chances, he led her to Robert de Baudricourt.

Joan came, on May 13, 1428, in her simple red dress, and walked straight up to the captain among his men. She knew him, she said, by what her Voices had told her, but she may also have heard him described by her father. She told him that the Dauphin must keep quiet, and risk no battle, for before the middle of Lent next year (1429) God would send him succor. She added that the kingdom belonged, not to the Dauphin, but to her Master, who willed that the Dauphin should be crowned, and she herself would lead him to Reims, to be anointed with the holy oil.

"And who is your Master?" said Robert.

"The King of Heaven!"

Robert, very naturally, thought that Joan was crazed, and shrugged his shoulders. He bluntly told Lassois to box her ears, and take her back to her father. So she had to go home; but here new troubles awaited her. The enemy came down on Domremy and burned it; Joan and her family fled to Neufchâteau, where they stayed for a few days. She and her parents soon went back to Domremy.

In Domremy they found that the enemy had ruined everthing. Their cattle were safe, for they had been driven to Neufchâteau, but when Joan looked from her father's garden to the church, she saw nothing but a heap of smoking ruins. She had to go to say her prayers now at the church of Greux. These things only made her feel more deeply the sorrows of her country. The time was drawing near when she had prophesied that the Dauphin was to receive help from heaven—namely, in the Lent of 1429. In that year the season was held more than commonly sacred, for Good Friday and the Annunciation fell on the same day. So, early in January, 1429, Joan the Maid turned her back on Domremy, which she was never to see

again. Her cousin Lassois came and asked leave for Joan to visit him
again; she said good-bye to her father and mother, and to her friend
Mengette, but to her dearest friend Hauvette she did not even say
good-bye, for she could not bear it. She went to her cousin's house
at Burey, and there she stayed for six weeks, hearing bad news of
the siege of Orleans by the English. Meanwhile, Robert de Baudricourt, in Vaucouleurs, was not easy in his mind, for he was likely
to lose the protection of René of Anjou, the Duc de Bar, who was
on the point of joining the English. Thus Robert may have been
more inclined to listen to Joan than when he bade her cousin box
her ears and take her back to her father. Robert was now half
disposed to send her to the king and let her take her chance.

On February 23, 1429, the gate of the little castle of Vaucouleurs,
"the Gate of France," which is still standing, was thrown open.
Seven travelers rode out, among them two squires, Jean de Nouillompont and Bertrand de Poulengy, with their attendants, and Joan
the Maid. "Go, and let what will come of it come!" said Robert de
Baudricourt. He did not expect much to come of it. It was a long
journey—they were eleven days on the road—and a dangerous. But
Joan laughed at danger. "God will clear my path to the king, for to
this end I was born." Often they rode by night, stopping at mon-
asteries when they could. Sometimes they slept out under the sky.
Though she was so young and so beautiful, with the happiness of
her long desire in her eyes, and the glory of her future shining on
her, these two young gentlemen never dreamed of paying their court
to her and making love, as in romances they do, for they regarded
her "as if she had been an angel." "They were in awe of her," they
said, long afterwards, long after the angels had taken Joan to be
with their company in heaven. And all the knights who had seen her
said the same. On March 6 Joan arrived in Chinon, where for two
or three days the king's advisers would not let him see her. At
last they yielded, and she went straight up to him, and when he
denied that he was the king, she told him that she knew well who
he was.

"There is the king," said Charles, pointing to a richly dressed noble.

"No, fair sire. You are he!"

Weeks had passed, and Joan had never yet seen a blow struck in war. She used to exercise herself in horsemanship, and knightly sports of tilting, and it is wonderful that a peasant girl became at once one of the best riders among the chivalry of France. The young Duc d'Alençon, lately come from captivity in England, saw how gallantly she rode, and gave her a horse.

It was now determined that Joan should be taken to Poictiers, and examined before all the learned men, bishops, doctors, and higher clergy who still were on the side of France. During three long weeks the learned men asked her questions, and no doubt they wearied her terribly. But they said it was wonderful how wisely this girl, "who did not know A from B," replied to their puzzling inquiries. She told the story of her visions, of the command laid upon her to rescue Orleans. Said Guillaume Aymeri, "You ask for men-at-arms, and you say that God will have the English to leave France and go home. If this is true, no men-at-arms are needed; God's pleasure can drive the English out of the land."

"In God's name," said the Maid, "the men-at-arms will fight, and God will give the victory." Then came the learned Seguin; "a right sour man was he," said those who knew him.

Seguin was a Limousin, and the Limousins spoke in a queer accent at which the other French were always laughing.

"In what language do your Voices speak?" asked he.

"In a better language than *yours,*" said Joan, and the bishops smiled at the country quip.

"We may not believe in you," said Seguin, "unless you show us a sign."

"I did not come to Poictiers to work miracles," said Joan; "take me to Orleans and I shall show you the signs that I am sent to do." And show them she did.

At last, after examining witnesses from Domremy, and the Queen of Sicily and other great ladies to whom Joan was entrusted, the clergy found nothing in her but "goodness, humility, frank maidenhood, piety, honesty, and simplicity." As for her wearing a man's dress, the Archbishop of Embrun said to the king, "It is more becoming to do these things in man's gear, since they have to be done amongst men."

The king therefore made up his mind at last. Jean and Pierre, Joan's brothers, were to ride with her to Orleans; her old friends, her first friends, Jean de Nouillompont and Bertrand de Poulengy, had never left her. She was given a squire, Jean d'Aulon, a very good man, and a page, Louis de Coutes, and a chaplain. The king gave Joan armor and horses, and offered her a sword. But her Voices told her that behind the altar of St. Catherine de Fierbois, where she heard Mass on her way to Chinon, there was an old sword, with five crosses on the blade, buried in the earth. That sword she was to wear. A man whom Joan did not know, and had never seen, was sent from Tours, and found the sword in the place which she described. The sword was cleaned of rust, and the king gave her two sheaths, one of velvet, one of cloth of gold, but Joan had a leather sheath made for use in war. She also commanded a banner to be made, with the Lilies of France on a white field. There was also a picture of God, holding the round world, and two angels at the sides with the sacred words, JHESU MARIA. On another flag was the Annunciation, the Virgin holding a lily, and the angel coming to her. In battle, when she led a charge, Joan always carried her standard, that she might not be able to use her sword. She wished to kill nobody, and said, "she loved her banner forty times more than her sword."

At last the men-at-arms who were to accompany Joan were ready. She rode at their head, as André de Laval and Guy de Laval saw her and described her in a letter to their mother. She was armed in white armor, but unhelmeted, a little ax in her hand, riding a great black charger, that reared at the door of her lodging and would not let her mount.

"'Lead him to the Cross!' cried she, for a Cross stood on the roadside, by the church. There he stood as if he had been stone, and she mounted. Then she turned to the church, and said, in her girlish voice, 'You priests and churchmen, make prayers and processions to God.' Then she cried, 'Forward, Forward!' and on she rode, a pretty page carrying her banner, and with her little ax in her hand." And so Joan went to war. She led, she says, ten or twelve thousand soldiers. Among the other generals were Xaintrailles and La Hire. Joan made her soldiers confess themselves; as for La Hire, a brave, rough soldier, she forbade him to swear, as he used to do, but, for his weakness, she permitted him to say, *By my bâton!*

About half past six in the morning the actual fight began. The French and Scottish leaped into the fosse, they set ladders against the walls, they reached the battlements, and were struck down by English swords and axes. Cannon balls and great stones and arrows rained on them. "Fight on!" cried the Maid; "the place is ours." At one o'clock, she set a ladder against the wall with her own hands, but was deeply wounded by an arrow, which pierced clean through between neck and shoulder. Joan wept, but seizing the arrow with her own hands she dragged it out. The men-at-arms wished to say magic spells over the wound to "charm" it, but this the Maid forbade as witchcraft.

"Yet," says Dunois, "she did not withdraw from the battle, nor took any medicine for the wound; and the onslaught lasted from morning till eight at night, so that there was no hope of victory. Then I desired that the army should go back to the town, but the Maid came to me and bade me wait a little longer. Next she mounted her horse and rode into a vineyard, and there prayed for the space of seven minutes or eight. Then she returned, took her banner, and stood on the brink of the fosse. The English trembled when they saw her, but our men returned to the charge and met with no resistance. The English fled or were slain, and we returned gladly into Orleans." The people of Orleans had a great share in this victory. Seeing the English hard pressed, they laid long beams across the broken arches of the bridge, and charged by this perilous way. The triumph was even more that of the citizens than of the army. Homer tells us how Achilles, alone and unarmed, stood by the fosse and shouted, and how all the Trojans fled. But here was a greater marvel; and the sight of the wounded girl, bowed beneath the weight of her banner, frighted stouter hearts than those of the men of Troy.

From that hour May 8 is kept a holiday at Orleans in honor of Joan the Maiden. Never was there such a deliverance. In a week the Maid had driven a strong army, full of courage and well led, out of forts like Les Tourelles. The Duc d'Alençon visited it, and said that with a few men-at-arms he would have felt certain of holding it for a week against any strength however great. But Joan not only gave the French her spirit: her extraordinary courage in leading a new charge after so terrible a wound, "six inches deep," says d'Alençon, made the English think that they were fighting a force not of this world. And that is exactly what they were doing.

The Maid had shown her sign, as she promised; she had rescued Orleans. Her next desire was to lead Charles to Reims, through a country occupied by the English, and to have him anointed there with the holy oil. Till this was done she could only regard him as Dauphin—king, indeed, by blood, but not by consecration.

Here are the exploits which the Maid and the loyal French did in one week. She took Jargeau on June 11; on June 15 she seized the bridge of Meun; Beaugency yielded to her on June 17; on June 18 she defeated the English army at Pathay. Now sieges were long affairs in those days, as they are even today, when cannon are so much more powerful than they were in Joan's time. Her success seemed a miracle to the world.

At last, with difficulty, Charles was brought to visit Reims, and consent to be crowned like his ancestors. Seeing that he was never likely to move, Joan left the town where he was and went off into the country. This retreat brought Charles to his senses. The towns which he passed by yielded to him; Joan went and summoned each. "Now she was with the king in the center, now with the rearguard, now with the van." The town of Troyes, where there was an English garrison, did not wish to yield. There was a council in the king's army: they said they could not take the place.

"In two days it shall be yours, by force or by good will," said the Maid.

"Six days will do," said the chancellor, "if you are sure you speak truth."

Joan made ready for an attack. She was calling "Forward!" when the town surrendered. Reims, after some doubts, yielded also, on July 16, and all the people, with shouts of *"Noel!"* welcomed the king. On July 17 the king was crowned and anointed with the Holy Oil by that very Archbishop of Reims who always opposed Joan. The Twelve Peers of France were not all present—some were on the English side—but Joan stood by Charles, her banner in her hand. "It bore the brunt, and deserved to share the renown," she said later to her accusers.

When the ceremony was ended, and the Dauphin Charles was a crowned and anointed king, the Maid knelt weeping at his feet.

"Gentle king," she said, "now is accomplished the will of God, who desired that you should come to Reims to be consecrated, and to prove that you are the true king and the kingdom is yours."

Then all the knights wept for joy.

The king bade Joan choose her reward. Already horses, rich armor, jeweled daggers, had been given to her. These, adding to the beauty and glory of her aspect, had made men follow her more gladly, and for that she valued them. She, too, made gifts to noble ladies, and gave much to the poor. She only wanted money to wage the war with, not for herself. Her family was made noble; on their shield, between two lilies, a sword upholds the crown. Her father was at Reims, and saw her in her glory. What reward, then, was Joan to choose? She chose nothing for herself, but that her native village of Domremy should be free from taxes. This news her father carried home from the splendid scene at Reims.

The name of Joan was now such a terror to the English that men deserted rather than face her in arms. At this time the truce with Burgundy ended, and the duke openly set out to besiege the strong town of Compiègne, held by de Flavy for France. Joan hurried to Compiègne, whence she made two expeditions which were defeated by treachery. Perhaps she thought of this, perhaps of the future, when in the church of Compiègne she declared one day to a crowd of children whom she loved that she knew she was sold and betrayed. Old men who had heard her told this tale long afterwards.

Burgundy had invested Compiègne, when Joan, with four hundred men, rode into the town secretly at dawn. That day Joan led a sally against the Burgundians. Her Voices told her nothing, good or bad, she says. The Burgundians were encamped at Margny and at Clairoix, the English at Venette, villages on a plain near the walls. Joan crossed the bridge on a gray charger, in a surcoat of crimson silk, rode through the redoubt beyond the bridge, and attacked the Burgundians. Flavy in the town was to prevent the English from attacking her in the rear. He had boats on the river to secure Joan's retreat if necessary.

Joan swept through Margny, driving the Burgundians before her; the garrison of Clairoix came to their help; the battle was doubtful. Meanwhile the English came up; they could not have reached the Burgundians to aid them, but some of the Maid's men, seeing the English standards, fled. The English followed them under the walls of Compiègne; the gate of the redoubt was closed to prevent the English from entering with the runaways. Like Hector under Troy, the Maid was shut out from the town which she came to save.

Joan was with her own foremost line when the rear fled. They told her of her danger, she heeded not. For the last time rang out in that girlish voice: *"Allez avant! Forward, they are ours!"*

Her men seized her bridle and turned her horse's head about. The English held the entrance from the causeway; Joan and a few men (her brother was one of them) were driven into a corner of the outer wall. A rush was made at Joan. "Yield! yield! give your faith to me!" each man cried.

"I have given my faith to Another," she said, "and I will keep my oath."

Her enemies confess that on this day Joan did great feats of arms, covering the rear of her force when they had to fly.

Some French historians hold that the gates were closed by treason that the Maid might be taken. We may hope that this was not so; the commander of Compiègne held this town successfully for the

king, and was rescued by Joan's friend, the brave Pothon de Xaintrailles.

The sad story that is still to tell shall be shortly told. There is no
word nor deed of the Maid's, in captivity as in victory, that is not to
her immortal honor. But the sight of the wickedness of men, their
cowardice, cruelty, greed, ingratitude, is not a thing to linger over.

Joan was now kept in a high tower at Beaurevoir, and was allowed
to walk on the leads. She knew she was sold to England, she had
heard that the people of Compiègne were to be massacred. She
would rather die than fall into English hands, "rather give her soul
to God, than her body to the English." But she hoped to escape and
relieve Compiègne. She, therefore prayed for counsel to her Saints;
might she leap from the top of the tower? Would they not bear her
up in their hands? St. Catherine bade her not to leap; God would
help her and the people of Compiègne.

Then, for the first time as far as we know, the Maid wilfully dis-
obeyed her Voices. She leaped from the tower. They found her, not
wounded, not a limb was broken, but stunned. She knew not what
had happened; they told her she had leaped down. For three days
she could not eat, "yet was she comforted by St. Catherine, who bade
her confess and seek pardon of God, and told her that, without fail,
they of Compiègne should be relieved before Martinmas." This
prophecy was fulfilled.

About the trial and the death of the Maid, I have not the heart to
write a long story. Some points are to be remembered. The person
who conducted the trial, itself illegal, was her deadly enemy, the
false Frenchman, the Bishop of Beauvais, Cauchon. Next, Joan was
kept in strong irons day and night, and she, the most modest of
maidens, was always guarded by five brutal English soldiers of the
lowest rank. Again, she was not allowed to receive the Holy Com-
munion, as she desired with tears. Thus weakened by long captivity
and ill usage, she, an untaught girl, was questioned repeatedly for
three months, by the most cunning and learned doctors in law of the
Paris University. Often many spoke at once, to perplex her mind.

But Joan always showed a wisdom which confounded them, and which is at least as extraordinary as her skill in war. She would never swear an oath to answer *all* their questions. About herself, and all matters bearing on her own conduct, she would answer. About the king and the secrets of the king, she would not answer. If they forced her to reply about these things, she frankly said, she would not tell them the truth. The whole object of the trial was to prove that she dealt with powers of evil, and that her king had been crowned and aided by the devil. Her examiners, therefore, attacked her day by day, in public and in her dungeon, with questions about these visions which she held sacred, and could only speak of with a blush among her friends.

All through her trial, her Voices bade her "answer boldly," in three months she would give her last answer, in three months "she would be free with great victory, and come into the Kingdom of Paradise." In three months from the first day of her trial she went free through the gate of fire. Boldly she answered, and wisely.

Enough. They burned Joan the Maid. She did not suffer long. Her eyes were fixed on a cross which a priest, Martin L'Advenu, held up before her. She maintained, he says, to her dying moment, the truth of her Voices. With a great cry of JESUS! she gave up her breath, and her pure soul was with God.

THE GREAT DISCOVERIES

By HENDRIK WILLEM VAN LOON

With Illustrations by the Author

THE Crusades had been a lesson in the liberal art of traveling. But very few people had ever ventured beyond the well-known beaten track which led from Venice to Jaffe. In the thirteenth century the Polo brothers, merchants of Venice, had wandered across the great Mongolian desert and after climbing mountains as high as the moon, they had found their way to the court of the great Khan of Cathay, the mighty emperor of China. The son

On the way to the court of the Great Khan of Cathay.

of one of the Polos, by the name of Marco, had written a book about their adventures, which covered a period of more than twenty years

The astonished world had gaped at his descriptions of the golden towers of the strange island of Zipangu, which was his Italian way of spelling Japan. Many people had wanted to go east, that they might find this gold-land and grow rich. But the trip was too far and too dangerous and so they stayed at home.

Of course, there was always the possibility of making the voyage by sea. But the sea was very unpopular in the Middle Ages and for many very good reasons. In the first place, ships were very small. The vessels on which Magellan made his famous trip around the world which lasted many years, were not as large as a modern ferryboat. They carried from twenty to fifty men, who lived in dingy quarters (too low to allow any of them to stand up straight), and the sailors were obliged to eat poorly cooked food, as the kitchen arrangements were very bad and no fire could be made whenever the weather was the least bit rough. The medieval world knew how to pickle herring and how to dry fish. But there were no canned goods, and fresh vegetables were never seen on the bill of fare as soon as the coast had been left behind. Water was carried in small barrels. It soon became stale and then tasted of rotten wood and iron rust and was full of slimy growing things. As the people of the Middle Ages knew nothing about microbes (Roger Bacon, the learned monk of the thirteenth century seems to have suspected their existence, but he wisely kept his discovery to himself) they often drank unclean water and sometimes the whole crew died of typhoid fever. Indeed the mortality on board the ships of the earliest navigators was terrible. Of the two hundred sailors who in the year 1519 left Seville to accompany Magellan on his famous voyage around the world, only eighteen returned. As late as the seventeenth century, when there was a brisk trade between western Europe and the Indies, a mortality of 40 per cent was nothing unusual for a trip from Amsterdam to Batavia and back. The greater part of these victims died of scurvy, a disease which is caused by lack of fresh vegetables and which affects the gums and poisons the blood until the patient dies of sheer exhaustion.

Under those circumstances you will understand that the sea did not attract the best elements of the population. Famous discoverers like Magellan and Columbus and Vasco da Gama traveled at the head of crews that were almost entirely composed of ex-jailbirds, future murderers, and pickpockets out of a job.

These navigators certainly deserve our admiration for the courage and the pluck with which they accomplished their hopeless tasks, in the face of difficulties of which the people of our own comfortable world can have no conception. Their ships were leaky. The rigging was clumsy. Since the middle of the thirteenth century they had possessed some sort of a compass (which had come to Europe from China by way of Arabia and the Crusades) but they had very bad and incorrect maps. They set their course by God and by guess. If luck was with them they returned after one, or two, or three years. In the other case, their bleached bones remained behind on some lonely beach. But they were true pioneers. They gambled with luck. Life to them was a glorious adventure. And all the suffering, the thirst and the hunger and the pain were forgotten when their eyes beheld the dim outlines of a new coast, or the placid waters of an ocean that had lain forgotten since the beginning of time.

Again I wish I could make this book a thousand pages long. The subject of the early discoveries is so fascinating. But history, to give you a true idea of past times, should be like those etchings which Rembrandt used to make. It should cast a vivid light on certain important causes, on those which are best and greatest. All the rest should be left in the shadow or should be indicated by a few lines. And in this chapter I can only give you a short list of the most important discoveries.

Keep in mind that all during the fourteenth and fifteenth centuries the navigators were trying to accomplish just *one thing*—they wanted to find a comfortable and safe road to the empire of Cathay (China), to the islands of Zipangu (Japan) and to those mysterious islands, where grew the spices which the medieval world had come to like since the days of the Crusades, and which people needed in those days before the introduction of cold storage, when meat and fish spoiled very quickly and could only be eaten after a liberal sprinkling of pepper or nutmeg.

The Venetians and the Genoese had been the great navigators of

the Mediterranean, but the honor for exploring the coast of the
Atlantic goes to the Portuguese. Spain and Portugal were full of that
patriotic energy which their age-old struggle against the Moorish in-
vaders had developed. Such energy, once it exists, can easily be
forced into new channels. In the thirteenth century, King Alphonso
III had conquered the kingdom of Algarve in the southwestern
corner of the Spanish peninsula and had added it to his dominions.
In the next century, the Portuguese had turned the tables on the
Mohammedans, had crossed the straits of Gibraltar and had taken
possession of Ceuta, opposite the Arabic city of Ta'Rifa (a word
which in Arabic means "inventory", and which by way of the
Spanish language has come down to us as "tariff"), and Tangiers,
which became the capital of an African addition to Algarve.

They were ready to begin their career as explorers.

In the year 1415, Prince Henry, known as Henry the Navigator,
the son of John I of Portugal and Philippa, the daughter of John of
Gaunt (about whom you can read in Richard II, a play by William
Shakespeare) began to make preparations for the systematic exploration of northwestern Africa. Before this, that hot and sandy coast
had been visited by the Phoenicians and by the Norsemen, who remembered it as the home of the hairy "wild man" whom we have
come to know as the gorilla. One after another, Prince Henry and
his captains discovered the Canary Islands, rediscovered the island
of Madeira which a century before had been visited by a Genoese
ship, carefully charted the Azores which had been vaguely known to
both the Portuguese and the Spaniards, and caught a glimpse of the
mouth of the Senegal River on the west coast of Africa, which they
supposed to be the western mouth of the Nile. At last, by the middle
of the fifteenth century, they saw Cape Verde, or the Green Cape,
and the Cape Verde Islands, which lie almost halfway between the
coast of Africa and Brazil.

But Henry did not restrict himself in his investigations to the
waters of the ocean. He was Grand Master of the Order of Christ.
This was a Portuguese continuation of the crusading order of the
Templars which had been abolished by Pope Clement V in the year
1312 at the request of King Philip the Fair of France, who had

The great discoveries in the Western Hemisphere.

improved the occasion by burning his own Templars at the stake
and stealing all their possessions. Prince Henry used the revenues
of the domains of his religious order to equip several expeditions
which explored the hinterland of the Sahara and of the coast of
Guinea.

But he was still very much a son of the Middle Ages and spent

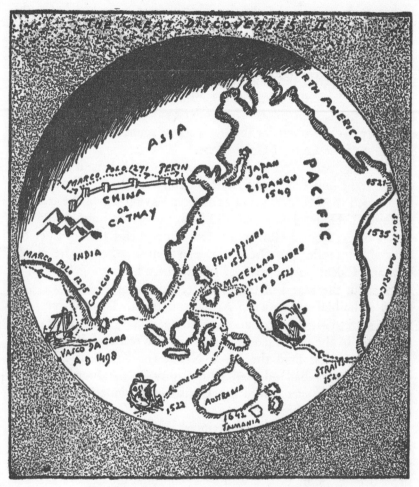

The great discoveries in the Eastern Hemisphere.

a great deal of time and wasted a lot of money upon a search for the mysterious "Prester John," the mythical Christian Priest who was said to be the Emperor of a vast empire "situated somewhere in the east." The story of this strange potentate had first been told in Europe in the middle of the twelfth century. For three hundred years people had tried to find "Prester John" and his descendants.

Henry took part in the search. Thirty years after his death, the riddle was solved.

In the year 1486 Bartholomew Diaz, trying to find the land of Prester John by sea, had reached the southernmost point of Africa. At first he called it the Storm Cape, on account of the strong winds which had prevented him from continuing his voyage toward the east, but the Lisbon pilots who understood the importance of this discovery in their quest for the India water route, changed the name into that of the Cape of Good Hope.

One year later, Pedro de Covilham, provided with letters of credit on the house of Medici, started upon a similar mission by land. He crossed the Mediterranean and, after leaving Egypt, he traveled southward. He reached Aden, and from there, traveling through the waters of the Persian Gulf which few white men had seen since the days of Alexander the Great, eighteen centuries before, he visited Goa and Calcut on the coast of India where he got a great deal of news about the island of the Moon (Madagascar) which was supposed to lie halfway between Africa and India. Then he returned, paid a secret visit to Mecca and to Medina, crossed the Red Sea once more and in the year 1490 he discovered the realm of Prester John, who was no less than the Black Negus (or King) of Abyssinia, whose ancestors had adopted Christianity in the fourth century, seven hundred years before the Christian missionaries had found their way to Scandinavia.

These many voyages had convinced the Portuguese geographers and cartographers that while the voyage to the Indies by an eastern sea route was possible, it was by no means easy. Then there arose a great debate. Some people wanted to continue the explorations east of the Cape of Good Hope. Others said, "No, we must sail west across the Atlantic and then we shall reach Cathay."

Let us state right here that most intelligent people of that day were firmly convinced that the earth was not as flat as a pancake, but was round. The Ptolemean system of the universe, invented and duly described by Claudius Ptolemy, the great Egyptian geographer who had lived in the second century of our era, which had served the simple needs of the men of the Middle Ages, had long been discarded by the scientists of the Renaissance. They had accepted the doctrine of the Polish mathematician, Nicolaus Copernicus, whose studies had convinced him that the earth was one of a number of round planets which turned around the sun, a discovery which he did not venture to publish for thirty-six years (it was printed in 1543, the year of his death) from fear of the Holy Inquisition, a Papal court which had been established in the thirteenth century when the heresies of the Albigenses and the Waldenses in France and in Italy (very mild heresies of devoutly pious people who did not believe in private property and preferred to live in Christlike poverty) had for a moment threatened the absolute power of the bishops of Rome. But the belief in the roundness of the earth was common among the nautical experts and, as I said, they were now debating the respective advantages of the eastern and the western routes.

Among the advocates of the western route was a Genoese mariner by the name of Cristoforo Colombo. He was the son of a wool merchant. He seems to have been a student at the University of Pavia where he specialized in mathematics and geometry. Then he took up his father's trade, but soon we find him in Chios in the eastern Mediterranean traveling on business. Thereafter we hear of voyages to England, but whether he went north in search of wool or as the captain of a ship we do not know. In February of the year 1477, Colombo (if we are to believe his own words) visited Iceland, but very likely he only got as far as the Faröe Islands which are cold enough in February to be mistaken for Iceland by anyone. Here Colombo met the descendants of those brave Norsemen who in the tenth century had settled in Greenland and who had visited America in the eleventh century, when Leif's vessel had been blown to the coast of Vineland, or Labrador.

What had become of those far western colonies no one knew. The American colony of Thorfinn Karlsefne, the husband of the widow of Leif's brother, Thorstein, founded in the year 1003, had been discontinued three years later on account of the hostility of the Eskimos. As for Greenland, not a word had been heard from the settlers since the year 1440. Very likely the Greenlanders had all

died of the Black Death, which had just killed half the people of
Norway. However that might be, the tradition of a "vast land in the
distant west" still survived among the people of the Faröe and Iceland and Colombo must have heard of it. He gathered further information among the fishermen of the northern Scottish islands and
then went to Portugal where he married the daughter of one of the
captains who had served under Prince Henry the Navigator.

From that moment on (the year 1478) he devoted himself to
the quest of the western route to the Indies. He sent his plans for
such a voyage to the courts of Portugal and Spain. The Portuguese,
who felt certain that they possessed a monopoly of the eastern route,
would not listen to his plans. In Spain, Ferdinand of Aragon and
Isabella of Castile, whose marriage in 1469 had made Spain into a
single kingdom, were busy driving the Moors from their last strong-
hold, Granada. They had no money for risky expeditions. They
needed every peseta for their soldiers.

Few people were ever forced to fight as desperately for their
ideas as this brave Italian. But the story of Colombo (or Colon or
Columbus, as we call him), is too well known to bear repeating.
The Moors surrendered Granada on the second of January of the
year 1492. In the month of April of the same year, Columbus signed
a contract with the King and Queen of Spain. On Friday, the 3rd of
August, he left Palos with three little ships and a crew of 88 men,
many of whom were criminals who had been offered indemnity of
punishment if they joined the expedition. At two o'clock in the
morning of Friday, the 12th of October, Columbus discovered land.
On the fourth of January of the year 1493, Columbus waved farewell
to the 44 men of the little fortress of La Navidad (none of whom
was ever again seen alive) and returned homeward. By the middle
of February he reached the Azores, where the Portuguese threatened
to throw him into jail. On the fifteenth of March, 1493, the admiral
reached Palos and together with his Indians (for he was convinced
that he had discovered some outlying islands of the Indies and
called the natives red Indians) he hastened to Barcelona to tell his
faithful patrons that he had been successful and that the road to the

gold and silver of Cathay and Zipangu was at the disposal of their most Catholic Majesties.

Alas, Columbus never knew the truth. Toward the end of his life, on his fourth voyage, when he had touched the mainland of South America, he may have suspected that all was not well with his discovery. But he died in the firm belief that there was no solid continent between Europe and Asia and that he had found the direct route to China.

Meanwhile, the Portuguese, sticking to their eastern route, had been more fortunate. In the year 1498, Vasco de Gama had been able to reach the coast of Malabar and return safely to Lisbon with a cargo of spice. In the year 1502 he had repeated the visit. But along the western route, the work of exploration had been most disappointing. In 1497 and 1498 John and Sebastian Cabot had tried to find a passage to Japan, but they had seen nothing but the snow-bound coasts and the rocks of Newfoundland, which had first been sighted by the Northmen five centuries before. Amerigo Vespucci, a Florentine who became the Pilot Major of Spain, and who gave his name to our continent, had explored the coast of Brazil, but had found not a trace of the Indies.

In the year 1513, seven years after the death of Columbus, the truth at last began to dawn upon the geographers of Europe. Vasco Nuñez de Balboa had crossed the Isthmus of Panama, had climbed the famous peak in Darien, and had looked down upon a vast expanse of water which seemed to suggest the existence of another ocean.

Finally in the year 1519 a fleet of five small Spanish ships under command of the Portuguese navigator, Ferdinand de Magellan, sailed westward (and not eastward, since that route was absolutely in the hands of the Portuguese who allowed no competition) in search of the Spice Islands. Magellan crossed the Atlantic between Africa and Brazil and sailed southward. He reached a narrow channel between the southernmost point of Patagonia, "the land of the people with the big feet," and the Fire Island (so named on account of a fire, the only sign of the existence of natives, which the sailors watched one night). For almost five weeks the ships of Magellan were at the mercy of the terrible storms and blizzards which swept through the straits. A mutiny broke out among the sailors. Magellan suppressed it with terrible severity and sent two of his men on shore where they were left to repent of their sins at leisure. At last the storms quieted down, the channel broadened, and

The channel broadened, and Magellan entered a new ocean.

Magellan entered a new ocean. Its waves were quiet and placid. He called it the Peaceful Sea, the Mare Pacifico. Then he continued in a western direction. He sailed for ninety-eight days without seeing land. His people almost perished from hunger and thirst and ate the rats that infested the ships, and when these were all gone they chewed pieces of sail to still their gnawing hunger.

In March of the year 1521 they saw land. Magellan called it the land of the Ladrones (which means robbers) because the natives stole everything they could lay hands on. Then farther westward to the Spice Islands!

Again land was sighted. A group of lonely islands. Magellan called them the Philippines, after Philip, the son of his master

Charles V, the Philip II of unpleasant historical memory. At first
Magellan was well received, but when he used the guns of his ships
to make Christian converts he was killed by the aborigines, together
with a number of his captains and sailors. The survivors burned one
of the remaining three ships and continued their voyage. They
found the Moluccas, the famous Spice Islands; they sighted Borneo
and reached Tidore. There, one of the two ships, too leaky to be of
further use, remained behind with her crew. The "Vittoria," under
Sebastian del Cano, crossed the Indian Ocean, missed seeing the
northern coast of Australia (which was not discovered until the first
half of the seventeenth century, when ships of the Dutch East India
Company explored this flat and inhospitable land), and after great
hardships reached Spain.

This was the most notable of all voyages. It had taken three years.
It had been accomplished at a great cost of both men and money.
But it had established the fact that the earth was round, and that
the new lands discovered by Columbus were not a part of the Indies
but a separate continent. From that time on, Spain and Portugal
devoted all their energies to the development of their Indian and
American trade. To prevent an armed conflict between the rivals,
Pope Alexander VI had obligingly divided the world into two equal
parts by a line of demarcation which followed the 50th degree of
longitude west of Greenwich, the so-called division of Tordesillas of
1494. The Portuguese were to establish their colonies to the east of
this line, the Spaniards were to have theirs to the west. This accounts
for the fact that the entire American continent, with the exception
of Brazil, became Spanish and that all of the Indies and most of
Africa became Portuguese until the English and the Dutch colonists
(who had no respect for Papal decisions) took these possessions
away in the seventeenth and eighteenth centuries.

When news of the discovery of Columbus reached the Rialto of
Venice, the Wall street of the Middle Ages, there was a terrible
panic. Stocks and bonds went down 40 and 50 per cent. After a
short while, when it appeared that Columbus had failed to find the
road to Cathay, the Venetian merchants recovered from their fright.
But the voyages of da Gama and Magellan proved the practical possi-

bilities of an eastern water route to the Indies. Then the rulers of
Genoa and Venice, the two great commercial centers of the Middle
Ages and the Renaissance, began to be sorry that they had refused
to listen to Columbus. But it was too late. Their Mediterranean became an inland sea. The overland trade to the Indies and China
dwindled to insignificant proportions. The old days of Italian glory
were gone. The Atlantic became the new center of commerce and
therefore the center of civilization. It has remained so ever since.

See how strangely civilization has progressed since those early
days, fifty centuries before, when the inhabitants of the Valley of
the Nile began to keep a written record of history. From the river
Nile, it went to Mesopotamia, the land between the rivers. Then
came the turn of Crete and Greece and Rome. An inland sea became
the center of trade and the cities along the Mediterranean were the
home of art and science and philosophy and learning. In the sixteenth century it moved westward once more and made the countries
that border upon the Atlantic become the masters of the earth.

There are those who say that the world war and the suicide of
the great European nations has greatly diminished the importance of
the Atlantic Ocean. They expect to see civilization cross the American continent and find a new home in the Pacific. But I doubt this.

The westward trip was accompanied by a steady increase in the
size of ships and a broadening of the knowledge of the navigators.
The flat-bottomed vessels of the Nile and the Euphrates were replaced by the sailing vessels of the Phoenicians, the Aegeans, the
Greeks, the Carthaginians and the Romans. These in turn were discarded for the square-rigged vessels of the Portuguese and the Spaniards. And the latter were driven from the ocean by the full-rigged
craft of the English and the Dutch.

At present, however, civilization no longer depends upon ships.
Aircraft has taken and will continue to take the place of the sailing
vessel and the steamer. The next center of civilization will depend
upon the development of aircraft and water power. And the sea
once more shall be the undisturbed home of the little fishes, who
once upon a time shared their deep residence with the earliest ancestors of the human race.

CHRISTMAS WITH QUEEN BESS

By JOHN BENNETT

Illustrations by REGINALD BIRCH

I

NICK looked up from the music rack and shivered. He had forgotten the fire in studying his song, and the blackened ends of the burnt-out logs lay smouldering on the hearth. The draught, too, whistled shrilly under the door, in spite of the rushes that he had piled along the crack.

The fog had been gone for a week. It was snapping cold; and through the peepholes he had thawed upon the window pane with his breath, he could see the hoarfrost lying in the shadow of the wall in the court below.

How forlorn the green old dial looked out there alone in the cold, with the winter dust whirling around it in little eddies upon the wind! The dial was fringed with icicles, like an old man's beard; and even the creeping shadow on its face, which told mid-afternoon, seemed frozen where it fell.

Mid-afternoon already, and he so much to do! Nick pulled his cloak about him, and turned to his song again:

> "Sir Fly hangs dead on the window pane;
> The frost doth wind his shroud—"

But there he stopped; for the boys were singing in the great hall below, and the whole house rang with the sound of the roaring chorus:

> "Down-a-down, hey, down-a-down,
> Hey derry derry down-a-down!"

Nick put his fingers in his ears, and began all over again:

"Sir Fly hangs dead on the window pane;
      The frost doth wind his shroud;
   Through the halls of his little summer house
      The north wind cries aloud."

But it was no use; all he could hear was:

"Down-a-down, hey, down-a-down,
      Hey derry derry down-a-down!"

How could a fellow study in a noise like that? He gave it up in despair, and kicking the chunks together, stood upon the hearth, warming his hands by the gathering blaze while he listened to the song:

"Cold's the wind, and wet's the rain;
      Saint Hugh, be our good speed!
   Ill is the weather that bringeth no gain,
      Nor helps good hearts in need.

"Down-a-down, hey, down-a-down,
      Hey derry derry down-a-down!"

He could hear Colley Warren above them all. What a voice the boy had! Like a golden horn blowing in the fresh of a morning breeze. It made Nick tingle, he could not tell why. He and Colley often sang together, and their voices made a quivering in the air like the ringing of a bell. And often, while they sang, the viols standing in the corner of the room would sound aloud a deep, soft note in harmony with them, although nobody had touched the strings; so that the others cried out that the instruments were bewitched, and would not let the boys sing any more. Colley Warren was Nick's best friend—a dark-eyed, quiet lad, as gentle as a girl, and with a mouth like a girl's mouth, for which the others sometimes mocked him, though they loved him none the less.

It was not because his voice was loud that it could be so distinctly heard; but it was nothing like the rest, and came through all the others like sunshine through a mist. Nick pulled the stool up closer, and sat down in the chimney corner, humming a second to the tune,

and blowing little glory holes in the embers with the bellows. He
liked the smell of a wood fire, and liked to toast his toes. He was a
trifle drowsy, too, now that he was warm again to the marrow of
his bones; perhaps he dozed a little.

But suddenly he came to himself again with a sense of a great
stillness fallen over everything—no singing in the room below, and
silence everywhere but in the court, where there was a trampling as
of horses standing at the gate. And while he was still lazily wonder-
ing, a great cheer broke out in the room below, and there was a
stamping of feet like cattle galloping over a bridge; and then, all at
once, the door opened into the hallway at the foot of the stair, and
the sound burst out as fire bursts from the cockloft window of a
burning barn, and through the noise and over it Colley Warren's
voice calling him by name: "Skylark! Nick Skylark! Ho there,
Nick! Where art thou?"

He sprang to the door and kicked the rushes away. All the hall
was full of voices, laughing, shouting, singing, and cheering. There
were footsteps coming up the stair. "What there, Skylark! Ho, boy!
Nick, where art thou?" he could hear Colley calling above them all.
Out he popped his nose: "Here I am, Colley—what's to do? *Whatever in the world!*" and he ducked his head like a mandarin; for
whizz—flap! two books came whirling up the stairs and thumped
against the panel by his ears.

"The news—the news, Nick! Have ye heard the news?" the lads
were shouting as if possessed. "We're going to court! Hurrah, hurrah!" And some, with their arms about one another, went whirling
out at the door and round the windy close like very madcaps, cutting such capers that the horses standing at the gate kicked up
their heels, and jerked the horse boys right and left like bundles
of hay.

Nick leaned over the railing and stared.

"Come down and help us sing!" they cried. "Come down and
shout with us in the street."

"I canna come down—there's work to do!"

"Thy 'canna' be hanged, and thy work likewise! Come down
and sing, or we'll fetch thee down. The Queen hath sent for us!"

"The Queen—hath sent—for us?"

"Ay, sent for us to come to court and play on Christmas day!
Hurrah for Queen Bess!"

At that shrill cheer the startled horses fairly plunged into the
street, and the carts that were passing along the way were jammed
against the opposite wall. The carriers bellowed, the horse boys
bawled, the people came running to see the row, and the apprentices
flew out of the shops bareheaded, waving their dirty aprons and
cheering lustily, just for the fun of the chance to cheer.

"It's true!" called Colley, his dark eyes dancing like stars on the
sea. "Come down, Nick, and sing in the street with us all! We are
going to Greenwich Palace on Christmas day to play before the
Queen and the court—for the first time, Nick, in a good six years;
and ye're not to work till the new masque comes from the Master of
the Revels! Come down, Nick, and sing with us out in the street;
for we're going to court, we're going to court to sing before the
Queen! Hurrah, hurrah!"

"Hurrah for good Queen Bess!" cried Nick; and up went his cap
and down went he on the baluster rail like a runaway sled, head
first into the crowd, who caught him laughing as he came. Then all
together they cantered out like a parcel of colts in a fresh, green
field, and sang in the street before the school till the people cheered
themselves hoarse to hear such music on such a wintry day; sang
until there was no other business on all the thoroughfare but just to
listen to their songs; sang until the undermasters came out with their
staves and drove them into the school again, to keep them from
straining their throats by singing so loudly and so long in the frosty
open air.

But a fig for staves and for undermasters! The boys clapped fast
the gates behind them, and barred the undermasters out in the street,
singing twice as loudly as before, and mocking at them with wry
faces through the bars; and then trooped off up the old precentor's
private stair and sang at his door until the old man could not hear
his own ears, and came out storming and grim as grief.

But when he saw the boys all there, and heard them cheering him
three times three, he could not storm to save his life, but only stood

there, black and thin, against the yellow square of light, smiling a quaint smile that half was wrinkle and half was pride, shaking his lean forefinger at them as if he were beating time, and nodding until his head seemed almost nodding off.

"Hurrah for Master Nathaniel Gyles!" they shouted.

"Primus Magister Scholarum, Custos Morum, Quartus Custos Rotulorum," said the old man softly to himself, the firelight from behind him falling in a glory on his thin white hair. "Be off, ye rogues! Ye are not fit to waste good language on; or, faith, I'd Latin ye all as dumb as fishes in the depths of the briny sea!"

"Hurrah for the fishes in the sea!"

"Soft, ye knaves! Save thy throats for good Queen Bess!"

"Hurrah for good Queen Bess!"

"Be still, I say, ye good-for-nothing varlets; or ye sha'n't have pie and ale tonight. But marry, now, ye *shall* have pie—ay pie and ale without a stint; for ye are good lads, and ye have pleased the Queen at last; and I am as proud of ye as a peacock is of his own tail!"

"Hurrah for the Queen—and the pie—and the ale! Hurrah for the peacock and his tail!" shouted the boys; and straightway, seeing that they had made a rhyme, they gave a cheer shriller and longer than all the others put together, and went clattering down the stairway, singing at the top of their lungs:

> "Hurrah for the Queen, and the pie and the ale!
> Hurrah for the peacock, hurrah for his tail!
> Hurrah for hurrah, and hurrah again—
> "We're going to court on Christmas day
> To sing before the Queen!"

"Good lads, good lads!" said the old precentor to himself, as he turned back into his little room. His eyes were shining proudly in the candlelight, yet the tears were running down his cheeks. A queer old man, Nat Gyles, and dead this many a long, long year; yet that night no man was happier than he.

But Master Gaston Carew, who had come for Nick, stood in the gathering dusk by the gate below, and stared up at the yellow square of light with a troubled look upon his reckless face.

II

It was a frosty morning when they all marched down to the boats that bumped along Paul's wharf.

The roofs of London were white with frost and rosy with the dawn. In the shadow of the walls the air lay in still pools of smoky blue; and in the east the horizon stretched like a swamp of fire. The winking lights on London Bridge were pale. The bridge itself stood cold and gray, mysterious and dim as the stream below, but here and there along its crest red-hot with a touch of flame from the burning eastern sky. Out of the river, running inland with the tide, came steamy shreds that drifted here and there. Then over the roofs of London town the sun sprang up like a thing of life, and the veil of twilight vanished in bright day with a million sparkles rippling on the stream.

Warm with piping roast and cordial, keen with excitement, and blithe with the sharp, fresh air, the red-cheeked lads skipped and chattered along the landing like a flock of sparrows alighted by chance in a land of crumbs.

"Into the wherries, everyone!" cried the old precentor. *"Ad unum omnes,* great and small!"

"Into the wherries!" echoed the undermasters.

"Into the wherries, my bullies!" roared old Brueton the boatman, fending off with a rusty hook as red as his bristling beard. "Into the wherries, yarely all, and we's catch the turn o' the tide! 'Tis gone high water now!"

Then away they went, three wherries full, and Master Gyles behind them in a brisk sixpenny tilt boat, resplendant in new ash-colored hose, a cloak of black velvet fringed with gold, and a brand-new periwig curled and frizzed like a brush heap in a gale of wind.

How they had worked for the last few days! New songs, new dances, new lines to learn; gallant compliments for the Queen, who was as fond of flattery as a girl; new clothes, new slippers and caps to try, and a thousand whatnots more. The school had hummed like a busy mill from morning until night. And now that the grinding was done and they had come at last to their reward—the hoped-for summons to the court, which had been sought so long in vain—the boys of St. Paul's bubbled with glee until the undermasters were in a cold sweat for fear their precious charges would pop from the wherries into the Thames, like so many exuberant corks.

They cheered with delight as London Bridge was shot and the boats went flying down the Pool, past Billingsgate and the oyster-men, the White Tower and the Traitors' Gate, past the shipping, where brown, foreign-looking faces stared at them above sea-battered bulwarks.

The sun was bright and the wind was keen; the air sparkled, and all the world was full of life. Hammers beat in the builders' yards; wild bargees sang hoarsely as they drifted down to the Isle of Dogs; and in slow ships that crept away to catch the wind in the open stream below, with tawny sails drooping and rimmed with frost, they heard the hail of salty mariners.

The tide ran strong, and the steady oars carried them swiftly down. London passed; then solitary hamlets here and there; then dun fields running to the river's edge like thirsty deer.

In Deptford Reach some lords who were coming down by water passed them, racing with a little Dutch boat from Deptford to the turn. Their boats had holly bushes at their prows and holiday gar-lands along their sides. They were all shouting gaily, and the stream was bright with their scarlet cloaks, Lincoln-green jerkins, and gold embroidery. But they were very badly beaten, at which they laughed, and threw the Dutchmen a handful of silver pennies. Thereupon the Dutchmen stood up in their boat and bowed like jointed ninepins; and the lords, not to be outdone, stood up likewise in their boats and bowed very low in return, with their hands upon their breasts. Then everybody on the river laughed, and the boys gave three cheers for the merry lords and three more for the sturdy Dutchmen. The Dutchmen shouted back, "Goot Yule!" and bowed and bowed until their boat turned round and went stern foremost down the stream, so that they were bowing to the opposite bank, where no one was at all. At this the rest all laughed again till their sides ached, and cheered them twice as much as they had before.

And while they were cheering and waving their caps, the boatmen rested upon their oars and let the boats swing with the tide which thereabout set strong against the shore, and a trumpeter in the Earl of Arundel's barge stood up and blew upon a long horn bound with a banner of blue and gold.

Instantly he had blown, another trumpet answered from the south, and when Nick turned, the shore was gay with men in brilliant livery. Beyond was a wood of chestnut trees as blue and leafless as a grove of spears; and in the plain between the river and the wood stood a great palace of gray stone, with turrets, pinnacles, and battlemented walls, over the topmost tower of which a broad flag blazoned with golden lions and silver lilies square for square whipped the winter wind. Amid a group of towers large and small a lofty stack poured out a plume of sea-coal smoke against the milky sky, and on the countless windows in the wall the sunlight flashed with dazzling radiance.

There were people on the battlements, and at the port between two towers where the Queen went in and out the press was so thick that men's heads looked like the cobbles in the street.

The shore was stayed with piling and with timbers like a wharf so that a hundred boats might lie there cheek by jowl and scarcely rub their paint. The lords made way; and the children players came ashore through an aisle of uplifted oars. They were met by the yeomen of the guard, tall, brawny fellows clad in red, with golden rose on their breasts and backs, and with them marched up to the postern, two and two, Master Gyles the last of all, as haughty as a Spanish don come courting fair Queen Bess.

A smoking dinner was waiting them, of whitebait with red pepper, and a yellow juice so sour that Nick's mouth drew up in a knot, but it was very good. There were besides, silver dishes full of sugared red currants, and heaps of comfits and sweetmeats, which Master Gyles would not allow them even to touch, and saffron cake with raisins in them, and spiced hot cordial out of tiny silver cups. Bare-headed pages clad in silk and silver lace waited upon them as if they were fledgling kings; but the boys were too hungry to care for that or to try to put on airs, and waded into the meat and drink as if they had been starved for a fortnight.

But when they were done Nick saw that the table off which they had eaten was inlaid with pearl and silver filigree, and that the tablecloth was of silk with woven metalwork and gems set in it worth more than a thousand crowns. He was very glad he had eaten first, for such wonderful service would have taken away his appetite.

And truly a wonderful palace was the Queen's Plaisance, as Greenwich House was called. Elizabeth was born in it, and so loved it most of all. There she pleased oftenest to receive and grant audiences to envoys from foreign courts. And there, on that account, as was always her proud, jealous way, she made a blinding show of glory and of wealth, of science, art, and power, that England, to the eyes which saw her there, might stand in second place to no dominion in the world, however rich or great. It was a very house of gold.

Over the door where the lads marched in was the Queen's device, golden rose, with a motto set below in letters of gold, "Dieu et non droit"; and upon the walls were blazoned coats of noble arms on branching golden trees, of purest metal and finest silk, costly beyond compare. The royal presence chamber shone with tapestries of gold, of silver and of oriental silks, of as many shifting colors as the birds of paradise, and wrought in exquisite design. The throne was set with diamonds, with rubies, garnets, and sapphires, glittering like a pastry-crust of stars, and garnished with gold-lace work, pearls, and ornament; and under the velvet canopy which hung above the throne was embroidered in seed pearls, "Vivat Regina Elizabetha!" There was no door without a gorgeous usher, no room without a page, no corridor without a guard, no post without a man of noble birth to fill it.

On the walls of the great gallery were masterly paintings of great folk, globes showing all the stars fast in the sky, and drawings of the world and all its parts, so real that one could see the savages in the New World hanging to the under side by their feet, like flies upon the ceiling. How they stuck was more than Nick could make out; and where they landed if they chanced to slip and fall troubled him a deal, until in the sheer multiplication of wonders he could not wonder any more.

When they came to rehearse in the afternoon the stage was hung with stiff, rich silks that had come in costly cedar chests from the looms of old Cathay; and the curtain behind which the players came and went was broidered with gold thread in flowers and birds like meteors for splendor. The gallery, too, where the musicians sat, was draped with silk and damask.

Some of the lads would have made out by their great airs as if this were all a common thing to them; but Nick stared honestly with round eyes, and went about with cautious feet, chary of touching things, and feeling very much out of place and shy.

It was all too grand, too wonderful—amazing to look upon, no doubt, and good to outface foreign envy with, but not to be endured every day nor lived with comfortably. And as the day went by each passing movement with new marvels, Nick grew more and more uneasy for some simple little nook where he might just sit down and be quiet for a while, as one could do at home, without fine pages peering at him from the screens, or splendid guards patrolling at his heels wherever he went, or obsequious ushers bowing to the floor at every turn, and asking him what he might be pleased to wish. And by the time night fell and the attendant came to light them to their beds, he felt like a fly on the rim of a wheel that went so fast he could scarcely get his breath or see what passed him by, yet of which he durst not let go.

The palace was much too much for him.

III

Christmas morning came and went as if on swallow-wings in a gale of royal merriment. Four hundred sat to dinner that day in Greenwich halls, and all the palace streamed with banners and green garlands.

Within the courtyard two hundred horses neighed and stamped around a water fountain playing in a bowl of ice and evergreen. Grooms and pages, hostlers and dames, went hurry-skurrying to and fro; cooks, bakers and scullions steamed about, leaving hot, mouth-watering streaks of fragrance in the air; bluff men-at-arms went whistling here and there; and serving-maids with rosy cheeks ran breathlessly up and down the winding stairways.

The palace stirred like a mighty pot that boils to its utmost verge, for the hour of the revelries was come.

Over the beechwood and far across the black heath where Jack Cade marshaled the men of Kent, the wind trembled with the boom of the castle bell. Within the walls of the palace its clang was muffled by a sound of voices that rose and fell like the wind upon the sea.

The ambassadors of Venice and France were there, with their courtly trains. The Lord High Constable of England was come to sit below the Queen. The earls, too, of Southampton, Montgomery, Pembroke and Huntington were there; and William Cecil, Lord Burleigh, the Queen's High Treasurer, to smooth his care-lined forehead with a Yuletide jest.

Up from the entry ports came shouts of "Room! room! room for my Lord Strange! Room for the Duke of Devonshire!" and about the outer gates there was a tumult like the cheering of a great crowd.

The palace corridors were lined with guards. Gentlemen pensioners under arms went flashing to and fro. Now and then through the inner throng some handsome page with wind-blown hair and rainbow-colored cloak pushed to the great door, calling: "Way, sirs, way for my Lord—way for my Lady of Alderstone!" and one by one, or in blithe groups, the courtiers, clad in silks and satins, velvets, jewels, and lace of gold, came up through the lofty folding doors to their places in the hall.

There, where the Usher of the Black Rod stood, and the gentlemen of the chamber came and went with golden chains about their necks, was bowing and scraping without stint, and reverent civility; for men that were wise and noble were passing by, men that were handsome and brave; and ladies sweet as a summer day, and as fair to see as spring, laughed by their sides and chatted behind their fans, or daintily nibbled comfits, lacking anything to say.

The windows were all curtained in, making a nighttime in midday; and from the walls and galleries flaring links and great

bouquets of candles threw an eddying flood of yellow light acros
the stirring scene. From clump to clump of banner staves and bur
nished arms, spiked above the wainscot, garlands of red-berrie
holly, spruce, and mistletoe were twined across the tapestry, till a
the room was bound about with a chain of living green.

There were sweet odors floating through the air, and hazy thread
of fragrant smoke from perfumes burning in rich braziers; an
under foot was the crisp, clean rustle of new rushes.

From time to time, above the hum of voices, came the sound o
music from a room beyond—cornets and flutes, fifes, lutes, an
harps, with an organ exquisitely played, and voices singing to it
and from behind the players' curtain, swaying slowly on its ring
at the back of the stage, came a murmur of whispering childisl
voices, now high in eager questioning now, low, rehearsing som
doubtful fragment of a song.

Behind the curtain it was dark—not total darkness, but twilight
for a dull glow came down overhead from the lights in the hal
without, and faint yellow bars went up and down the dusk fror
crevices in the screen. The boys stood here and there in nervou
groups. Now and then a sharp complaint was heard from the tire
woman when an impatient lad would not stand still to be dressed

Master Gyles went to and fro, twisting the manuscript of th
Revel in his hands, or pausing kindly to pat some faltering lad upo
the back. Nick and Colley were peeping by turns through a hole ir
the screen at the throng in the audience chamber.

They could see a confusion of fans, jewels, and faces, and nov
and again could hear a burst of subdued laughter over the steadil
increasing buzz of voices. Then from the gallery above, all at onc
there came a murmur of instruments tuning together; a voice in th
corridor was heard calling, "Way here, way here!" in masterfu
tones; the tall folding doors at the side of the hall swung wide, anc
eight dapper pages in white and gold came in with the Master o
Revels. After them came fifty ladies and noblemen clad in white anc
gold, and a guard of gentlemen pensioners with glittering halberds

There was a sharp rustle. Every head in the audience chambe
louted low. Nick's heart gave a jump—for the Queen was there!

She came with an air that was at once serious and royal, bearing
erself haughtily, yet with a certain grace and sprightliness that
ecame her very well. She was quite tall and well made, and her
uickly changing face was long and fair, though wrinkled and no
onger young. Her complexion was clear and of an olive hue; her
ose was a little hooked; her firm lips were thin; and her small
lack eyes, though keen and bright, were pleasant and merry withal.
Her hair was a coppery, tawny red, and false, moreover. In her ears
ung two great pearls; and there was a fine small crown studded
ith diamonds upon her head, beside a necklace of exceeding fine
old and jewels about her neck. She was attired in a white silk
own bordered with pearls the size of beans, and over it wore a
antle of black silk, cunningly shot with silver threads. Her ruff
as vast, her farthingale vaster; and her train, which was very long,
as borne by a marchioness who made more ado about it than
lizabeth did of ruling her realm.

"The Queen!" gasped Colley.

"Dost think I didna know it?" answered Nick, his heart begin-
ing to beat tattoo as he stared through the peephole in the screen.
He saw the great folk bowing like a gardenful of flowers in a
orm, and in its midst Elizabeth erect, speaking to those about her
a lively and good-humored way, and addressing all the foreigners
ccording to their tongue—in French, Italian, Spanish, Dutch; but
ers was a funny Dutch, and while she spoke she smiled, and made
joke upon it in Latin, at which they all laughed heartily, whether
ey understood what it meant or not. Then, with her ladies in
aiting, she passed to a dais near the stage, and stood a moment,
ately, fair, and proud, while all her nobles made obeisance, then
t and gave a signal for the players to begin.

"Rafe Fullerton!" the prompter whispered shrilly; and out from
ehind the screen slipped Rafe, the smallest of them all, and down
e stage to speak the foreword of the piece. He was frightened,
nd his voice shook as he spoke, but everyone was smiling, so he
ok new heart.

"It is a masque of Summertime and Spring," said he, "wherein
oth claim to be best-loved, and have their say of wit and humor,

and each her part of songs and dances suited to her time, th, sprightly galliard and the nimble jig for Spring, the slow pavan, the stately peacock dance for Summer time. And win who may fair Summer time or merry Spring, the winner is but that beside ou, Queen!"—with which he snapped his fingers in the faces of then, all—"God save Queen Bess!"

At that the Queen's eyes twinkled, and she nodded, highly pleased, so that everyone clapped mightily.

The play soon ran its course amid great laughter and applause, Spring won. The English ever loved her best, and the quick-paced, galliard took their fancy, too. "Up and be doing!" was its tune, and, it gave one a chance to cut fine capers with his heels.

Then the stage stood empty and the music stopped.

At this strange end a whisper of surprise ran through the hall. The Queen tapped with the inner side of her rings upon the broad, arm of her chair. From the look on her face she was whetting he, tongue. But before she could speak, Nick and Colley, dressed as a, farmer boy and girl, with a garland of house-grown flowers about, them, came down the stage from the arras, hand in hand, bowing,

The audience chamber grew very still—*this* was something new, Nick felt a swallowing in his throat, and Colley's hand winced in, his grip. There was no sound but a silky rustling in the room.

Then suddenly the boys behind the players' curtain laughed to, gether, not loud, but such a jolly little laugh that all the people, smiled to hear it. After the laughter came a hush.

Then the pipes overhead made a merry sound as of shepherds, piping on oaten straws in new grass where there are daisies; and, there was a little elfish laughter of clarionets, and a fluttering among, the cool flutes like spring wind blowing through crisp young leaves, in April. The harps began to pulse and throb, with a soft cadence, like raindrops falling into a clear pool where brown leaves lie upon, the bottom and bubbles float above green stones and smooth white, pebbles. Nick lifted up his head and sang.

It was a happy little song of the coming and the triumph of the, spring. The words were all forgotten long ago. They were not, much: enough to serve the turn, no more; but the notes to which hey went were like barn swallows twittering under the eaves, gold-inches clinking in purple weeds beside old roads, and robins singing n common gardens at dawn. And wherever Nick's voice ran Col-ey's followed, the pipes laughing after them a note or two below; while the flutes kept gurgling softly to themselves as a hill brook gurgles through the woods, and the harps ran gently up and down ike rain among the daffodils. One voice called, the other answered; here were echo-like refrains; and as they sang Nick's heart grew ull. He cared not a stiver for the crowd, the golden palace, or the great folk there—the Queen no more—he only listened for Colley's voice coming up lovingly after his own and running away when he ollowed it down, like a lad and a lass through the bloom of the May. And Colley was singing as if his heart would leap out of his ound mouth for joy to follow after the song they sung, till they ame to the end and the skylark's song.

There Colley ceased, and Nick went singing on alone, for-getting, caring for, heeding nought but the song that was in his hroat.

The Queen's fan dropped from her hand upon the floor. No one aw it or picked it up. The Venetian ambassador scarcely breathed.

Nick came down the stage, his hands before him, lifted as if he aw the very lark he followed with his song, up, up, up into the un. His cheeks were flushed and his eyes were wet, though his voice vas a song and a laugh in one.

Then they were gone behind the curtain, into the shadow and he twilight there, Colley with his arms about Nick's neck, not quite aughing, not quite sobbing. The manuscript of the Revel lay torn n two upon the floor, and Master Gyles had a foot upon each piece. In the hall beyond the curtain was a silence that was deeper than hush, a stillness rising from the hearts of men.

Then Elizabeth turned in the chair where she sat. Her eyes were s bright as a blaze. And out of the sides of her eyes she looked at ae Venetian ambassador. He was sitting far out on the edge of his hair, and his lips had fallen apart. She laughed to herself. "It is a ood song, signor," said she, and those about her started at the ound of her voice. "*Chi tace confessa*—it is so! There are no songs

like English songs—there is no spring like an English spring—the
is no land like England, *my* England!" She clapped her hands. "
will speak with those lads," said she.

Straightway certain pages ran through the press and came behin
the curtain where Nick and Colley stood together, still tremblin
with the music not yet gone out of them, and brought them throug
the hall to where the Queen sat, every one whispering, "Look
as they passed.

On the dais they knelt together, bowing, side by side. Elizabet
with a kindly smile, leaning a little forward, raised them with h
slender hand. "Stand, dear lads," said she, heartily. "Be lifted up l
thine own singing, as our hearts have been uplifted by thy son
And name me the price of that same song—'twas sweeter than th
sweetest song we ever heard before."

"Or ever shall hear again," said the Venetian ambassador, und
his breath, rubbing his forehead as if just wakening out of a drean

"Come," said Elizabeth, tapping Colley's cheek with her fa
"what wilt thou have of me, fair maid?"

Colley turned red, then very pale. "That I may stay in the pala
forever and sing for your Majesty," said he. His fingers shivered
Nick's.

"Now that is right prettily asked!" she cried, and was well please
"Thou shalt indeed stay for a singing page in our household—
voice and a face like thine are merry things upon a rainy Monda
And thou, Master Lark," said she, fanning the hair back fro
Nick's forehead with her perfumed fan—"thou that comest up o
of the field with a song like the angels sing—what wilt thou hav
that thou mayst sing in our choir and play on the lute for us?"

Nick looked up at the torches on the wall, drawing a deep, lor
breath. When he looked down again his eyes were dazzled and l
could not see the Queen.

"What wilt thou have?" he heard her ask.

"Let me go home," said he.

There were red and green spots in the air. He tried to cou
them, since he could see nothing else, and everything was very sti
but they all ran into one purple spot which came and went like

refly's glow, and in the middle of the purple spot he saw the ueen's face coming and going.

"Surely, boy, that is an ill-considered speech," said she, "or thou ost deem us very poor, or most exceeding stingy!" Nick hung is head, for the walls seemed tapestried with staring eyes. "Or else is home of thine must be a very famous place."

The maids of honor tittered. Further off somebody laughed. Nick oked up, and squared his shoulders.

They had rubbed the cat the wrong way.

It is hard to be a stranger in a palace, young, country-bred, and ughed at all at once; but down in Nick Attwood's heart was a ubborn streak that all the flattery on earth could not cajole, nor dicule efface. He might be simple, shy, and slow, but what he ved he loved: that much he knew; and when they laughed at him r loving home they seemed to mock not him, but home— and *that* uched the fighting-spot.

"I would rather be there than here," said he.

The Queen's face flushed. "Thou are more curt than courteous," id she. "Is it not good enough for thee here?"

"I could na live in such a place."

The Queens' eyes snapped. "In such a place? Marry, art thou so oice? These others find no fault with the life."

"Then they be born to it," said Nick, "or they could abide no ore than I—they would na fit."

"Haw, haw!" said the Lord High Constable.

The Queen shot one quick glance at him. "Old pegs have been ade to fit new holes before today," said she; "and the trick can done again." The Constable smothered the rest of that laugh in s hand. "But come, boy, speak up; what hath put thee so out of nceit with our best-beloved palace?"

"There is na one thing likes me here. I canna bide in a place fine, for there's not so much as a corner in it feels like home. I uld na sleep in the bed last night."

"What, how? We commanded good beds!" exclaimed Elizabeth, grily, for the Venetian ambassador was smiling in his beard. This shall be seen to."

"Oh, it *was* a good bed—a very good bed indeed, your Majesty!"
cried Nick. "But the mattress puffed up like a cloud in a bag, an
almost smothered me; and it was so soft and so hot that it gave m
a fever."

Elizabeth leaned back in her chair and laughed. The Lord Hig
Constable hastily finished the laugh that he had hidden in his han
Everybody laughed. "Upon my word," said the Queen, "it is an od
skylark cannot sleep in feathers! What didst thou do, forsooth?"

"I slept in the coverlid on the floor," said Nick. "It was na hurt—
I dusted the place well—and I slept like a top."

"Now verily," laughed Elizabeth, "if it be floors that thou do
desire, we have acres to spare—thou shalt have thy pick of the lo
Come, we are ill used to begging people to be favored—thou'lt stay?

Nick shook his head.

"*Ma foi!*" exclaimed the Queen, "it is a queer fancy makes
face at such a pleasant dwelling! What is it sticks in thy throat?

Nick stood silent. What was there to say? If he came here I
never would see Stratford town again; and *this* was no abiding-pla
for him. They would not even let him go to the fountain himself
draw water with which to wash, but fetched it, three at a time, i
a silver ewer and a copper basin with towels and a flask of perfum

Elizabeth was tapping with her fan. "Thou art bedazzled like
she said. "Think twice—preferment does not gooseberry on tl
hedgerow every day; and this is a rare chance which hangs ripenir
on thy tongue. Consider well. Come, thou wilt accept?"

Nick slowly shook his head.

"Go then, if thou wilt go!" said she; and as she spoke sl
shrugged her shoulders, illy pleased, and turning toward Colle
took him by the hand and drew him closer to her, smiling at h
guise. "Thy comrade hath more wit."

"He hath no mother," Nick said quietly, loosing his hold at la
on Colley's hand. "I would rather have my mother than his wit

Elizabeth turned sharply back. Her keen eyes were sparklin
yet soft.

"Thou art no fool," said she.

A little murmur ran through the room.

She sat a moment, silent, studying his face. "Or if thou art,
upon my word I like the breed. It is a stubborn, forward dog; but

Illustration by Reginald Birch.

Hold-fast is his name. Ay, sirs," she said, and sat up very straight,
looking into the faces of her court, "Brag is a good dog, but Hold-
fast is better. A lad who loves his mother thus makes a man who
loveth his native land—and it's no bad streak in the blood. Master
Skylark, thou shalt have thy wish; to London thou shalt go this
very night."

"I do na live in London," Nick began.

"What matters the place?" said she. "Live wheresoever thine heart
doth please. It is enough—so. Thou mayst kiss our hand." She held
her hand out, bright with jewels. He knelt and kissed it as if it
were all a doing in a dream, or in some unlikely story he had read.
But a long while after he could smell the perfume from her slender
fingers on his lips.

Then a page standing by him touched his arm as he arose, and
bowing backward from the throne, came with him to the curtain
and the rest. Old Master Gyles was standing there apart. It was too
dark to see his face, but he laid his hand upon Nick's head.

"Thy cake is burned to a coal," said he.

THE MOUNTAIN MAN

By CONSTANCE LINDSAY SKINNER

SILENT SCOT strained uselessly at the rope binding his wris
behind his back. And once more he swallowed the gorge
humiliation which, despite his philosophy, *would* rise every now an
again, like an undigested potato.

A few hours ago he had been on his way from Bunyan's Town o
the Pennsylvania frontier to join his father and mother and young
brothers in the Carolinian mountains. In deerskin clothes, cap an
moccasins, with long-barreled rifle, carved powderhorn and leather
shot pouch, he had slipped noiselessly along, the freest—and, he ha
believed, the wariest—lad in the forest. To be sure, he had veere
rather far eastward, even to the ford of the Brandywine River; b
he had done so purposely. There was a man at the ford whom
greatly admired. This man had visited Bunyan's Town a few yea
before and had given him praise and a bit of silver for excelling a
the other boys as a runner, jumper and marksman. Silent Scot ha
not expected to speak with this man, who would be much too bu
at present for a friendly chat. No: he had only meant to hide amon
the trees until he caught a glimpse of him—of George Washingto
in the uniform of an American general.

And now look what had happened to him! He had walked righ
into the camp of a British outpost. To think that such a disgra
should overtake him. Andrew MacPhail, whom the English an
German Quakers in Bunyan's Town called "Silent Scot" because
could go through the forest, even in the dry midsummer, without
twig crackling under his feet, noiseless and swift as a hawk in air-
Silent Scot whom men twice and thrice his sixteen years were prou
to acclaim as the best scout on their section of the border! He swa
lowed again, with shame.

The tree to which they had tied him was a white birch. That w
clever of them, he admitted. There was no chance of his getting fr
by fraying the rope on its smooth bark. Their lantern was on th

ound, banked around with brush. He could barely see the faces of
s two red-coated captors. He gathered from their conversation that
ey would do nothing more to him until a third man arrived, some
1e named "Ferguson." What would this Ferguson do when he
1me? Hang him, probably. "Andy MacPhail," he muttered, "I'm
llin' ye the truth. I'm not so verra proud of ye!"

He wondered what time it was; not far from dawn, he thought.
[is chances of escape were slim enough now; after the light broke
1ey would be even slimmer. His disgust threatened to choke him.
He held his breath suddenly, every nerve taut. His sense of hear-
g, keener than that of his guards and trained to distinguish among
1e vibrations of the woods, had caught a sound he knew was not
1ade by breeze or rabbit. He heard it again, the faintest swish.
hen a man stepped into the dim, narrow radius of the lantern.
he two British soldiers sprang up and saluted. They spoke in low
nes, but Silent Scot heard the words "rebel spy" twice. He cogi-
ted. Rebel? Oh, yes, he was a rebel; there was no insult for him in
1at word. But spy! That had an ugly sound. No brave man liked
1at name. If they had said "Scout"—but spy! Well, whose fault was
that he was being insulted? His own! Hadn't he walked jauntily
to the very arms of these insolent redcoats at dusk? His shame
1d rage boiled over.

"Come an' peck me off the bark o' this tree, ye two red-breasted
oodpeckers, an' I'll make ye eat that word for a worm!" he roared
them.

The newcomer snatched up the lantern, hooded it in his scarf and
ld it up to the prisoner's face. Silent Scot saw a fold of the scarf
1der the tiny disk of light; it was patterned in plaid. The sight of
1at Highland tartan stirred him, almost made him forget his anger.
e leaned forward and peered sharply into Ferguson's face. Dimly
saw tight, stern lips and a prominent nose in a long lean, hard
ce, and eyes that looked black yet somehow seemed to burn like
ve coals. They were the eyes of a Highland Scot, with a fiery zeal
his soul. Andy had seen them before, like that; the eyes of a
ountain preacher exhorting his flock in exaltation, the eyes of a
lted bard chanting old war ballads with the old frenzy.

"You're Scotch," Ferguson said abruptly, after a searching surve of the tall, rangy lad with bronzed and ruddy skin, blue eyes, shock of light yellow hair like a huge corn tassel and a wide, inne cent, good-humored mouth.

"Ay, but that's nothing against me nor yet 'tis nothing again the Scotch." Andy spoke casually, as a man who knew his ow worth.

"A Highlander, too."

"Oh, ay, and that does no harm to the Hielanders, neither."

"You told me that when you doubled all the s's in 'red-breasste woodpeckerss.' The Highland blood comes out in the s's when man's in a rage." A flicker that might have been meant for a smil passed over Ferguson's face.

"I'd not be speakin' against the Hielanders if I was you, M Ferguson—seein' ye're one yersel'," Andy said in dignified rebuk

"How do you know that?" Ferguson asked quickly. There wa no trace of Scotch accent in his speech.

"An' why wouldn't I know it, seein' ye stuck yer plaidie in m face wi' the lantern?" Andy asked truculently.

"So I did. You're a sharp lad to have noticed that."

Now, if Ferguson had spoken sarcastically Andy would not hav minded. He could use sarcasm himself on occasion with tellin effect. But it was only too evident that Ferguson was not being sa castic. No; he, Silent Scot, was being sincerely praised for seein what was directly under his nose! He, Silent Scot, whose eyes we like a lance for keenness; who could read the subtlest signs of h forest world more swiftly and accurately than his Indian teacher *he* was being called "sharp" because he had observed a handful thick woolen goods thrust close to his eyes! It was disgraceful! H swallowed twice, unable to speak.

"My men say you're a rebel spy, and you say you're not. But we' soon see. It will be in this letter they took from your jerkin Ferguson sat down on a log, with the lantern beside him, and rea the paper which the soldiers had seized in searching their prisone He looked up presently. "Lad, this seems to be a letter from or Robert Marvin—and a Quaker judging by his 'thees' and 'thous' to one Duncan MacPhail saying that his son, Andrew, is going home because the debt is discharged. I'll thank you to tell me the meaning of it. And, mind you, no lies!" he added harshly.

"I've no need to tell ye lies, Mr. Ferguson," Andy answered with what dignity he could muster so soon after the degrading praise of his sharpness. "The letter is written by an honest Quaker man in Bunyan's Town to my father in Carolina. When my father went south he owed Mr. Marvin a debt and hadn't the money to pay it. So he left me with Mr. Marvin to work out the debt. An' now 'tis paid an' I'm going to my father."

"So you say, my lad; and so does the letter say. But this bit of country here is not on the road to Carolina." Ferguson rose abruptly and held the lantern up to Andy's face again. "What were you doing here?" he ripped the question out sharply.

Not wishing to answer without due consideration, Silent Scot sneezed deliberately, twice.

"Oh, ay; 'tis not precisely on the road, nor yet 'tis not so far off the road. Ye're right in what ye say, Mr. Ferguson." He spoke slowly and meditatively while he thought quickly. Perhaps these men did not know how close Washington and his army were. He must be careful. "But when a man's finding his way by the sun at dead o' night, an' in a strange land beside, 'tis likely he'll wander an' come out where he never wanted to be. An' that's precisely what's happened to me, Mr. Ferguson. Tied to a tree like a poor fool of a collie dog that's been chasin' sheep," he wound up bitterly.

Again the faint, swift flicker that might have been a smile went over Ferguson's face.

"Ay, my lad. You've sat yourself down in a platter of trouble. The rebel army is not far off; and dawn will bring fighting. And it is less than an hour to dawn. Mind you," he said harshly, "if you'd been a rebel and a spy I'd have hanged you to yon tree without pity. But I can see you're nobody but a simple country lad, who knows nothing at all. And that's well for you, Andrew MacPhail."

"Ay," said Andy huskily. He, Silent Scot, scout of scouts, called a know-nothing! He swallowed hard.

"Ay, dawn will bring fighting." Ferguson's voice deepened suddenly with passion; his intense eyes, fixed on Andy, looked as if they did not see him but flamed toward some splendid vision beyond him. "'Tis a great day you'll be seeing, lad! The king's loyal men will drive the rebels before them like chaff before the wind. Oh, would God have given me a hundred lives! I'd fling them on a hundred swords to keep Britain's honor clear." He swung away abruptly. Andy felt little quivers through the roots of his hair, as when the kilted bards sang.

"He's a strong man, is Ferguson. His eyes burned into me like a shot," he admitted in grudging admiration. He could catch a few words, here and there, of Ferguson's orders to his men, but they conveyed no meaning to him. Presently the redcoats saluted and disappeared in the darkness. He could hear their clumsy feet for some moments, going toward the river. Ferguson came over and loosed him from the tree, but left his wrists tied. "Sit on this log with me, lad. You'll be tired of standing. Tell me, now, where were you born?"

"In Aberdeen near Braemar; for my father was one of the shepherds carin' for Lord Mar's sheep."

"Aberdeen, you say? I'm from Aberdeen myself! Lord Pitfour was my father—the old lord. Lad, it's a grand thing to be born with hills about you. And, if I could choose, I'd say, let me die among hills. I've seen many places, but there's none bonnier than Aberdeen, though it is long since I left it. I was twelve years old when I ran off to be a drummer boy for the king's men in Flanders. Seven years we fought the French; and I grew from drummer boy to soldier."

"Ay, the Seven Years' War. They had it over here, too. I've heard Mr. Marvin tell about it."

"And since then I've been about the world with scarcely a look at Scotland, and always with a sword in my hand," Ferguson went on as if Andy had not spoken.

"A sword," Andy repeated, "I don't think much o' swords." And he added innocently. "Ye should learn to shoot, Mr. Ferguson."

Ferguson looked at him quickly; his eyes kindled, and the stern gravity of his face was broken for an instant by that humorous flicker.

"Lad, if we had but a clear day before us and no foes to fight, I'd be pleased to match you at shooting!"

"Oh, ho," Andy laughed softly. "Ye'd be a verra foolish man to try it, Mr. Ferguson! For I'm not braggin' when I tell ye that the old men of Bunyan's Town, where I come from, say there's never been a lad in Pennsylvania could match me but Daniel Boone. An' there's no man twice my years today can stand up beside me at shootin'."

Ferguson sprang up, and darted into the shadows and as swiftly back again with a rifle in his hands.

"Take a look at that," he said, passing it slowly in front of the lantern and turning it so that Andy could see every part of it.

"I never saw a gun like that," Andy said at last slowly. "'Tis shorter in the barrel than mine. A verra pretty gun."

"Ay, lad, and a quick one. I can load, fire, and reload in half the time it takes with any other gun. And she shoots straight."

"Where did you get her?"

"Lad, I made her!"

"What's that you say?" amazed.

"I designed this gun, Andrew. And she was cast for me in the arsenal at Woolwich. The King himself would ride over to see me fire her. He'd come with generals and admirals and sporting gentlemen and grand ladies, too, just to watch Pat Ferguson with rifle or pistol hitting every mark he aimed at. The King could tell you how he's seen me aim at a robin on the fence, toss my pistol in the air, catch it, and shoot the robin's head off. My eye and hand are as sure as that. You say you're not bragging to tell me you're the best marksman in Pennsylvania. Well, lad, I'm not bragging when I tell you that Pat Ferguson is the best marksman in the British Army. And maybe that means the crack shot of the world, for we're better shots than the French or Germans. Do you still want to match me at shooting?"

"Ay," said Andy stolidly. "For I can see 'twould be a match worthy o' me."

Ferguson slapped him on the knee.

"That's fine! You're a proud lad, and that's what I like," he exclaimed heartily. "I hope we'll meet, and shoot, in a happier day."

He set the rifle aside and extinguished the lantern. In the gray light, whitening rapidly now, Andy could see a wide forest-fringed meadow like a green apron thrown off by one of the hills, with the Brandywine, a twisted silver band, running about the edges of it. He saw a rabbit start and, with little sidelong leaps and darts through the long grass, make for a clump of brush. A meadow lark rose, shaking the dew from her wings. Her thin, golden thread of song hung above his head for an instant as she passed, soaring, over Ferguson's lookout. There was a flash of sky blue, like a garland of lupins whipping through the air, and a score of bluebirds slanted over the meadow and the softly gleaming river and were gone from his sight.

Andy looked about the camp carefully and decided that Ferguson had not done so badly with it. Naturally, a British soldier, even though a Highlander, could not be expected to show so much intelligence about such things as an American frontiersman. It was an excellent site, at the woods' edge midway on the incline of a hill; but the trees were not the best for a hiding place. They were mostly birches, growing rather well apart; and their sheer trunks of white and silver gray were conspicuous in themselves and tended to show up anything of a different color near them. Ferguson had recognized that peril and had piled cut willows among the trees so that they would look like a natural growth of underbrush to any one viewing them from the other side of the meadow; but Andy felt sure that they would not deceive him. *He* would know, as soon as he saw them, that they had no roots in the ground, and that they were bundles of twigs and not whole bushes. He knew the ways of growing willows. If *he* had made that breastwork the enemy could not have told the difference without laying hands on it. His self-respect, so sorely downed during the past night, began to mount again.

Ferguson came to him with a rope in his hand.

"Andrew MacPhail, the fortune of war has made you my prisoner; but that's nothing against your dignity as a brave man," he said formally. "I believe there's no harm in you, but I'd be false

THE MOUNTAIN MAN

to my duty if I took chances with you. So I'm obliged to bind you to the logs so that you can't make a stir or rise up and show yourself." He stooped and quickly made Andy secure. "The rebels under General Washington are lying in the woods yonder. And their scouts will be peering like hawks at every spot of brush. This is the day that will see the Rebellion put down. And I'm praying 'tis I will fire the first shot. For 'tis likely they'll send out an officer and a man or two with him to reconnoiter. But he will never ride back."

His burning, gloomy eyes were fixed on Andy again as if they did not see him but something beyond him. He wheeled away and dropped on his knees behind the willow breastwork, his rifle in his hands.

The brilliant yellow light of the September sun, rising now over the eastern knolls, made the heavy dew of the meadow sparkle like the jewels in some royal crusader's breastplate, and the river tide shimmer like brandished steel. With his heart beating tumultuously and his eyes strained on the wall of trees opposite, Andy watched silently.

What should he do? he asked himself. Rather, what *could* he do? Shout? Ferguson would kill him in a wink. Well, that wouldn't matter so much, he thought, if his shout would do any good. But the danger was that the American officer might think it a signal from one of his own scouts and come on instead of dashing back. His sole hope was that there were frontier scouts like himself over there. It was second nature with them not to show themselves erect in the open; in war, they distrusted every clump of trees and every field of long grass. They knew how the Indian scout would crawl on his belly a few inches at a time, lie still in the calms between the gusts of wind or the little breezes, then creep on again while they blew and made the whole surface move so that the shaking of the grass in his part of the field would not be observed. They knew how the Indian warriors would crouch under cover, noiselessly, for days, if need be, waiting for the settlers to grow careless and come outside the palisades so that they could shoot them down from ambush. A frontiersman might even now be snaking through the grass at the far end of the field. If so, before he got within range of Ferguson's rifle, he would know that the willows of the lookout never grew out of the soil in this fashion. Officers were fine gentlemen, Andy believed. Likely they came from Philadelphia and Richmond and Boston, and had no training for this sort of thing. Reconnoitering was a scout's work. Surely they wouldn't let an officer try it?

He saw movement where the trees seemed to be thinnest. Then a man rode into the field and paused. Three other mounted men followed him. They came on a little way together and paused again. Two of them now veered to the left, and the third to the right. The man who had emerged first cantered briskly across the meadow directly toward the lookout.

"I can't yet tell a rebel's rank by his uniform. But from the proud look of him and his horse, I'd say yon man riding to his death is no less than a colonel," Ferguson said grimly.

The American officer came on twenty yards and reined in. He was mounted on a fine bay horse, Andy saw; and he wore a dark green and blue uniform with a high cocked hat. He looked about him; with face upturned, he swept his glance slowly over the hillside. The boy in the lookout knew that face. He had traveled miles out of his way just to see it once again.

Washington! Andy's heart died within him and a dumb cry strangled in his throat. It was Washington himself who sat there on his horse in the sunlit meadow, a living target for the crack shot of the world.

There was nothing that he could do, nothing. He looked at Ferguson and, frozen with horror, watched him raise his rifle and take aim. An eternity of agony rolled by while he waited for the shot. Then, scarcely able to believe his eyes, he saw Ferguson's finger withdraw from the trigger, saw the rifle lowered. What had happened? He darted a glance at the field. Washington had swung his horse round; his back was toward them now. Slowly he trotted away. He was still well within range, an easy mark. Again Ferguson raised his rifle and again lowered it without firing. Silently both occupants of the lookout watched the rider rejoin his companions

and, with them, disappear into the forest. Ferguson sprang up, with
a sharp word to someone who was coming through the coppice.

The whole wood back of them was astir now. Andy caught the
flare of red coats among the green leafage. Vaguely he realized that
the men who had captured him the night before had returned; that
Ferguson was talking while one of them cut the rope that had bound
him to a log. He heard something about being taken back behind
the lines. Then he was moving, being led off through the forest.
It didn't matter. He could think of nothing but the picture of
Washington less than a hundred yards from Ferguson's rifle, offering first his breast and then his back to the crack shot of the world,
who had lowered his gun without firing! Why? The question beat
at his brain like hail on oak leaves. Why hadn't Ferguson fired?
He had said that he wanted to fire the first shot of the day; he had
expected an officer to ride out, had lain in wait eager to kill him.
Ay, and he had called Washington, as he came out of the forest,
"Yon man riding to his death!" Then why hadn't he shot him?
Was it a miracle, such as saved Moses and Elijah? Had God stricken
Ferguson blind, or peopled the meadow with ten thousand angels in
chariots of fire about Washington? If there had been fiery chariots
there, Ferguson would have seen them, whoever else was blind.
Andy felt sure of that. There was a strange spirit in Ferguson, like
the spirit in Highland preachers and bards, making them see
things not visible to common men. Chariots and horses of fire!
Ay, that would be a grand and glorious sight to hear a man tell
about!

"God, don't let Ferguson get killed till I've a chance to ask him,"
Andy prayed fervently.

A half mile further on, his guard led him by a detour along the
crests of the low, rounded hills; for the army was sweeping in full
force across the lower ground. It was the first large army on the
march Andy had ever seen. For a time he forgot the chariots of
fire and the great man whom God had saved. He stared, breathless,
at the monstrous mêlée; teams of men, bent until their brows were
near to the dust, like Israelite slaves under the Egyptian lash, dragging the great guns; horses plunging; flags streaming, gold lace

and bayonets sparkling; bare knees bobbing rhythmically as chips of new wood bob on the dark eddy of a stream, and plaidies waving, as a Highland regiment passed; the skirling of the bagpipes and the shriek of bugles, the sullen, sinister thudding of drums and of thousands of feet and hoofs on the dry ground; and red coats like thousands of autumnal berries snapped from miles of bushes and lashed on by a mad gale.

His guard led him sharply down the far side of a knoll to a large farmhouse, with outhouses and cornfields. The ground was gashed deep by heavy wheels, and the broken cornstalks looked as if one of the hills had rolled over on them. All about were the black smudges of extinguished campfires. The ruinous sight shocked Andy, who had suffered lean winters when other red warriors had devastated the border fields.

"Ye've made a grand mess of yon farm!" he said, in tones of severe reproof. The guard gave him a sour look and shoved him into a shed, where four soldiers were playing cards.

"Here's a boy that got lost going to Carolina. Lieutenant Ferguson's taking a liking to him. Here's his gun and hunting knife and powderhorn and shot pouch." He cut the cords about Andy's wrists. "Ferguson says give him some food and let him sleep." Then with a scowling, "Mind you, rebel; no tricks now!" he was gone.

Andy did full justice to the food, but he was too excited to be sleepy, in spite of the fact that he had been awake all night. However, he lay down presently and closed his eyes; because he wanted to think, and to plan. Especially did he want to plan, for he could not linger in this pleasant spot. He had to go to Carolina. He rolled as close as possible to his confiscated weapons and drowsed with a busy brain. How he loved that rifle, and the powderhorn which his Indian friend, Tuleko, had carved for him! But it was hopeless to think of regaining them unnoticed. He sighed. But there was his hunting knife. Certainly he should be able to slip that inside one of his leggings. He could make his hunting knife serve his needs all the way to Carolina. Even before his twelfth year, long before he had owned firearms, he had killed birds and small game with a sapling, cut and sharpened at one end by his knife, with its bunch of roots at the other end to give it weight and balance. Thrown tomahawk fashion, with sure aim, it could be relied on to keep a traveler from hunger. With his knife he could cut and whittle a fire stick of hickory; and so make a camp fire every night to cook his food or to dry his clothes after swimming a creek or tramping in the rain. He knew how to make fire as the Indians made it for centuries before ever they traded beaver skins for the white man's matches. Yes, Silent Scot would be free of troubles if he could only get hold of his knife. He snorted, and tossed an inch nearer to it, and flung out an arm. A soldier jumped up and bent over him, putting a hand on his shoulder. Silent Scot half opened his eyes, then closed them again as if the lids were too heavy to stay up without propping. The soldier went back to his card game. The next time he snorted and tossed, one of the card players made a jesting remark but did not come to look at him. After a while they paid no attention.

Throughout his pretended slumbers he could hear the roar of cannon. It sounded to him as if all the thunders of the sky had gathered over the ford of the Brandywine to split the world in twain. There were nearer sounds, too—dashing hoofs, messengers probably, he thought; and feet tramping by, men bearing the wounded to shelter, perhaps. Later on he heard wild shouts. What was that? The American Army in retreat? His guards rushed to the door, yelling for more news. Andy retrieved his knife and hid it inside his legging. The British winning! That made it more urgent than ever for him to get to Carolina, deliver his letter, and then go as scout with the American Army. They needed scouts, he felt sure, after what he had seen today! Washington himself obliged to do scout duty! If he, Andy MacPhail, had been over there with the American soldiers he would not have permitted that! As he considered it, his thoughts reverted to the incident which had so puzzled him. Why had Ferguson lowered his gun without firing?

He was sitting up, yawning, and still apparently drowsy after a comforting supper, when the man who had brought him in stepped into the doorway and beckoned to him.

"Ferguson wants you."

Andy jumped up and followed him to the farmhouse. He would

have his nagging question answered now, he thought with a thrill of excitement. He would make that fierce, glum man answer!

"Dr. Giffen, here's the lad he sent me for," Andy heard his guide say to one of a group of men in the kitchen.

"Very well, Horton, take him in," the doctor said, with a casual glance at Andy. Then, as they moved off in the direction of a door that stood ajar, he stopped him. "You must not excite him, my boy. He is in a bad way."

"Ye mean he's wounded?" Andy asked. "Is he hurtit bad, doctor?"

"Yes, his right arm is shot to pieces."

"His *right arm!*" Andy repeated, aghast; and added slowly, more to himself than to the doctor, "Him that was the crack shot o' the world."

"He will never shoot again. It is a harder blow for him than for most men. He'd have taken death instead gladly if he'd been given his choice."

Andy made no reply. Habitually silent-lipped as well as silent-footed, what few words he used in his daily life went from him now. He saw that Dr. Giffen admired Ferguson and was grieved for him. But no doctor could understand as he, Silent Scot, understood what this blow meant to the man in there. Wasn't his own heart sore hurt because he must slip away this evening and leave behind him the rifle he loved, his dearest friend, the comrade of his long hunts and of all his daring adventures in the red man's country? But sometime he would own another rifle. He would fire many a straight and pretty shot. Ay, there was no joy in the world like that; and he would have it again! But Ferguson, who had made that new, magical, quick-firing gun; Ferguson, the crack shot o' the world—— He, Silent Scot, was doubtless the only other man living who understood just what that shattered right arm meant to Pat Ferguson.

"Wait outside, Horton," Ferguson said. Andy had an impression of white linen swathings, of colorless lips tightened to a thin line, of damp black hair, of black eyes smoldering deep in a gray, drawn face. He saw a bit of fringe, wet and stained, hanging down from the rolled plaidie under Ferguson's head. He had no idea what he would say to Ferguson, except that, some time before he left the room, he would ask a certain question which, if unanswered, would give him no peace all his life long. But he *did* know what he would *not* say. He would not say one word about the shattered arm. That was too vast a grief for pity; words would be an insult. Ferguson would know what he felt and why he made no mention of it. For they two were not only crack marksmen, brothers of the rifle clan, they were Scots and Highlanders, the same silent, strong people—mountain men, both.

"Good evenin', Mr. Ferguson," Andy said politely. "I'm verra pleased to see ye again."

"And I am as pleased to see you again, Andrew MacPhail," Ferguson replied with similar courtesy; "I sent for you to give you back your letter—now that I know there is no harm in it." He extended it to him in his left hand. "And I wanted to ask you a question."

"Now, that's verra strange," said Andy, "for I'm wantin' to ask ye a question yersel'."

"Yours will keep. Lad, did you know who the officer was who rode toward us this morning? I'm asking, because when I looked at you, after he'd gone, your face was white as frost."

Silent Scot's expression did not change. He was master of his face, as more than one befooled Indian warrior could have told. He thought fast. He liked Ferguson; they were friends. He would have liked to speak the truth to him from an open heart. But he must remember that in this war they were on opposite sides, foes. If he admitted having recognized Washington, Ferguson might believe that he had been scouting for the Americans when he stumbled into the British camp. In that case, he would order him well guarded. No, he couldn't take the chance of that. He must hurry on to Carolina; because, as he saw it, his first duty was to deliver the old Quaker's letter to his father, to let him know that the shadow of debt—so obnoxious to Highland pride—no longer darkened the honor of the MacPhails. After that, he would be free to offer his services as scout to the nearest Patriot army. He must not run the risk of being clapped into a British prison until the end of the war. He had seen today how badly the Americans needed scouts.

"'Tis not a bonny sight to see a man killed, Mr. Ferguson," he said evasively. "An' him sittin' so grand on a fine bay horse! Didn't ye say he was no less than a colonel? There's not so many grand colonels in Bunyan's Town, where I come from, Mr. Ferguson." Andy smiled disarmingly, his little blue eyes twinkling. Apparently the wounded man was satisfied with his answer, for he did not press the question.

"I know who he was, lad. That was General Washington himself."

"General Washington!" Andy echoed with excellently simulated amazement. "And ye didn't shoot him! *Why?*"

"I didn't know him then. I found out later who he was."

"But when ye thought 'twas a colonel, Mr. Ferguson, and ye'd told me not ten minutes before how ye hoped to fire the first shot, and how yon man was ridin' surely to his death——" Andy's words rushed out pellmell now. "What did ye see, man? Tell me that! *What did ye see in the field around him?*"

"See?" Ferguson repeated, puzzled. "Why, nothing."

"*Then why didn't ye shoot?*" His voice quavered and the color rose in his cheeks. Ferguson's drawn face was touched for an instant with a mild surprise.

"Didn't you see, lad, that just as I was aiming at his breast, he swung round and showed me his back? Well, 'tis not a pleasant thing to shoot an unoffending individual in the back, who is acquitting himself very coolly of his duty. As he rode off it came to me that maybe I was forgetting my own duty in letting an officer of those rebels and traitors go free to plague the King's loyal men later on the field. And I leveled at him again, but the idea disgusted me."

"An' if ye *had* known 'twas Washington?" Andy asked eagerly.

"Then maybe my duty would have been so plain I couldn't have escaped it. Washington, the most dangerous rebel of them all!" he said broodingly, the sullen, fiery look kindling in his eyes. "But I am not sorry I didn't know. I've never shot my foe in the back, Andrew. And I think no man's fit to be called a soldier that will foul an honest gun with a cowardly shot like that. No, *I'm not sorry I didn't know!*" Ferguson's eyelids closed and his lips tightened quickly to still a twitch of pain.

For some minutes Andy did not speak. He was thinking hard. At first he had been disappointed that Ferguson had not seen glorious chariots of fire. But now? Well, he didn't know. Never to foul your gun with a coward's shot—there was something splendid in that, too.

"I'm verra proud to be acquainted wi' ye, Mr. Ferguson," he said presently, with dignity, "for I can see ye're a verra fine man."

Ferguson opened his eyes. "I'll say the same to you, Andrew. I wish I could let you go on to your father, lad," he said kindly, "but that is impossible. Though we're friends now, and both Aberdeen men, too, I couldn't give you back your gun. And how would you get to Carolina without a rifle to hunt with? Poor lad, you'd starve."

"Ay, ay. Fancy a poor, simple lad like me goin' to Carolina wi'out a rifle!" Andrew said noncommittally, wagging his head. "But I'm thinkin' ye should take a bit o' sleep now, Mr. Ferguson. So I'll be sayin' good night."

"I'll see you again in the morning," Ferguson said. "You know the way back to your quarters? If not, there are scores of men about to direct you—and to prevent you from running away to the rebels. Tell Horton I want him."

Andy went out. He found Horton in the kitchen and gave him Ferguson's message. The yards were full of men and horses and baggage. Through the gathering dusk little cook fires dotted the field with flames. His trained eye noted quickly the positions of inanimate objects which would afford shelter. On the whole the prospect was as promising as he could have hoped for. Ferguson had had no fear that he would try to escape from a yard full of men. But Andy much preferred a yard full of men who were not watching him, to one or two who were!

It took him nearly half an hour to get beyond the camp—snaking his way under and behind wagons, behind tents, through deep ruts in the fields, to the river. He skirted the ford to the bank of the smoother, deeper tide beyond it. There he paused and made sure that his letter and his knife were safely disposed of and protected. Ferguson might send men after him. If they found his trail and followed it, they would lose it here—in water.

He was sorry that he would not see Ferguson in the morning; but he had to go to Carolina. The sooner he got to Carolina with his letter, the sooner he would be able to join the army and prevent Washington from taking risks like that! He hoped he would meet Ferguson again some day. That hope was a prophecy, though Andy did not know it. He would meet Ferguson again in scenes of adventure such as the boy slipping down the low bank to the Brandywine's edge that night could not have even imagined.

He meditated briefly on all that had happened to him—and looked on the bright side.

" 'Tis no' so great a shame to me, after all, that they caught me," he told himself; "but if I hadna got away from them—Oh, ay; *that would have been verra disgracefu'!*"

Yes, on the whole, Silent Scot had justified his name and his fame as an impeccable scout. Now he was on his way to Carolina without a care on his mind. A tiny yellow moon peeped at him over a hill. Stars flickered dimly on the river, lighting a path for him. Andy dropped noiselessly into the water and swam downstream, comfortable and contented as a beaver.

SALT-WATER TEA

By ESTHER FORBES

Illustration by Tom Hall

O N SUNDAYS the boys might relax a little, breakfast when they pleased, only they must turn up clean and shining in time to go to church with Aunt and Uncle and listen to the inflammatory Reverend Sam Cooper. Doctor Cooper was putting more politics than gospel into his sermons that fall and more fear of "taxation without representation" than God into his congregation.

England had, by the fall of 1773, gone far in adjusting the grievances of her American colonies. But she insisted upon a small tax on tea. Little money would be collected by this tax. It worked no hardship on the people's pocketbooks, only three-pence a pound. The stubborn colonists, who were insisting they would not be taxed unless they could vote for the men who taxed them, would hardly realize that the tax had been paid by the East India Company in London before the tea was shipped over here. After all, thought Parliament, the Americans were yokels and farmers—not political thinkers. And the East India tea, even after the tax was paid, would be better and cheaper than any the Americans ever had had. Weren't the Americans, after all, human beings? Wouldn't they care more for their pocketbooks than their principles?

Shivering—for the last week in October was bitterly cold—Johnny built up the fire in the attic. From the back window he could see that the roofs of the Afric Queen were white with frost.

A sharp rat-tat on the shop door below woke Rab.

"What time's it?" he grumbled, as people do who think they are disturbed too early Sunday morning.

"Seven and past. I'll see what's up."

It was Sam Adams himself. When either cold or excited, his palsy increased. His head and hands were shaking. But his strong, seamed face, which always looked cheerful, today looked radiant. Sam Adams was so pleased that Johnny, a little naïvely, thought he must have word that Parliament had backed down again. The expected ships had not sailed.

"Look you, Johnny. I know it's the Lord's Day, but there's a placard I must have printed and posted secretly tonight. The Sons of Liberty will take care of the posting, but Mr. Lorne must see to the printing. Could you run across and ask him to step over? And Rab —where's he?"

Rab was coming down the ladder.

"What's up?" said Rab sleepily.

"The first of the tea ships, the *Dartmouth,* is entering the harbor. She'll be at Castle Island by nightfall."

"So they dared send them?"

"Yes."

"And the first has come?"

"Yes. God give us strength to resist. That tea cannot be allowed to land."

When Johnny got back with Mr. Lorne, Rab had Mr. Adams's text in his hands, reading it as a printer reads, thinking first of spacing and capitals, not of the meaning.

"I can set that in no time. Two hundred copies? They'll be fairly dry by nightfall."

"Ah, Mr. Lorne," said Adams, shaking hands, "without you printers the cause of liberty would be lost forever."

"Without you"—Mr. Lorne's voice shook with emotion—"there would not have been any belief in liberty to lose. I will, as always, do anything—everything you wish."

"I got word before dawn. It's the *Dartmouth* and she will be as far as Castle Island by nightfall. If that tea is landed—if that tax is paid—everything is lost. The selectmen will meet all day today and I am calling a mass meeting for tomorrow. This is the placard I will put up."

He took it from Rab's hands and read:

"Friends! Brethren! Countrymen! That worst of Plagues, the detested tea shipped for this Port by the East India Company, is now arrived in the Harbour: the hour of destruction, of manly opposition to the machinations of Tyranny, stares you in the Face; Every Friend to his Country, to Himself, and to Prosterity, is now called upon to meet at Faneuil Hall, at nine o'clock this day [that, of course, is tomorrow, Monday], at which time the bells will ring to make united and successful resistance to this last, worst and most destructive measure of Administration . . . Boston, Nov. 29, 1773."

Then he said quietly: "Up to the last moment—up to the eleventh hour, we will beg the Governor's permission for the ships' return to London with their cargo. We have twenty days."

Johnny knew that by law any cargo that was not unloaded within twenty days might be seized by the custom-house and sold at auction.

"Mr. Lorne, needless to say the Observers will meet tonight. There are *private* decisions to be made before the mass meeting tomorrow at nine."

Johnny pricked up his ears. Ever since he had come to Mr. Lorne's (and Rab said he might be trusted with anything—possibly with men's lives) he had now and then summoned the members of the Observers' Club. They were so close to treason they kept no list of members. Rab made Johnny memorize the twenty-two names. They met in Rab and Johnny's attic.

"Johnny," said Mr. Lorne, anxious and overanxious to please Mr. Adams, "start right out."

"No, sir, if you please. Noon will be better. That will give the members time to get home from church. And, as usual, Johnny, make no stir. Simply say, 'Mr. So and So owes eight shillings for his newspaper.'"

Johnny nodded. That meant the meeting would be tonight at eight o'clock. If he said one pound eight shillings, it would mean the next night at eight. Two pounds, three and six would mean the day after at three-thirty. It gave him a feeling of excitement and pleasure to be even on the fringes of great, secret, dangerous events.

Today he could not make his rounds on horseback. A constable might stop him and ask embarrassing questions. There was a law against riding out on Sunday for either business or pleasure.

The Reverend Samuel Cooper he "dunned" as he was shaking hands with his parishioners at the end of the service. He nodded as Johnny told him that eight shillings were due on the paper, but a fashionable woman standing by said it was a fair scandal for boys to be intruding into God's house and dunning a clergyman, and if collecting bills wasn't work, what was? She would call a constable and have the "impertinent imp" whipped for Sabbath-breaking. Mr. Cooper had to cough so he could pretend not to be laughing, and he winked at Johnny in spite of the dignity of his black clericals, white bands, and great woolly wig.

"I'll tell my brother William, too, eh?" he offered. "Brother William and I will both pay you tonight."

Johnny found four more of the members also at this meeting and then headed for Beacon Hill. At all the great mansions he commonly went to the back door, either to leave newspapers or to "collect bills." A skinny, slippery-looking old black slave in the kitchen told him Mr. Hancock was in bed with a headache. No, she would *not* permit Johnny to go to his bedchamber. So the boy went to the front door, rang the bell, hoping some other less obdurate servant might let him in. The old slave guessed what he was up to and got there first.

Might he not send a note up to Mr. Hancock? They wrangled a little and at last she said yes he might. She was preparing a catnip tea to send to the master. He could write a note and put it on the tray. In the kitchen he wrote his note—"Mr. Hancock owes the *Boston Observer* eight shillings," folded it, and on the outside wrote, "Mr. Hancock, Esquire."

Near-by was William Molineaux's house. Its seedy appearance advertised to the whole world that its owner was close to bankruptcy. Mr. Molineaux was standing in his orchard, shaking his cane at a couple of small boys he had treed in an apple tree. He had a terrible temper, which he thoroughly enjoyed. Although Johnny told him three times about those eight shillings, he was not sure whether the idea had penetrated the wild Irishman's skull or not. Nor did he care.

His good friend, Josiah Quincy, plump little John Adams, and James Otis he found together at the Quincy house. They were still sitting over their port and cracking nuts. James Otis did not even look up when Johnny entered. He was hunched up in his chair, his thick-skulled, heavy head hung forward. He was busy drawing a row of little people on the paper before him. Quincy, having already heard about the meeting that night, put a finger to his lips and shook his head, at the same time glancing at the heavy, lonely figure of Otis. Johnny guessed that neither he nor John Adams wanted Otis notified of the meeting, although he was a member.

For four years Otis had been crazy and sane, turn and turn about, on again and off again. He was the most brilliant man of them all, thought in the largest terms, nor ever merely of Boston; was passionate in his demand for the rights of Englishmen everywhere— over here and in Old England, too. Now he was not even listening to what was going on about him. His heavy head was swinging back and forth. John Adams and Josiah Quincy were watching him so intently their heads were also moving a little. Johnny stole out and closed the door softly after him. He guessed that in a day or two he'd hear it whispered, James Otis had got into a mad freak and fired guns from the windows of his house: James Otis had been seen leaving Boston in a closed chaise with a doctor and in a straitjacket.

Next he went to Doctor Church. He was a queer man surely. He was still in his bedgown and slippers, with paper, inkhorn, and pens about him, writing poetry. Johnny did not care for Molineaux because he bellowed and roared so loudly. But he disliked Doctor Church. He did not know one thing about him, but he felt the man was crooked, and he knew that Paul Revere and Joseph Warren felt as he felt about Church.

He went on to Mr. Revere's. The silversmith was busy drawing a political cartoon concerning tea and tyranny. He did not draw well

—not the way he made silver. As he drew, his children crowded about him, standing on the rungs of his chair, breathing down his neck, dropping crumbs of gingerbread into his hair; but Paul Revere took all this confusion as he took everything else, without any fussing.

"I believe I owe you eight shillings?" he said, with a wide smile on his dark, ruddy face. The eyes gleamed.

Now there was only Doctor Warren left; he'd go back and help Rab set out all those chairs in the attic, get ready for the meeting that night.

Doctor Warren was back from Roxbury. He was sitting in his surgery, still in his riding boots and spurs.

"Eight shillings, sir," said Johnny.

"I guessed we'd meet tonight. I'll be there . . . but wait a moment. I promised this article to Mr. Lorne this morning—got held up. Woman fell out of an apple tree. Broken thigh . . . " He went on writing.

He was a fine-looking young man, with fresh skin and thick blond hair and very bright blue eyes.

Even a horse boy merely entering that surgery would feel confidence in him and his skill. Johnny took off the red mittens Aunt Lorne had knit for him and stretched his hands toward the fire blazing on the hearth.

.   .   .   .   .   .

Outside, Johnny could hear shouting, yelling, whistles, the running of feet. With the coming of night, the Sons of Liberty were abroad, tacking up Mr. Adams's placards. Tonight Rab was not out with them, although he had been off once or twice of late helping to frighten the tea consignees out of Boston to the protection of a handful of British soldiers stationed on Castle Island. Johnny was too young to be a "Son." But when the Observers met, the boys always stayed in the room below to run errands for them, and it was always Rab who mixed the fragrant punch with which the meetings ended.

All over Boston was a feeling of excitement. Everyone knew that the *Dartmouth* was but a few miles away. Great events were brewing. Johnny went to the door to see what the clamor was. A courageous Tory was chasing the men whom he had found tacking a placard on his property. They had let him chase them thus far to dark Salt Lane and now had turned on him. Such street brawling made Johnny sick. He closed the door, sat down beside Rab, and began slicing lemons, oranges, and limes.

"Rab . . ."

"Yes?"

"What will they decide . . . those men upstairs?"

"You heard Sam Adams. If *possible,* the ships will sail home again with their tea. We've got twenty days."

"But if the Governor won't agree?"

"He won't. You don't know Hutchinson. I do. And you saw how happy Sam was this morning? He knows the Governor a lot better than I do."

"And then . . . and what next, Rab?"

Johnny heard blows and oaths from the street outside. His hands shook. He put down the knife so Rab wouldn't know. They were doing something—something awful, to the Tory.

"As soon as we go upstairs with our punch, we'll know. Look at Sam Adams. If he looks as pleased as an old dog fox with a fat pullet in his mouth, we'll know they've agreed to violence if everything else fails. He doesn't care much any more about patching up our differences with England. He'd just about welcome a war."

"But the King's warships are in the harbor. They'll protect the tea. They'll fight."

"We can fight, too." Rab was putting the last delicate touches to his kettleful of brew, for tonight the punch would be hot. He was grating nutmegs, cautiously sprinkling in cloves, and breaking up cinnamon bark.

"Taste it, Johnny. That Madeira Mr. Hancock brought with him is first-class."

But Johnny heard a low moaning in the street, close to the shut door. That Tory, who had been so brave—and foolish—as to follow the Sons of Liberty down a black alley was alone now—was sobbing, not from pain but from humiliation. Johnny declined to taste the punch.

Mr. Lorne called down the ladder.

"Boys, ready with your punch?"

"They made up their minds fast tonight," said Rab. "I rather thought they would."

Johnny carried a handful of pewter cups and the big wooden bowl. Rab followed with two pitchers of his spicy brew.

The attic where the boys commonly slept looked strange enough with those chairs pulled out and arranged for the meeting. John Hancock sat in the moderator's chair. His face looked white and drawn. Probably his head still ached. Beside him was Sam Adams leaning toward him, whispering and whispering. Johnny thought how the Tories were saying that Sam Adams seduced John Hancock, even as the Devil had seduced Eve—by a constant whispering in his ear.

Adams turned his face as Johnny set down the wooden bowl on the baize-covered box before the moderator. Johnny had never seen an old dog fox with a fat pullet in his mouth, but he recognized the expression when he saw it. Rab poured the punch and instantly the tense silence was broken. The men were on their feet, crowding up about the bowl. Rab and Johnny were well known. Here was Paul Revere clinking his cup with Rab, and John Hancock was telling Johnny how far too well his old slave woman guarded his privacy. Actually three men had come to the house to tell him the first of the tea ships had been sighted, but he had not known anything was afoot until he got Johnny's "bill" on his tray. Then he guessed what had happened.

"Here's to December the sixteenth."

"Hear! Hear!"

They drank to that last day, the day on which the tea must be destroyed—unless it was allowed to return to England. And Johnny saw that Sam Adams had carried them all with him. They did not honestly want the tea returned and a peaceful settlement made. They wanted grievances and more grievances . . . well, yes, armed warfare. Things were in such a state they did not honestly believe there could be any permanent, friendly settlement with the mother country.

Sam Adams was standing at the far end of the room and Mr. Hancock still sat, his head in his hands. Adams clapped slightly and instantly conversation stopped.

"Gentlemen," he said, "tonight we have made our decision—and know the method by which the detested tea can be destroyed, if the ships are not allowed to return. Here we have with us two of exactly —ah—the sort of boys or young men we intend to use for our great purpose. Two boys in whom we have implicit trust. If it is the wish of the assembled club members, I suggest we approach them with our proposition tonight . . . enlist their aid. Twenty days will be up before we know. We'd best get on with our plans."

The members once more took their seats, but the pewter cups of punch were passing from hand to hand. Only Will Molineaux was too restless to sit. He was muttering to himself. Ben Church sat alone. He often did. No one really liked him.

All agreed the boys were to be told.

"First," Adams said to the boys, "raise your right hands. Swear by the great name of God Himself never, for as long as you live, to divulge to anyone the secret matters now trusted to you. Do you so swear?"

The boys swore.

Hancock was not looking at them. He sat with his aching head in his hands.

"There's no chance—not one—those ships will be allowed to return. The mass meetings which will be held almost daily demanding the return of the tea are to arouse public opinion and to persuade the world we did not turn to violence until every other course had been blocked to us. When the twenty days are up, on the night of the sixteenth of December, those ships are going to be boarded. That tea will be dumped in Boston Harbor. For each ship, the *Dartmouth,* the *Eleanor,* and the brig, the *Beaver,* we will need thirty stout, honest, fearless men and boys. Will you be one, Rab?"

He did not say Rab and Johnny, as the younger boy noticed. Was this because he thought Johnny too cripple-handed for chopping open tea chests—or merely because he knew Rab better and he was older?

"Of course, sir."

"How many other boys could you find for the night's work? Strong and trustworthy boys—for if one ounce of tea is stolen, the whole thing becomes robbery—not a protest."

Rab thought.

"Eight or ten tonight, but give me a little time so I can feel about a bit and I can furnish fifteen or twenty."

"Boys who can keep their mouths shut?"

"Yes."

Paul Revere said, "I can furnish twenty or more from about North Square."

"Not one is to be told in advance just what the work will be, nor who the others are, nor the names of the men who instigated this tea party—that is, the gentlemen gathered here tonight. Simply, as they love their country and liberty and hate tyranny, they are to gather in this shop on the night of December sixteenth, carrying with them such disguises as they can think of, and each armed with an axe or hatchet."

"It will be as you say."

The discussion became more general. Each of these three groups must have a leader, men who could keep discipline.

"I'll go for one," said Paul Revere.

Doctor Warren warned him. "Look here, Paul, it has been decided this work must be done by apprentices, strangers—folk little known about Boston. The East India Company may bring suit. If you are recognized . . . "

"I'll risk it."

Uncle Lorne was motioning to the boys to leave the conspirators. They did not want to leave, but they did.

.   .   .   .   .

Both the boys were in their truckle beds. The loft still smelled of tobacco and the spices of the punch.

Johnny moved restlessly on his bed.

"Rab?"

"Uh?"

"Rab . . . those boys you promised. Am I one?"

"Of course."

"But my hand . . . What will we have to do?"

"Chop open tea chests. Dump tea in the harbor."

"Rab?"

"Hummmmm?"

"How can I ever . . . chop?"

"You've twenty days to practice in. Logs in back yard need splitting."

"Rab . . ."

But the older boy was asleep.

Johnny was so wide awake he couldn't close his eyes. Old Meeting struck midnight. He settled himself again. Surely if he tried hard enough he could sleep. He was thinking of those tea ships, the *Dartmouth,* the *Eleanor,* the *Beaver,* great white sails spread softly, sweeping on and on through the night to Boston. Nearer, nearer. He was almost asleep, twitched, and was wide awake. He would not think of the tea ships, but of those logs in the back yard he would practice on. He would take an axe in his left hand and chop, chop, chop . . . so he fell asleep.

Something large and white was looming up over him—about to run him down. He struggled awake, sat up, and found he was sweating. It was the great sails of the tea ships.

From the bed next to him he heard the soft, slow breathing of the older boy. So much more involved than Johnny in the brewing storm, Rad had been able to drop off immediately. Somehow Johnny must draw something of Rab's calm, his nerveless strength. He began to breathe in unison with the sleeping boy—so slowly, so softly. He fell into a heavy sleep.

. . . . .

Next morning Johnny was up and out in the back yard early. At first it seemed impossible to hold an axe in a left hand, steady it

with his bad right. He gritted his teeth and persevered. Rab said
nothing of his struggles. He merely set type, pulled proofs as usual
But often he was gone from home, and Johnny knew he wa*
"feeling about" for those fifteen to twenty boys he had promised.
Would the others go and Johnny be left behind? He could not
bear the thought, and Rab had promised him that in twenty
days he might learn to chop. Having finished the logs in Mr.
Lorne's back yard, he began chopping (free gratis) for the Afric
Queen.

Almost every day and sometimes all day, the mass meetings at
Old South Church went on. Tempers grew higher and higher.
Boston was swept with a passion it had not known since the Boston
Massacre three years before. Riding this wild storm was Sam Adams
and his trusty henchmen, directing it, building up the anger until,
although the matter was not publicly mentioned, they would all see
the only thing left for them to do was to destroy the tea.

Sometimes Rab and Johnny went to these meetings. It happened
they were there when the Sheriff arrived and bade the meeting
forthwith to disperse. He said it was lawless and treasonable. This
proclamation from Governor Hutchinson was met with howls and
hisses. They voted to disobey the order.

Sometimes the boys slipped over to Griffin's Wharf. By the eighth
of December the *Eleanor* had joined the *Dartmouth*. These were
strange ships. They had unloaded their cargoes—except the tea. The
Town of Boston had ordered them not to unload the tea and the
law stated they could not leave until they had unloaded. Nor would
the Governor give them a pass to return to England. At Castle
Island the British Colonel Leslie had orders to fire upon them if
they attempted to sneak out of the harbor. The *Active* and the
Kingfisher, British men-of-war, stood by ready to blast them out of
the water if they obeyed the Town and returned to London with
the tea. The ships were held at Griffin's Wharf as though under an
enchantment.

Here was none of the usual hustle and bustle. Few of the crew
were in sight, but hundreds of spectators gathered every day merely
to stare at them. Johnny saw Rotch, the twenty-three-year-old

Quaker who owned the *Dartmouth,* running about in despair. The Governor would not let him leave. The Town would not let him unload. Between them he was a ruined man. He feared a mob would burn his ship. There was no mob, but night and day armed citizens guarded the ships. They would see to it that no tea was smuggled ashore and that no harm was done to the ships. Back and forth paced the guard. Many of their faces were familiar to Johnny. One day even John Hancock took his turn with a musket on his shoulder, and the next night he saw Paul Revere.

Then on the fifteenth, the third of the tea ships arrived. This was the brig, the *Beaver.*

. . . .

The next day, the sixteenth, Johnny woke to hear the rain drumming sadly on the roof, and soon enough once more he heard all the bells of Boston cling-clanging, bidding the inhabitants come once more, and for the last time, to Old South to demand the peaceful return of the ships to England.

By nightfall, when the boys Rab had selected began silently to congregate in the office of the *Observer,* behind locked doors, the rain stopped. Many of them Johnny knew. When they started to assume their disguises, smootch their faces with soot, paint them with red paint, pull on nightcaps, old frocks, torn jackets, blankets with holes cut for their arms, they began giggling and laughing at each other. Rab could silence them with one look, however. No one passing outside the shop must guess that toward twenty boys were at that moment dressing themselves as "Indians."

Johnny had taken some pains with his costume. He had sewed for hours on the red blanket Mrs. Lorne had let him cut up and he had a fine mop of feathers standing upright in the old knitted cap he would wear on his head, but when he started to put on his disguise, Rab said no, wait a minute.

Then he divided the boys into three groups. Beside each ship at the wharf they would find a band of men. "You," he said to one group of boys, "will join the boarding party for the *Dartmouth.* You for the *Eleanor.* You for the *Beaver.*" Each boy was the speak softly to the leader and say, "Me Know You," for that was the countersign. They would know the three leaders because each of them would wear a white handkerchief about the neck and a red string about the right wrist. Then he turned to Johnny.

"You can run faster than any of us. Somehow get to Old South Church. Mr. Rotch will be back from begging once more the Governor's permission for the ships to sail within a half-hour. Now, Johnny, you are to listen to what Sam Adams says next. Look you. If Mr. Adams then says, 'Now may God help my country,' come back here. Then we will take off our disguises and each go home and say nothing. But if he says, 'This meeting can do nothing more to save the country,' you are to get out of that crowd as fast as you can, and as you get into Cornhill begin to blow upon this silver whistle. Run as fast as you are able back here to me and keep on blowing. I'll have boys posted in dark corners, close enough to the church, but outside the crowd. Maybe we'll hear you the first time you blow."

About Old South, standing in the streets, inside the church, waiting for Rotch to return with the very last appeal that could be made to the Governor, was the greatest crowd Boston had ever seen— thousands upon thousands. There was not a chance, not one, Johnny could ever squirm or wriggle his way inside, but he pushed and shoved until he stood close to one of the doors. Farther than this he could not go—unless he walked on people's heads. It was dark already.

Josiah Quincy's voice rang out from within. "I see the clouds roll and the lightning play, and to that God who rides the whirlwind and directs the storm, I commit my country . . ."

The words thrilled Johnny, but this was not what he was waiting for, and it was not Sam Adams speaking. He was bothered with only one thing. Quincy had a beautiful carrying voice. It was one thing to hear him and another Sam Adams, who did not speak well at all.

The crowd made way for a chaise. "Rotch is back! Make way for Rotch!" Mr. Rotch passed close to Johnny. He was so young he looked almost ready to cry. This was proof enough that the Governor had still refused. Such a turmoil followed Rotch's entry, Johnny could not hear any one particular voice. What chance had he of hearing Sam Adam's words? He had his whistle in his hand, but he was so jammed into the crowd about the door that he did not believe he would be able to get his hand to his mouth.

"Silence!" That was Quincy again. "Silence, silence; Mr. Adams will speak." Johnny twisted and turned and brought his whistle to his lips.

And suddenly there was silence. Johnny guessed there were many in that crowd who, like himself, were hanging on those words. Seemingly Mr. Adams was calmly accepting defeat, dismissing the meeting, for now he was saying,

"This meeting can do nothing more to save the country."

Johnny gave his first shrill blast on his whistle, and he heard whistles and cries seemingly in all directions, Indian war whoops, and "Boston Harbor a teapot tonight!" "Hurrah for Griffin's Wharf!" "Salt-water tea!" "Hi, Mohawks, get your axes and pay no taxes!"

Johnny was only afraid all would be over before Rab and his henchmen could get to the wharf. Still shrilling on the whistle, he fought and floundered against the tide of the crowd. It was sweeping toward Griffin's Wharf, he struggling to get back to Salt Lane. Now he was afraid the others would have gone on without him. After all, Rab might have decided that Johnny's legs and ears were better than his hands—and deliberately let him do the work that best suited him. Johnny pushed open the door.

Rab was alone. He had Johnny's blanket coat, his ridiculous be-feathered knitted cap in his hands.

"Quick!" he said, and smootched his face with soot, drew a red line across his mouth running from ear to ear. Johnny saw Rab's eyes through the mask of soot. They were glowing with dark excitement he had seen but twice before. His lips were parted. His teeth looked sharp and white as an animal's. In spite of his calm demeanor, calm voice, he was charged and surcharged with a will to action, a readiness to take and enjoy any desperate chance. Rab had come terrifying alive.

They flung themselves out of the shop.

"Roundabout!" cried Rab. He meant they would get to the wharf by back alleys.

"Come, follow me. *Now* we're really going to run."

He flew up Salt Lane in the opposite direction from the waterfront. Now they were flinging themselves down back alleys (faster and faster). Once they had a glimpse of a blacksmith shop and other "Indians" clamoring for soot for their faces. Now slipping over a back-yard fence, now at last on the waterfront, Sea Street, Flounder Alley. They were running so fast it seemed more like a dream of flying than reality.

The day had started with rain and then there had been clouds, but as they reached Griffin's Wharf the moon, full and white, broke free of the clouds. The three ships, the silent hundreds gathering upon the wharf, all were dipped in the pure white light. The crowds were becoming thousands, and there was not one there but guessed what was to be done, and all approved.

Rab was grunting out of the side of his mouth to a thick-set, active-looking man, whom Johnny would have known anywhere, by his walk and the confident lift of his head, was Mr. Revere. "Me Know You."

"Me Know You," Johnny repeated this countersign and took his place behind Mr. Revere. The other boys, held up by the crowd, began arriving, and more men and boys. But Johnny guessed that many who were now quietly joining one of these three groups were acting on the spur of the moment, seeing what was up. They had blacked their faces, seized axes, and come along. They were behaving as quietly and were as obedient to their leaders as those who had been so carefully picked for the work of destruction.

There was a boatswain's whistle, and in silence one group boarded the *Dartmouth*. The *Eleanor* and the *Beaver* had to be warped in to the wharf. Johnny was close to Mr. Revere's heels. He heard him calling for the captain, promising him, in the jargon everyone talked that night, that not one thing should be damaged on the ship except only the tea, but the captain and all his crew had best stay in the cabin until the work was over.

Tom Hall

They broke open the chests and flung the tea into the harbor.

Captain Hall shrugged and did as he was told, leaving his cabin boy to hand over the keys to the hold. The boy was grinning with pleasure. The "tea party" was not unexpected.

"I'll show you," the boy volunteered, "how to work them hoists. I'll fetch lanterns, mister."

The winches rattled and the heavy chests began to appear—one hundred and fifty of them. As some men worked in the hold, others broke open the chests and flung the tea into the harbor. But one thing made them unexpected difficulty. The tea inside the chests was wrapped in heavy canvas. The axes went through the wood easily enough—the canvas made endless trouble. Johnny had never worked so hard in his life.

He had noticed a stout boy with a blackened face working near him. The boy looked familiar, but when he saw his white, fat hands, Johnny knew who he was and kept a sharp eye on him. It was Dove. He was not one of the original "Indians," but a volunteer. He had on an enormous pair of breeches tied at each knee with rope. Even as Johnny upended a chest and helped get the tea over the rail, he kept an eye on Dove. The boy was secretly scooping tea into his breeches. This theft would come to several hundred dollars in value, but more important it would ruin the high moral tone of the party. Johnny whispered to Rab, who put down the axe he had been wielding with such passion and grabbed Dove. It wasn't much of a scuffle. Soon Dove was whining and admitting that a little tea had happened to "splash" into his breeches. Johnny got them off and kicked them and the many pounds of tea they held into the harbor.

"He swim good," he grunted at Rab, for everyone was talking "Indian" that night.

Rab picked up the fat Dove as though he were a rag baby and flung him into the harbor. The tea was thicker than any seaweed and its fragance was everywhere.

Not a quarter of a mile away, quite visible in the moonlight, rode the *Active* and the *Kingfisher*. Any moment the tea party might be interrupted by British marines. There was no landing party. Governor Hutchinson had been wise in not sending for their help.

The work on the *Dartmouth* and the *Eleanor* finished about the same time. The *Beaver* took longer, for she had not had time to unload the rest of her cargo, and great care was taken not to injure it. Just as Johnny was about to go over to see if he could help on the *Beaver,* Mr. Revere whispered to him. "Go get brooms. Clean um' deck."

Johnny and a parcel of boys brushed the deck until it was clean as a parlor floor. Then Mr. Revere called the captain to come up and inspect. The tea was utterly gone, but Captain Hall agreed that beyond that there had not been the slightest damage.

It was close upon dawn when the work on all three ships was done. And yet the great, silent audience on the wharf, men, women, and children, had not gone home. As the three groups came off the ships, they formed in fours along the wharf, their axes on their shoulders. Then a hurrah went up and a fife began to play. This was almost the first sound Johnny had heard since the tea party started—except only the crash of axes into tea chests, the squeak of hoists, and a few grunted orders.

Standing quietly in the crowd, he saw Sam Adams, pretending to be a most innocent bystander. It looked to Johnny as if the dog fox had eaten a couple of fat pullets, and had a third in his mouth.

As they started marching back to the center of the town, they passed the Coffin House at the head of Griffin's Wharf. A window opened.

"Well, boys," said a voice, so cold one hardly knew whether he spoke in anger or not, "you've had a fine, pleasant evening for your Indian caper, haven't you? But mind . . . you've got to pay the fiddler yet."

It was the British Admiral Montague.

"Come on down here," someone yelled, "and we'll settle that score tonight."

The Admiral pulled in his head and slapped down the window.

Johnny and Rab knew, and men like the Observers knew, but best of all Sam Adams knew, that the fiddler would have to be paid. England, unable to find the individuals who had destroyed this valuable property, would punish the whole Town of Boston—

make every man, woman and child, Tories and Whigs alike, suffer until this tea was paid for. Nor was she likely to back down on her claim that she might tax the colonists any way she pleased.

Next day, all over Boston, some of them with a little paint still showing behind their ears, boys were so lame they could scarce move their fingers, but none of them—not one—told what it was that had lamed them so. They would stand about and wonder who "those Mohawks" might have been, or what the British Parliament might do next, but never say what they themselves had been doing, for each was sworn to secrecy.

Only Paul Revere showed no signs of the hard physical strain he had been under all the night before. Not long after dawn he had started on horseback for New York and Philadelphia with an account of the Tea Party. He could chop open tea chests all night, and ride all day.

THE STORY OF MOLLY PITCHER

By AGNES REPPLIER

Illustration by H. J. FORD.

IT is a strange and interesting thing to see how history repeats itself in a series of noble and picturesque incidents which are so much alike that they might be easily mistaken for one another. Perhaps in the years to come they will be mistaken for one another, and then those learned scholars who love to deny all the things that are worth believing will say, as they say now of William Tell and the apple: "Whenever an event is represented as happening in different countries and among different nations, we may be sure that it never happened at all." Yet to Spain belongs Augustina, the Maid of Saragossa; to England, brave Mary Ambree; and to America, Molly Pitcher, the stout-hearted heroine of Monmouth; and these three women won for themselves honor and renown by the same valorous exploits. Augustina is the most to be envied, for her praises have been sung by a great poet; Mary Ambree has a noble ballad to perpetuate her fame; Molly Pitcher is still without the tribute of a verse to remind her countrymen occasionally of her splendid courage in the field.

The Spanish girl was of humble birth, young, poor, and very handsome. When Saragossa was besieged by the French during the Peninsular War, she carried food every afternoon to the soldiers who were defending the batteries. One day the attack was so fierce, and the fire so deadly, that by the gate of Portillo not a single man was left alive to repulse the terrible enemy. When Augustina reached the spot with her basket of coarse and scanty provisions, she saw the last gunner fall bleeding on the walls. Not for an instant did she hesitate; but springing over a pile of dead bodies, she snatched the match from his stiffening fingers and fired the gun herself. Then calling on her countrymen to rally their broken ranks, she led them back so unflinchingly to the charge that the French were driven from the gate they had so nearly captured, and the honor of Spain was saved. When the siege was lifted and the city free a pension was settled on Augustina, together with the daily pay of an artilleryman, and she was permitted to wear upon her sleeve an embroidered shield bearing the arms of Saragossa. Lord Byron, in his poem "Childe Harold," has described her beauty, her heroism, and the desperate courage with which she defended the breach:

> "Who can avenge so well a leader's fall?
> What maid retrieve when man's flushed hope is lost!
> Who hang so fiercely on the flying Gaul,
> Foiled by a woman's hand before a battered wall?"

For the story of Mary Ambree we must leave the chroniclers— who to their own loss and shame never mention her at all—and take refuge with the poets. From them we learn all we need to know, and it is quickly told. Her lover was slain treacherously in the war between Spain and Holland, the English being then allies of the Dutch; and, vowing to avenge his death, she put on his armor and marched to the siege of Ghent, where she fought with reckless courage on its walls. Fortune favors the brave, and wherever the maiden turned her arms the enemy was repulsed, until at last the gallant Spanish soldiers vied with the English in admiration of this valorous foe:

> "If England doth yield such brave lassies as thee,
> Full well may she conquer, faire Mary Ambree."

Even the Great Prince of Parma desired to see this dauntless young girl, and finding her as chaste as she was courageous and beautiful, he permitted her to sail home without any molestation from his army.

> "Then to her own country she back did returne,
> Still holding the foes of faire England in scorne;
> Therefore English captaines of every degree
> Sing forth the brave valours of Mary Ambree."

And now for Molly Pitcher, who, unsung and almost unremembered, should nevertheless share in the honors heaped so liberally upon the Spanish and English heroines. "A red-haired, freckled-faced young Irishwoman," without beauty and without distinction, she was the newly-wedded wife of an artilleryman in Washington's little army. On June 28, 1778, was fought the battle of Monmouth, famous for the admirable tactics by which Washington regained the advantages lost through the negligence of General Charles Lee, and also for the splendid charge and gallant death of Captain Moneton,

H. J. Ford

Strong, skillful, and fearless, she stood by the weapon.

an officer of the English Grenadiers. It was a Sunday morning, close and sultry. As the day advanced, the soldiers on both sides suffered terribly from that fierce, unrelenting heat in which America rivals India. The thermometer stood at 96° in the shade. Men fell dead in their ranks without a wound, smitten by sunstroke, and the sight of them filled their comrades with dismay. Molly Pitcher, regardless of everything save the anguish of the sweltering, thirsty troops, carried buckets of water from a neighboring spring, and passed them along the line. Back and forward she trudged, this strong, brave patient young woman, while the sweat poured down her freckled face, and her bare arms blistered in the sun. She was a long time in reaching her husband—so many soldiers begged for drink as she toiled by—but at last she saw him, parched, grimy, spent with heat, and she quickened her lagging steps. Then suddenly a ball whizzed past, and he fell dead by the side of his gun before ever the coveted water had touched his blackened lips. Molly dropped her bucket, and for one dazed moment stood staring at the bleeding corpse. Only for a moment, for, amid the turmoil of battle, she heard the order given to drag her husband's cannon from the field. The words roused her to life and purpose. She seized the rammer from the trodden grass, and hurried to the gunner's post. There was nothing strange in the work to her. She was too well versed in the ways of war for either ignorance or alarm. Strong, skillful, and fearless, she stood by the weapon and directed its deadly fire until the fall of Moneton turned the tide of victory. The British troops under Clinton were beaten back after a desperate struggle, the Americans took possession of the field, and the battle of Monmouth was won.

On the following day, poor Molly, no longer a furious Amazon, but a sad-faced widow, with swollen eyes, and a scanty bit of crape pinned on her broad young bosom, was presented to Washington, and received a sergeant's commission with half-pay for life. It is said that the French officers, then fighting for the freedom of the colonies, that is, against the English, were so delighted with her courage that they added to this reward a cocked hat full of gold pieces, and christened her "La Capitaine." What befell her in after-years has never been told. She lived and died obscurely, and her name has been well-nigh forgotten in the land she served. But the memory of brave deeds can never wholly perish, and Molly Pitcher has won for herself a little niche in the temple of Fame, where her companions are fair Mary Ambree and the dauntless Maid of Sara-gossa.

DANIEL BOONE'S RIFLE

By STEWART EDWARD WHITE
Map by Joseph E. Sandford

ON a rock by a roadside sat Andrew Burnett. The season was early spring: that time when the snow water is but just draining away, the red-winged blackbirds are new arrived in melody, and the wide washed sky is ahum with the vigor of fresh joy in the world. Nevertheless the lad's expression was somber, his eyes smoldered with a sullen resentment well emphasized by his straight black eyebrows that almost met over the bridge of his nose. He was thinking what a hard time he was having in life; and how downtrodden he was; and what—in the somewhat hazy future—he was going to do about it. This was not an unusual state of mind for his age, which was nineteen.

He was entirely absorbed. He did not hear the liquid-voiced blackbirds and meadow larks. He did not see the red squirrel that chirked and jerked toward him along the rails of the zigzag "snake" fence. He was even wholly unaware of a horseman galloping recklessly through the puddles, until a shower of mud brought him to his feet. He flared into furious resentment; unreasonable, for it was self-evident that the horseman was innocent of intention, but natural as the leap of his discontent toward an outlet.

"Look what you're doing, you dirty whelp!" he shouted.

The horse was thrown on its haunches; turned; walked slowly back, brought to a stand. The rider leaned forward in his saddle.

"What did you say?" he challenged softly.

His appearance further inflamed the other's anger. His clothing was of fine quality and in the height of prevailing fashion; his mount was self-evidently an animal of blood; the very expression of his finely featured, faintly disdainful face, the lift of his long, white hands raised the bristles on the country boy's contempt for the city macaroni. The fact that the stranger was also a lad, apparently not far from his own age, helped not at all.

Andrew repeated his sentiment.

198

"You tom fool, how could I see you, sitting there like a bump on a log!' retorted the horseman.

This was not unreasonable; but Andrew was in no mood for reason. He expanded his original idea. The city boy leaped nimbly from his horse. They fought whole-heartedly. Andrew was obviously the stronger: the stranger's quickness and certainty of movement equalized matters. They inflicted some damage on one another; thrashed about considerably; finally locked and went to earth. The horse trotted away, his reins dangling. The combatants struggled a moment or so without any perceptible advantage to either, rolled down the low bank, and plumped into a puddle. The icy shock of the water tore them apart. They arose dripping. Andrew, his dogged slow spirit catching its fuel fully, was in dash to resume. But the other was laughing.

"We're a sweet pair!" he cried. "Now why in tarnation were we both so cross? I'm not usually a crochety person. Are you?"

Andrew stopped, his mouth falling open. This was too abrupt for one of his disposition.

"Or *are* you?" inquired the other. "I don't believe it. 'Tain't reasonable. I didn't see you, you know. And why should I go off at half cock? That ain't reasonable either. Of course you were startled. Don't blame you."

"I take back the 'dirty whelp,'" conceded Andrew gruffly.

"Never mind about the 'dirty,'" amended the other. He glanced down humorously at his dripping finery, "And I take back——"

"Never mind the 'tom fool,'" interposed Andrew. "Reckon we're a pair of them."

"So that's all right My name is Russell Braidwood. I live in Philadelphia."

"Mine is Andy Burnett. I live at the farm yonder, up the lane."

"Well, what made you so cross?" enquired Russell.

"I'm sick of the farm," replied Andy, falling somber again.

"The same with me."

"What?"

"I'm sick of Philadelphia."

They sat together on the rock. The warm spring sun steamed

from their drenched garments. Overfield the blackbirds and the meadow larks distilled its brightness into song. A first bobolink overflowed its rapture. Drop after rapid drop, small water tinklings drained away the last of winter from the world. The red squirrel curved the sweep of his tail over his back and clasped his little hands to his head in an ecstatic worship of the fresh flood of life in the springtime. Of these things the two lads, absorbed in one another, had no consciousness; but now in the new expansiveness of feeling they flooded in.

Why was Andy sick of the farm? Well, there was his stepfather, who was harsh and stern in religion and rigid in discipline, and strong for the duty youth owed to those who had brought it into the world.

"Only he did not bring me into the world," interpolated Andy.

"Your mother?" asked Russell.

"My mother is dead," replied Andy briefly.

But that might be borne, and the hard, iron, grinding, endless work, and the lack of all amusement so necessary to youth. It was the future, the dull gray appalling future. The same thing over and over. And for what? A living, hardly wrung. And at the end of life the acres still demanding, still grudging, and the bent back of age, and possibly resignation. Like iron walls pressing in closer and closer. Why not break away from it?

"There's my grandmother. You do not know my grandmother. I can't desert her. And anyway I'm not of age. He wouldn't let me go. I'm too valuable to him," said Andy bitterly. "The only reason I'm here now is because he's gone to town for the day. You don't know him, either."

It was all very black. To youth two years until the coming of age was forever. To youth the inevitable passing away of age does not occur.

But Russell? How could he be sick of Philadelphia? A great city; leisure; amusement; money in his pocket; fine clothes; a horse to ride; position; family; the silver spoon in the mouth? This was difficult to understand.

Russell's bright face darkened. He brushed these things aside.

How did they count when one is in prison? In prison to position. Doing the same things over and over. One sickens of them, no matter how they glitter. In prison all one's life; sitting inside a cage while the world flashes by outside.

"They are set on my going into the Business; won't hear of anything else!" he cried bitterly, "Great-grandfather started the bank, and the Family have carried it on ever since. Sitting in an office at a desk. Just the same as being locked in by a jailer. God, I hate it! Next year; that's when my term begins!"

"Why don't you just break away?" Andy repeated the question that had been asked himself.

"I can't. There's the family. You don't know the family."

They contemplated their several hopelessness; and the world deepened to deep gloom in which the blackbirds, and the meadow larks, and the single bobolink, and the sunshine and the little water tinklings were not. As for the red squirrel, he had gone away.

"Hullo," cried Russell, making a belated discovery. "My horse is gone!"

"Oh, that's all right," Andy reassured him. "This is our lane to the barn. We'll find him at the gates. Come on up to the house and we'll catch him."

They trudged to the end of the lane; found the horse against the gates; led him through.

"You must come in to see my grandmother," urged Andy.

"I can't; I'm too filthy," objected Russell; then, seeing some urgency on the part of his new friend, he agreed. "All right. If she can stand it, I can."

They left the horse tied to a rail. The farmhouse was of the prosperous order, square, unornamented, relieved from being a box by six white columns that upheld a veranda roof above the second story. Its paint was old; but the structure was in repair. About it were remnants of what must have been a cherished garden; but these remnants were well attended. The picket fence was upright and intact. Before the front door stood two great locust trees. Behind the back door was an apple orchard and the long-armed sweep of a well.

Russell's vivid imagination, darting in the speculation it loved, brought him its findings: efficiency; tidy, careful efficiency; no thought of the ornamentation of life; only in the garden an awkward fumbling effort to preserve the memory, as it were, of a beauty whose full body had followed its vanished creator. He stopped appreciatively at a lilac bush, touching with sensitive finger its new buds.

"I like the soft feel," he explained.

"It used to be a nice garden—when my mother was alive," said Andy. "Most of the flowers are gone now. I work on it a little when I get time; but I can't do much. Grandmother likes it."

Russell raised his eyes and became aware of a little old lady in a rocking chair behind a front window. He swept his hat from his head in the approved fashion of the period. A moment later he stood before her, bowing again, and conscious of an amused scrutiny under which, in spite of himself, he felt his color rising. Though possessed of charmingly open qualities, and though nothing of a snob, Russell was nevertheless an aristocrat both by breeding and by the training of his day, which emphasized social differences even more strongly than is at present the case. That he should not find himself perfectly at ease in superiority before any old countrywoman was, in the harmless arrogance of his young conception, beyond his thought.

She was a little old lady, sitting in a Boston rocker. She wore a cap, very neat; and a voluminous black dress of heavy silk, and cobwebby half mitts of silk lace, and a pair of black satin soft shoes side by side on a hassock. Her only ornament was a cameo brooch at her throat. Her lap held knitting. On the floor at her side lay an ebony cane topped with ivory. The Boston rocker was uncushioned, and in it she sat uncompromisingly upright as one who sits in state; though not with rigidity but rather with the repose of energy. As Russell, raising his head from his bow of introduction, looked upon her thin, waxlike, veined hands, and the sad lines of past care in her tiny face, he thought to himself that he had never seen anyone so old, and a certain choke of pathos gripped his throat. As he met the snap and twinkle of her eyes, he thought he had never met anyone so unquenchably and agelessly young; so that pity became an affront, and any thought of pathos an impertinence. And as Russell, though sensitive to impression, was as yet too young for analysis, he ended by standing before her at ill-ease, like an awkward schoolboy, conscious and ashamed of his muddied garments and his general dishevelment.

But his ill-ease soon melted. Neither by look nor manner, save for a momentary deep twinkle in her eyes, did the old lady seem aware of the strange disarray of the two. The twinkle was amused, but it vanished unseen. To his astonishment, when he paused to think of it, Russell shortly found himself seated at her elbow chatting eagerly and easily, as to an equal not only in convention but in years, laughing delightedly over her quick pithy comments, sometimes caustic in content, but welling from the relish of deep quiet humor that mellowed them to a shared understanding that had no sting. Russell was of the vivacious and romantic disposition that expands under warmth. The old lady, tapping her Boston rocker into brisk motion, listened and questioned; and Russell glowed and chattered and had a wonderful youthful time telling about himself, secure in the comfort of some deep inner instinct that assured him that he would not later come to, as was so often the case, to look upon himself in reaction as a talkative fool.

As he talked he looked about him at the furnishings of the old room, and his eye fell upon a weapon on pegs over the fireplace. He checked what he was saying.

"What a beautiful piece!" he cried. "May I look at it? I love guns. All kinds of guns. They are a sort of passion with me."

"Bring it here, Andy," commanded the grandmother.

Russell handled the weapon reverently.

"Do you mind?" he begged, and put it to his face in the attitude of aim.

"I see you are a marksman also," observed the old lady. "You and Andy should match skill."

"I should love to try it—the rifle, I mean. It is in beautiful condition. But it is very old, isn't it?"

"I'll back it against anything newer," interposed Andy gruffly.

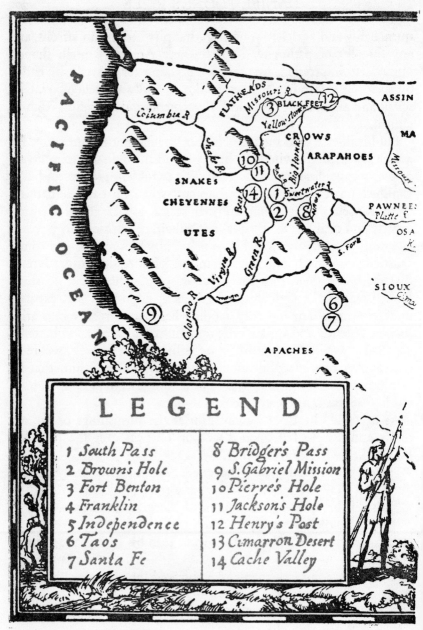

LEGEND

1 South Pass	8 Bridger's Pass
2 Brown's Hole	9 S. Gabriel Mission
3 Fort Benton	10 Pierre's Hole
4 Franklin	11 Jackson's Hole
5 Independence	12 Henry's Post
6 Taos	13 Cimarron Desert
7 Santa Fe	14 Cache Valley

Map by Joseph E. Sandford.

The Trail of Daniel Boone among

the Indian tribes of the West.

Russell turned the weapon over, examining its details. He looked up suddenly, a slight awe in his eyes.

"This inscription—" he stammered—"is it—was it really?"

"Colonel Boone's rifle? Yes," the old lady answered. "He gave it to my husband just before he left Kentucky for the West."

"Did you know Daniel Boone, ma'am?"

"Certainly." She paused; then went on in response to Russell's unspoken pleading. "You see, as a girl I rode over the Wilderness Road into Kentucky to join Colonel Boone's enterprise. I lived at Boonesborough until my husband died."

"Were you at the great fight at Boonesborough?" inquired Russell breathlessly.

The old lady let her knitting fall in her lap. She leaned against the back of her chair and her eyes softened in reminiscence.

"Yes: though I saw little of it. We women were busy within, cooking, carrying water to the men, molding bullets, tending the wounded."

Under urging she told more: nine days of bitter siege, the garrison so small that it must stand to arms day and night, the men gaunt and haggard from the strain; showers of burning arrows, fire, no water to spare, the roof swept by a hail of bullets.

"The British had supplied them with ammunition," said she. "The men said they picked up a hundred and twenty-five pounds of flattened bullets after the siege, and that takes no count of those imbedded in the logs."

The fort seemed doomed. Then a young man sprang to the roof and worked fully exposed to extinguish the fire.

"The Lord sustained us," observed the old lady piously. "For in all that hail of bullets he was not touched."

Shortly after this it became necessary for the women to take their places at the port holes to relieve the men for a brief rest. The limit of human endurance had been reached.

"So I fired with the rest. I cannot believe I did much damage; but I made a noise," she chuckled. "But it gave me opportunity to see Colonel Boone perform a noteworthy feat. One of the savages had a very good rifle, and he had climbed a high tree in which he was completely protected and from which he could overlook the compound within the fort. He hit one or two of our people before we suspected where he was; but especially he was killing our cattle, which were huddled in the center. When his position had been located Colonel Boone himself ascended into the tower. After a little the man in the tree, preparing for another shot, showed just the top of his head. Colonel Boone fired instantly and killed him. It was a very long distance away."

"Was he—did he use this rifle?"

"Yes, that was his favorite rifle always, though he had several." Russell gazed down at the weapon with awe.

"What is this other name—Farrell?" he enquired.

"He made the piece, I believe: though I am not certain. The Colonel was always particularly fond of it. He had some association with it, though I do not know what it was. That is why Mr. Burnett always took such pride in the fact that it was a gift to him, for at that time he did not know Colonel Boone so well as later."

"How did it happen?" urged Russell.

"Mr. Burnett was of the greatest assistance—so Colonel Boone always maintained—at the time Jemima Boone and three other girls were carried off by the savages," said the old lady, a trifle primly, as one reluctant to boast. But Russell, aflame with excitement would have no reticence. He learned how the four girls had been seized suddenly and spirited away; how their absence was not discovered for some hours; how the settlement was aroused to pursuit. Most of the men, under Mr. Calloway, cut across country on horseback in the probable direction of flight. Boone with eight picked men took the difficult job of following directly, on foot. For thirty miles they puzzled out a trail, blinded by every device of savage ingenuity; furthermore, they managed to do so rapidly enough to move faster than the Indians had done in their flight. At last the marauders, considering they had got clear away, abandoned attempts at conceal-ment and took the direct course.

"Colonel Boone had himself been captive of the savages," ex-plained Mrs. Burnett, "so he knew their devices."

He struck boldly across country and cut the trail again in ten miles. Shortly after they caught sight of the Indians making camp.

"Mr. Burnett has often told me that now came the moments of greatest danger for the girls," said the old lady, "for it was certain that the first act of the savages, on being surprised, would be to murder them. Colonel Boone picked out four men. One of them was Mr. Burnett. He was always very proud of this; for he was very young. They crept up. They knew that the least false move, a snapped bit of wood, even the rustle of a leaf would be the signal for the crash of tomahawks on the four girls' skulls."

At last Boone gave a signal. The four men fired and rushed forward instantly. The remainder of the party bounded down the hill, yelling as loudly as they could. The savages nearest the girls, who were huddled together "tattered, torn and despairing" at the foot of the tree, were killed at first fire. The others were for a brief but sufficient instant paralyzed by surprise. All but one. He leaped across the fire, his tomahawk upraised over the head of Jemima Boone. But before it could descend, its wielder collapsed, a knife in his throat.

"Mr. Burnett was always very skillful at throwing a knife," stated the old lady. "But Colonel Boone considered he had saved Jemima's life; as, indeed, he had; and a little later, when Mr. Burnett and I were married, the Colonel gave Mr. Burnett this rifle."

"I think this is the most wonderful thing I have ever heard!" cried Russell.

"Ours was the second wedding to take place in Kentucky. The first was of Sam Henderson and Betty Calloway; and within the year Frances Calloway married John Holden; and Jemima Boone married Flanders Calloway. Sam, John, and Flanders were the other three men, besides Colonel Boone and Mr. Burnett, in the rescue party; and Betty and Frances were the other two girls captured along with Jemima."

She stopped with an air of finality.

"You didn't tell Russell who the fourth girl was, Grandmother," said Andy with a mischievous grin.

A faint color crept into the old lady's cheeks.

"You know perfectly who it was, you rapscallion!" she replied sharply.

Russell stared up at her breathlessly in dawning comprehension.

"Not another word out of you!" The grandmother checked his eager questions. "It is too fine a day to sit within, listening to an old woman's chatter. I am tired. Take him away, Andy. Get along, both of you. Try your skill at the rifle. Show him how your grandfather taught you the knife should be thrown. Off with you, now!"

She would have no more of them; fairly bundled them out of the room with the dynamics of her energy, though physically she did not stir from her chair. Only at the door she stopped them with a word.

"I like your young man, Andrew," she observed. "Tell him to come see me again. I have often heard Colonel Boone say that there is nought like a good honest fight to begin friendship." She smiled faintly at their confusion; and deliberately closed her eyes. They hesitated a moment, and stole out.

DAVY CROCKETT LEGENDS

By CONSTANCE ROURKE

A FEW men had gathered about the fire in a tavern on the Forked Deer River in western Tennessee. The winter dusk had fallen. An old hunter was speaking, mournfully.

"Thar's a great rejoicing among the bears of the river country, and the alligators of the Mississippi are rolling up their shining ribs to the sun. The rattlesnakes has been coming out of their holes this autumn to frolic in the clearings, and the foxes goes to sleep in the goose pens. It's because the rifle of Crockett is silent forever, and the print of his moccasins is found no more in our woods."

"The painters and bears will miss him," said another hunter.

"He never missed *them*," said a man with red hair, who was bending over the barrel of a flintlock, oiling it.

"I heard Davy never died at all," said a hunter.

"I heard he was a-roaming over the prairies of Texas with a bear," said a traveler.

"Named Death Hug," said the red-haired man.

"He was carrying messages for Sam Houston," said the traveler, "and he was stopped by a big party of Mexican scouts. Quick as lightning Crockett mounted Death Hug and leapt clean over their heads." There was a pause. "Another time when he was carrying those messages, he met a squad of Mexicans just as he came up to a grove of oaks and Death Hug ran right up one of the oaks with Crockett on his back and then out on a limb as slick as a panther going to roost, and over to the limb of another oak, and another, and then they were down and away."

"And once he sighted a stallion on the prairie," said the old hunter, "wild as the whirlwind, and tall and strong. Crockett came within a hundred yards of him, and the stallion threw back his ears, spread his jaws, and came snorting at him. As the horse reared to plunge, Crockett seized his mane and mounted him as easy as a cowbird sits on the back of a brindle bull. The stallion made off like lightning and a big thunderstorm came up. Lightning struck all around but it flashed to either side of the horse as he ran and never struck him. The horse was off to the west and Crockett thought he was going to be flung against the Rocky Mountains. He ran for three days and three nights until he came to the Mad River, that poured down the mountainside boiling and hissing. There the horse ran under a tree, trying to push Crockett off his back, but Crockett pulled his mane and that stallion leapt over the tree and the boiling river besides. Then he stopped quiet and Crockett got off."

For twenty years after his death, stories were told of Davy Crockett as though he were still alive. It was said that he had been shot by a silver bullet that had made no wound and left no trace, and that he had feigned death at the Alamo, and had concealed himself when the battle was over. Then—in the story—he had set out to avenge the death of the five prisoners whom the Mexicans had put to the sword. He had found the slayers and had killed them with his hunting knife. Afterwards he was seen on the prairies far to the north, hunting buffalo.

"Sometimes Crockett rides wild horses, sometimes he rides Death Hug when he goes hunting buffalo," said the traveler. "Once he got trace of two mammoth buffaloes from the wilds of Oregon, that snorted blue fire and bellowed small thunder. When they got in a particular passion they used to butt trees down and bore a hole in the earth twenty feet deep before they could cool off their dispositions. Crockett put off to the spot where they were and found them just as the hurricane of their temper was up, and they were snorting young lightning and roaring bass music and had uprooted a few trees and tossed them into the air for practice. They were going to play toss with Crockett, too, but he slipped round and tied their tails fast together, got between them with their tails like traces and with each of his arms over their flanks drove them a hundred miles, and they were as tame as sucking sheep."

He went on: "Another buffalo was so big and noisy and kept up such a continual thunderstorm of roaring that he used to scare away the sunrise, and the prairies were dark for days, but Crockett shot him on the wing and invited some Comanche warriors to the feast.

It was night, and as they were making ready a great light appeared on the horizon. The light came nearer and nearer, and it was a prairie fire with billows of smoke and flame a-foaming and a-tossing in the air like waves at sea and a roaring like the sea. It came nearer and nearer to where Crockett was with the Comanches, as if it were going to sweep right over them, but a breeze came up and the fire swayed a little. The breeze got to be a great wind and the fire turned and went off in another direction. Away went Davy after it with all those buffalo steaks in his hands, holding them out in front of him and he kept going until the steaks was well roasted. Then he came back to the Comanches and they had their feast."

"They was one buffalo Crockett captured out on the prairies and he tamed him," said the man with red hair, "and he called him Mississippi. When Crockett came to one of those border towns Mississippi was with him, and Mississippi would go to a meeting every Sunday morning. He sang the bass of 'Old Hundred,' never missing a note, and that same critter would even lend the leader his horn for a tuning fork!"

"It's a caution what will happen in those border towns out on the wild prair*ee*."

It was not only hunters of the Great Valley who told stories about Crockett. Trappers from the far west said that they had seen him in the mountains of California, hunting grizzlies. Sailors back from long voyages in the South Seas declared that he was there, hunting pearls.

"Out there in the South Seas he was a-diving," said a sailor, "and he came to a cave. He crawled till he came to dry land under the deepest water of the ocean. It was dark, so he made a lamp wick out of his hair and soaked it with elbow grease and made a light by striking his knuckles on a rock.

"Crockett looked around and discovered that he had got in among thousands and thousands of pearl oysters that were fast asleep in their beds. He sang a song and danced a measure or two, and the oysters woke up. They all opened their shells for him and he came ashore with sacks and sacks of pearls."

Someone repeated this story in a stage coach that was traveling slowly at night in western Kentucky. The light in the coach was dim, showing the dark figures of men in every seat.

Other tales about Crockett were told as the coach rumbled, the wheels cracked, and the hooves of the horses thudded against hard clay, first at a walk, then at a trot, then at a walk again.

"I understand," said a man in a tall beaver hat, "I understand that Crockett has not lingered in the Far East, but has returned to the great prairies of North America to hunt the buffalo, the deer, and the elk. Only the other day I learned that he had crossed the Cannon Ball River and was following the crooked courses of the Missouri."

"I am credibly informed that Davy Crockett has now reached the Mississippi," said a small man with an air of importance. "In fact a friend of mine who has a dwelling on its bank witnessed a curious adventure of his. Crockett was out hunting one day when he noticed a wing-broken goose riding on the surface of the river. He struck out after it. You know that Davy Crockett can swim faster, dive deeper, stay down longer, and come out dryer than any man in all creation. Just as he was about to seize the goose a loud howl rose suddenly near him. Crockett jumped up out of the water like a sturgeon. It was a wolf, only a few feet away. At the same moment an alligator swam toward him from another direction and from overhead the whole flock of wild geese flew down upon him, hissing and flapping their wings.

"Davy dove down slantwise so as to come up far beyond the reach of all these critters, but when he struck the bottom of the river he was chased by a river calf and had to swim straight up to the surface again. The wolf, the alligator, the geese, were still there and the river calf was hotfoot after him besides! Crockett struck out for a sawyer and just then a little steamboat came whistling and tooting along with fire and black smoke, and scared all the critters away. Crockett asked for a passage on board. Death Hug came along at this moment, swimming in easy water, and Crockett requested a berth for him too. The captain was a fussy man and he refused to give a berth to Death Hug, so Crockett and his tame bear walked out of the water and into the woods where they cut down a very ancient hollow gum tree, hewed it open on one side with Crockett's

knife, corked up both ends, and launched their canoe into the river
just as the steamer got out of sight. Old Death Hug sat in the stern
and steered with his tail. He lit a pipe, and so did Crockett. Death
Hug paddled with his paws and Crockett with his hands. Smoking
like smokestacks, they made that hollow log canoe walk in and out
and along the water until the fishes stared, and soon they passed the
steamboat. After a while Death Hug wanted to go ashore, so the
canoe was drawn up on a bank. Crockett took a log for a pillow
and floated downstream, and was soon fast asleep.

"I suppose you gentlemen have heard what happened to him
next," queried the little man, as though he hoped they had not.

From the darkest corner of the coach a traveler spoke up. "I
reckon it's just about there he met up with Ben Hardin!"

Now a certain Ben Hardin was a member of Congress from Kentucky, an orator, and a good deal of a humorist. Ben Hardin in the
stories was a different figure altogether. Many tales were told of the
frolics and adventures of Crockett and this curious personage in the
Shakes and on the Mississippi—"the backbone of North America"—
where Crockett had once traveled with his staves. These stories are
full of wind, earthquakes, hurricanes, lightning. Not all of them
could have been related in a single evening, no matter how long
the journey.

Here are a few of them, set down as they were told in the talk
of the day.

As Davy Crockett was drifting downstream, asleep on his log
pillow, he was wakened by bumping into something. Before him
was a strange equipage for river travel. In the center of a log three
kegs had been fastened one on top of another, and on the topmost
keg was sitting a fat little man wearing a snug tarpaulin hat that
looked as bright as a new dollar. His trousers were of sailcloth, his
shoes thin and light with ribbons on them. He wore a big black
patch over one eye.

"Well, stranger," said Crockett, "you must have robbed a peddler
and got off with all his flashy trumpery."

"Why," said the fat little man, "the critter's got the lingo of a

Christian. I thought I had spoke to a catfish. I've plowed salt water for forty year and I've seen porpoises and dolphins and mermaids, and I've took many a Nantucket sleigh ride, but you're the queerest looking sea craft I ever come across, on soundings or off. Where you cruising, old rusty bottom?"

The little man's voice grew deeper and rougher as he spoke. He had a voice so rough it couldn't be written down but would have to be shown in a picture.

"You infernal heathen," said Crockett, "I suppose you're new down this way, but I'll tell you I'm a snorter by birth and education, and if you don't go floating along and leave me to finish my nap I'll give you a taste of my breed, beginning with the snapping turtle!"

At this rejoinder the fat little stranger looked as mad as a shovel full of hot coals. He took a string of tobacco out of his pocket and bit into it savagely. He bit off a string long and big enough to hang a buffalo with, and roared out, "I'll shiver your mizzen, you landlubber! You rock crab! You deck sweeper!"

Crockett's steam was up. "I'll double you up like a spare shirt. My name is Crockett—"

With this the stranger roared with laughter, and his laugh was as rough and noisy as his talk. Stooping down he reached out his hand. "Give us your flipper. I wouldn't hurt a hair of your head for all the world. I've been cruising up and down this river a-looking for you. Hurrah for Davy Crockett!"

The stranger explained that his name was Ben Hardin, and that he was a man who had seen great times. "My business is seeing," he said jovially, and added that he had been told he could see more with the black patch over one eye than any other man could see with it off. He said he had been captain of ships that had turned bottom upward and sailed along to their destinations on their masts. He said that he had leaned his back against a hurricane. He said that he drank bitters made out of whiskey and rusty cannon balls, and slept coiled up like a cable. The last time he counted he was going on into his ninety-ninth year.

As Hardin was talking, a noise was heard like low thunder, then a distant roaring like the voice of old Niagara.

"Hello," said Crockett, "there's a storm coming."

"No, it's a steamer," said Ben Hardin.

"Maybe it's the echo of our voices," said Crockett.

The noise grew louder, the water began to squirm about, and Crockett's log and Hardin's little craft began playing seesaw. Then came a sudden roaring blast that would have made Niagara sound like a kitten. The trees on shore walked out by the roots and danced about. Houses came apart. Two boats on the river crashed into each other, and their ribs were stove in to the boilers. Crockett and Hardin thought it was time to be off.

When a streak of lightning glanced by, Crockett seized it by the fork and sprang upon it. For a man who had leaned his back against a hurricane, Ben seemed in a hurry to leave. He gave a leap and seized Crockett's hair. Crockett greased the lightning with some rattle snake oil he happened to have along and the way they left the tornado behind and slid across the land was astonishing to all nature.

When this feat became known people talked about greased lightning. They still do. "Quick as greased lightning."

When this adventure was over Crockett landed with his new friend in the woods, and he felt as good-natured as a soaped eel. He invited Hardin to come along to his cabin, where he promised him a bear steak, and the two went along through the woods as good friends as a tame hawk and a blind rooster.

But the way Ben walked was a caution, for he was used to the decks of a ship. When it came to walking among the tall masts of the backwoods he turned every way but the right way. He swung about like a bearskin hung to the limb of a tree.

One morning Ben wanted to go out hunting. So out they went and away went Ben, whistling and swinging his tarpaulin hat at every little creature that happened to be in sight. At last they got under an oak that was famous for breeding many generations of wild cats. Even its knots looked like wildcats' eyes. Just as they got beneath it and were going to take a seat on a root they heard something above them give a scratch and a grunt. Ben ran up the tree as light as a monkey up a ship's ladder. He hadn't gone further than heels out of sight when Crockett heard a sailor's regular rough language with all the trimmings. He looked up and saw a bear, and the creature had grabbed Ben by the shoulder. The way the old sea serpent fought back was a caution. Down they came to the ground, Ben and the bear, and rolled over and over. The leaves began to turn claret color so Crockett stepped up, squeezed the breath out of the bear, and gave Ben a swallow out of the lightning bottle. Ben swore that every claw of that bear was a whaler's harpoon.

Ben Hardin told Crockett that he was a whole squall and a hurricane at a frolic. Old sailors used to say that he could dance all the girls in all the seaports from Cadiz to Cape Cod out of their stockings. He danced till he wore away the stone steps in front of Crocketts' cabin.

"Well, old Salt-Rope," said Crockett, "I'll give you a frolic that'll last you for a seven years' cruise."

Now Ben had said that Crockett's daughter was as pretty as a dolphin. "I've seen dolphins and mermaids too," he added. The story was that she had once been captured by Indians, who carried her away and tied her to a tree, and meant to kindle a fire about her. But while they were gone for wood, panthers came and gnawed the ropes and set her free, and gathered about her as she ran through the forest and escorted her most of the way home.

"Anyway she's the true grit," said Crockett, " and she can dance anything from an earthquake reel to a square-toed double trouble shiver."

They all went to the Asphaltum Flats, where lightning couldn't strike because the flats were so hard. An old man with a hemlock fiddle played new tunes that went so fast a humming-bird's wing couldn't keep time with them. Crockett set Ben and the girl at it, and away they went, and the Asphaltum Flats looked like a prairie on fire. "After the first three tunes," Crockett said, "Old Ben began to grunt like a saw going through a pine knot. Then he staggered. My girl said nothing but kept on leading out every new tune. After the hundred and fifteenth tune Ben began to roll like a ship in a sea-storm and finally he fell over and curled up in his pigtail. But my girl was ready to go on."

Strange tales were told of Crockett's hunting exploits in wild country of the Northwest and of his encounters with Indians. One evening about dark Crockett and Hardin came to the great Indian Rock, which was the hardest stone in all creation.

"It was so 'tarnal high and so all flinty hard," said Crockett, "that it would turn off a common ordinary everyday streak of lightning and make it point down and look flat as a cow's tail."

They got under a shelf of this great rock, and Crockett struck a little fire from it with his knuckles to light their pipes, and they began puffing. They looked up and the whole stone around and on both ends was alive and red with Indians, all with guns and tomahawks. Ben reached for his flintlock, but Crockett saw that lightning would be the only thing so he rubbed himself against the shelf of the rock and struck his left eye two or three times. Then he stepped back and with a single wink sent such a blasting streak of hot lightning into the great rock that it parted into forty thousand pieces. There were red Indians shooting up into the sky like rockets and landing way out on the prairie. "We cut stick in such a shower of red Indians as was never seen before," said Crockett.

Another time Crockett and Ben Hardin were having a feast of roasted buffalo with some friendly Indians near one of their lodges. Afterwards Crockett danced a breakdown on a great flat rock nearby. He rattled off some clear music as he danced and all the Indians came out and sat around in a circle to watch him—all but the Indian chief, who began a regular Indian war dance in opposition. The Indians began to shout and whoop. Crockett went at it harder and danced until the old rock began to snap and smoke like a hemlock back log. Fire began to fly about, the Indian chief's feet began to singe, and the blankets of the others were all in a light blaze. Just as the Indians were all going to run off Crockett finished with a regular old "Grind the Bottle," and stamped the whole fire out again.

Farther to the north Crockett and Ben Hardin went wolf hunting. After the hunt one day, when Crockett was feeling hot and lazy, the old sailor bantered him for a race on the frozen river. Now Crockett was a rocket on skates. Skating, he could pass the swiftest Indians, and Indians could go fast as thought on their bone runners made of buffalo ribs. Up and down the frozen rivers of the north Crockett would go, leaping great air holes twenty feet or more across and skating on without losing a stroke. Death Hug was also a prime skater, though not so good as Crockett. For the race Death Hug started off ahead while Davy and Ben started even. They went so fast they struck fire against the wind. Sparks flew out of the ice and made Crockett's gun go off, so he lost a stroke but he skated ahead and grabbed Death Hug's tail. At the same moment Ben fell. He caught hold of the tail of Crockett's hunting shirt and down the river went the three for a hundred miles, like a toboggan, with Death Hug in the lead.

Traveling over the country in winter Davy and Death Hug came to the Niagara River, which was frozen. They were cutting all sorts of frolic flourishes on the ice when suddenly the great piece on which they were skating parted from the rest and headed toward the Falls. There were people all along the banks and Crockett waved at them. Suddenly Crockett and his bear were left on only a small wedge of ice that was sharp at one end. Death Hug put his paw to his nose, Crockett raised Uncle Sam's starry handkerchief, and they steered over the great hill of water as easy as though they were on a greased ship.

Then Crockett mounted his old pet alligator and steered right back up the roaring thunder-water as slick as a stream of wind going up a chimney.

"My old alligator walked up that monstrous great hill of water as easy as a wildcat goes up a white oak," said Crockett. "And my alligator opened his mouth as wide as the Black Cave, and the people were all astonished."

On the Upper Lower Fork of the Great Little Deep Shallow River Davy gathered all his animals around him. Death Hug was there, and Mississippi, the buffalo, that could sing "Old Hundred," and a cougar, a fox, and a hyena. Crockett's pet hyena could out-laugh an earthquake, and he was so wild that the northeast wind couldn't reach him and even lightning couldn't catch up with him.

"The lightning put out after him once," said Davy, "but he laughed it out of countenance and ran away, and when I followed him I had to run for seven days and seven nights. Then he turned round and came home with me as docile as a kitten."

Crockett gathered them all together under the Liberty Tree. It was the Fourth of July, so he took out his bag of patriotism and gave them an oration. "When I began my oration," said Crockett, "they opened their eyes and ears in the most teetotal attentive manner and showed a 'tarnal sight more respect than the members of Congress show one another during their speeches, and when I concluded by lifting my cap with twenty-six cheers for Uncle Sam and his states, with a little thrown in for Texas and Oregon, why choke me if those critters didn't follow with such a shout as set all the trees to shaking!"

Then Crockett taught all the animals the polka. Death Hug and the buffalo Mississippi and the old alligator could wear down an oak floor in a single night, all flipping their heels in regular polka step while Ben Hardin whistled the tunes. Ben could outwhistle the prettiest clarionet that ever talked music.

Stories about Crockett are still told in Kentucky and Tennessee and in the Ozark Mountains. Even now people in the Ozarks talk about him as though he were still living just over the next ridge.

They say that once he went bear hunting in the fall up on Whang-doodle Knob. At sundown he was tired out, so he lay down under a big old dead cedar tree and went to sleep. In his sleep he rolled over and nearly broke his powder horn. Above him was a little curved yellow branch and he hung his horn on it. The next morning the horn was gone and he couldn't find the branch. That night he came back to the Knob and soon the little crescent moon came up, riding low over the mountain. It came so close and looked so yellow it nearly blinded him, and there was his powder horn hanging from the tip. He reached it down and went along home to his cabin.

In the Ozarks they tell of another time when Crockett was out hunting and traveled far from his cabin and spent the night in the woods. The next morning at daybreak he took a far jump and landed on the sun, thinking that he would be carried over the mountain to his cabin. But he had forgotten that he was west of his cabin instead of east. So, traveling with the sun for twenty-four hours, he saw the whole world, and dropped off the next morning and landed on his own doorstep.

During his own lifetime Crockett had been spoken of as consorting on easy terms with the moon, with shooting stars, a fiery comet, and the lightning. In all the stories his close companions were wind, water, fire, the earth, and the wild creatures of forest and prairies. In a last story he is portrayed as stronger than the sun, and he appears once more in the hunting country of Tennessee.

This story belongs to the Winter of the Big Snow, the winter of 1835, when Crockett set out for Texas, when snow fell early through the wide stretches of the North, crept farther and farther down through the hardwood forests of Michigan, then through the softwood forests, through the long valleys of Wisconsin, down upon the prairie country of Illinois, into Kentucky and Tennessee. The story was told as if Crockett himself related it.

"On one of those winter mornings it was all screwen cold," said Crockett. "The forest trees were so stiff they couldn't shake and the very daybreak froze fast as it was trying to dawn. The tinderbox in my cabin would no more catch fire than a sunk raft at the bottom of the sea. All creation was in a fair way for freezing fast, so I thought I must strike a little fire from my fingers and travel out a few leagues and see what I could do about it. I brought my knuckles together like two thunderclouds, but the sparks froze up before I could collect 'em, so out I walked and tried to keep myself unfrozen by going along at a frolic gait, whistling the tune of 'Fire in the Mountains' and keeping going at three double-quick time. Well, after I had walked about a hundred miles up Daybreak Hill I reached Peak o' Day, and there I discovered what was the matter. The earth had actually frozen fast on her axis and couldn't turn round, and the sun had got jammed between two cakes of ice under the wheels, and there he had been shining and working to get loose till he was frozen fast in his cold sweat.

"'C-R-E-A-T-I-O-N,' thought I, 'this is the toughest sort of suspension, and it mustn't be endured—something must be done or human creation is done for!' It was so premature and antediluvian cold on top of Peak o' Day that my upper and lower teeth were all collapsed together as tight as a frozen oyster. So I took a big bear off my back that I'd picked up on my road, and threw him down on the ice and soon there was hot sweet bear oil on all sides. I took and squeezed him over the earth's axis until I'd thawed it loose, and I poured about a ton of sweet bear oil over the sun's face. Then I gave the earth's cog wheel one kick backward till I got the sun free and whistled 'Push Along, Keep Moving.' In about fifteen seconds the earth gave a grunt and began to roll around easy, and the sun walked up most beautiful, saluting me with such a wind of gratitude it made me sneeze.

"I lit my pipe by the blaze of his topknot and walked home, introducing people to the fresh daylight with a piece of sunrise in my pocket."

So when Davy Crockett set out for Texas the earth was no longer screwed up stiff and frozen fast, but rolled around. The sun walked up in the morning and down at night, though the days were bitter cold and the snow lay deep.

NAPOLEON

By HENDRIK WILLEM VAN LOON

Map by the Author

NAPOLEON was born in the year 1769, the third son of Carlo Maria Buonaparte, an honest notary public of the city of Ajaccio in the island of Corsica, and his good wife, Letizia Ramolino. He therefore was not a Frenchman, but an Italian whose native island (an old Greek, Carthaginian and Roman colony in the Mediterranean Sea) had for years been struggling to regain its independence, first of all from the Genoese, and after the middle of the eighteenth century from the French, who had kindly offered to help the Corsicans in their struggle for freedom and had occupied the island for their own benefit.

During the first twenty years of his life, young Napoleon was a professional Corsican patriot—a Corsican Sinn Feiner, who hoped to deliver his beloved country from the yoke of the bitterly hated French enemy. But the French revolution had unexpectedly recognized the claims of the Corsicans and gradually Napoleon, who had received a good training at the military school of Brienne, drifted into the service of his adopted country. Although he never learned to spell French correctly or to speak it without a broad Italian accent, he became a Frenchman. In due time he came to stand as the highest expression of all French virtues. At present he is regarded as the symbol of the Gallic genius.

Napoleon was what is called a fast worker. His career does not cover more than twenty years. In that short span of time he fought more wars and gained more victories, and marched more miles and conquered more square kilometers, and killed more people, and brought about more reforms, and generally upset Europe to a greater extent than anybody (including Alexander the Great and Jenghis Khan) had ever managed to do.

He was a little fellow and during the first years of his life his health was not very good. He never impressed anybody by his good looks and he remained to the end of his days very clumsy whenever he was obliged to appear at a social function. He did not enjoy a single advantage of breeding or birth or riches. For the greater part of his youth he was desperately poor and often he had to go without a meal or was obliged to make a few extra pennies in curious ways.

He gave little promise as a literary genius. When he competed for a prize offered by the Academy of Lyons, his essay was found to be next to the last and he was number 15 out of 16 candidates. But he overcame all these difficulties through his absolute and unshakable belief in his own destiny, and in his own glorious future. Ambition was the mainspring of his life. The thought of self, the worship of that capital letter "N" with which he signed all his letters, and which recurred forever in the ornaments of his hastily constructed palaces, the absolute will to make the name Napoleon the most important thing in the world next to the name of God, these desires carried Napoleon to a pinnacle of fame which no other man has ever reached.

When he was a half-pay lieutenant, young Bonaparte was very fond of the "Lives of Famous Men" which Plutarch, the Greek historian, had written. But he never tried to live up to the high standard of character set by these heroes of the older days. Napoleon seems to have been devoid of all those considerate and thoughtful sentiments which make men different from the animals. It will be very difficult to decide with any degree of accuracy whether he ever loved anyone besides himself. He kept a civil tongue to his mother, but Letizia had the air and manners of a great lady, and after the fashion of Italian mothers she knew how to rule her brood of children and command their respect. For a few years he was fond of Josephine, his pretty Creole wife, who was the daughter of a French officer of Martinique and the widow of the Vicomte de Beauharnais, who had been executed by Robespierre when he lost a battle against the Prussians. But the Emperor divorced her when she failed to give him a son and heir, and married the daughter of the Austrian Emperor because it seemed good policy.

During the siege of Toulon, where he gained great fame as commander of a battery, Napoleon studied Macchiavelli with industrious care. He followed the advice of the Florentine statesman and never kept his word when it was to his advantage to break it. The word "gratitude" did not occur in his personal dictionary. Neither, to be quite fair, did he expect it from others. He was totally indifferent to human suffering. He executed prisoners of war (in Egypt in 1798) who had been promised their lives, and he quietly allowed his wounded in Syria to be chloroformed when he found it impossible to transport them to his ships. He ordered the Duke of Enghien to be condemned to death by a prejudiced court-martial and to be shot, contrary to all law, on the sole ground that the "Bourbons needed a warning." He decreed that those German officers who were made prisoner while fighting for their country's independence should be shot against the nearest wall, and when Andreas Hofer, the Tyrolese hero, fell into his hands after a most heroic resistance, he was executed like a common traitor.

In short, when we study the character of the Emperor, we begin to understand those anxious British mothers who used to drive their children to bed with the threat that "Bonaparte, who ate little boys and girls for breakfast, would come and get them if they were not very good." And yet, having said these many unpleasant things about this strange tyrant, who looked after every other department of his army with the utmost care but neglected the medical service, and who ruined his uniforms with Eau de Cologne because he could not stand the smell of his poor sweating soldiers; having said all these unpleasant things and being fully prepared to add many more, I must confess to a certain lurking feeling of doubt.

Here I am sitting at a comfortable table loaded heavily with books, with one eye on my typewriter and the other on Licorice, the cat, who has a great fondness for carbon paper, and I am telling you that the Emperor Napoleon was a most contemptible person. But should I happen to look out of the window, down upon Seventh Avenue, and should the endless procession of trucks and carts come to a sudden halt, and should I hear the sound of the heavy drums and see the little man on his white horse in his old and much-worn green uniform, then I don't know, but I am afraid that I would leave my books and the kitten and my home and everything else to follow him wherever he cared to lead. My own grandfather did this

and Heaven knows he was not born to be a hero. Millions of other
people's grandfathers did it. They received no reward, but they expected none. They cheerfully gave legs and arms and lives to serve
this foreigner, who took them a thousand miles away from their
homes and marched them into a barrage of Russian or English or
Spanish or Italian or Austrian cannon and stared quietly into space
while they were rolling in the agony of death.

If you ask me for an explanation, I must answer that I have none.
I can only guess at one of the reasons. Napoleon was the greatest of
actors and the whole European continent was his stage. At all times
and under all circumstances he knew the precise attitude that would
impress the spectators most and he understood what words would
make the deepest impression. Whether he spoke in the Egyptian
desert, before the backdrop of the Sphinx and the pyramids, or
addressed his shivering men on the dew-soaked plains of Italy, made
no difference. At all times he was master of the situation. Even at
the end, an exile on a little rock in the middle of the Atlantic, a sick
man at the mercy of a dull and intolerable British governor, he held
the center of the stage.

After the defeat of Waterloo, no one outside of a few trusted
friends ever saw the great Emperor. The people of Europe knew
that he was living on the island of St. Helena—they knew that a
British garrison guarded him day and night—they knew that the
British fleet guarded the garrison which guarded the Emperor on his
farm at Longwood. But he was never out of the mind of either
friend or enemy. When illness and despair had at last taken him
away, his silent eyes continued to haunt the world. Even today he is
as much of a force in the life of France as a hundred years ago,
when people fainted at the mere sight of this sallow-faced man who
stabled his horses in the holiest temples of the Russian Kremlin, and
who treated the Pope and the mighty ones of this earth as if they
were his lackeys.

To give you a mere outline of his life would demand a couple of
volumes. To tell you of his great political reform of the French
state, of his new codes of laws which were adopted in most European
countries, of his activities in every field of public activity, would take

thousands of pages. But I can explain in a few words why he was so successful during the first part of his career and why he failed during the last ten years. From the year 1789 until the year 1804, Napoleon was the great leader of the great French Revolution. He was not merely fighting for the glory of his own name. He defeated Austria and Italy and England and Russia because he, himself, and his soldiers were the apostles of the new creed of "Liberty, Fraternity and Equality" and were the enemies of the courts while they were the friends of the people.

But in the year 1804, Napoleon made himself Hereditary Emperor of the French and sent for Pope Pius VII to come and crown him, even as Leo III, in the year 800 had crowned that other great King of the Franks, Charlemagne, whose example was constantly before Napoleon's eyes.

Once upon the throne, the old revolutionary chieftain became an unsuccessful imitation of a Habsburg monarch. He forgot his spiritual Mother, the Political Club of the Jacobins. He ceased to be the defender of the oppressed. He became the chief of all the oppressors and kept his shooting squads ready to execute those who dared to oppose his imperial will. No one had shed a tear when in the year 1806 the sad remains of the Holy Roman Empire were carted to the historical dustbin and when the last relic of ancient Roman glory was destroyed by the grandson of an Italian peasant. But when the Napoleonic armies had invaded Spain, had forced the Spaniards to recognize a king whom they detested, had massacred the poor Madrilenes who remained faithful to their old rulers, then public opinion turned against the former hero of Marengo and Austerlitz and a hundred other revolutionary battles. Then and only then, when Napoleon was no longer the hero of the revolution but the personification of all the bad traits of the Old Régime, was it possible for England to give direction to the fast-spreading sentiment of hatred which was turning all honest men into enemies of the French Emperor.

The English people from the very beginning had felt deeply disgusted when their newspapers told them the gruesome details of the Terror. They had staged their own great revolution (during the reign of Charles I) a century before. It had been a very simple affair compared to the upheaval of Paris. In the eyes of the average Englishman a Jacobin was a monster to be shot at sight and Napoleon was the chief devil. The British fleet had blockaded France ever since the year 1798. It had spoiled Napoleon's plan to invade India by way of Egypt and had forced him to beat an ignominious retreat, after his victories along the banks of the Nile. And finally, in the year 1805, England got the chance it had waited for so long.

Near Cape Trafalgar on the southwestern coast of Spain, Nelson annihilated the Napoleonic fleet, beyond a possible chance of recovery. From that moment on, the Emperor was landlocked. Even so, he would have been able to maintain himself as the recognized ruler of the continent had he understood the signs of the times and accepted the honorable peace which the powers offered him. But Napoleon had been blinded by the blaze of his own glory. He would recognize no equals. He could tolerate no rivals. And his hatred turned against Russia, the mysterious land of the endless plains with its inexhaustible supply of cannon fodder.

As long as Russia was ruled by Paul I, the half-witted son of Catherine the Great, Napoleon had known how to deal with the situation. But Paul grew more and more irresponsible, until his exasperated subjects were obliged to murder him, (lest they all be sent to the Siberian lead mines) and the son of Paul, the Emperor Alexander, did not share his father's affection for the usurper whom he regarded as the enemy of mankind, the eternal disturber of the peace. He was a pious man who believed that he had been chosen by God to deliver the world from the Corsican curse. He joined Prussia and England and Austria and he was defeated. He tried five times and five times he failed. In the year 1812 he once more taunted Napoleon until the French Emperor, in a blind rage, vowed that he would dictate peace in Moscow. Then, from far and wide, from Spain and Germany and Holland and Italy and Portugal, unwilling regiments were driven northward, that the wounded pride of the great Emperor might be duly avenged.

The rest of the story is common knowledge. After a march of two months, Napoleon reached the Russian capital and established his headquarters in the holy Kremlin. On the night of September 15 of the year 1812, Moscow caught fire. The town burned four days. When the evening of the fifth day came, Napoleon gave the order for the retreat. Two weeks later it began to snow. The army trudged through mud and sleet until November the 26th when the river Berezina was reached. Then the Russian attacks began in all seriousness. The Cossacks swarmed around the "Grande Armée" which was no longer an army but a mob. In the middle of December the first of the survivors began to be seen in the German cities of the East.

Then there were many rumors of an impending revolt. "The time has come," the people of Europe said, "to free ourselves from this insufferable yoke." And they began to look for old shotguns which had escaped the eye of the ever-present French spies. But ere they knew what had happened, Napoleon was back with a new army. He had left his defeated soldiers and in his little sleigh had rushed ahead to Paris, making a final appeal for more troops that he might defend the sacred soil of France against foreign invasion.

Children of sixteen and seventeen followed him when he moved eastward to meet the allied powers. On October 16, 18, and 19 of the year 1813, the terrible battle of Leipzig took place, where for three days boys in green and boys in blue fought each other until the Elster ran red with blood. On the afternoon of the 17th of October, the massed reserves of Russian infantry broke through the French lines and Napoleon fled.

Back to Paris he went. He abdicated in favor of his small son, but the allied powers insisted that Louis XVIII, the brother of the late king Louis XVI, should occupy the French throne, and surrounded by Cossacks and Uhlans, the dull-eyed Bourbon prince made his triumphal entry into Paris.

As for Napoleon, he was made the sovereign ruler of the little island of Elba in the Mediterranean where he organized his stable boys into a miniature army and fought battles on a chessboard.

But no sooner had he left France than the people began to realize what they had lost. The last twenty years, however costly, had been a period of great glory. Paris had been the capital of the world. The

fat Bourbon king who had learned nothing and had forgotten nothing during the days of his exile disgusted everybody by his indolence.

On the first of March of the year 1815, when the representatives
of the allies were ready to begin the work of unscrambling the map

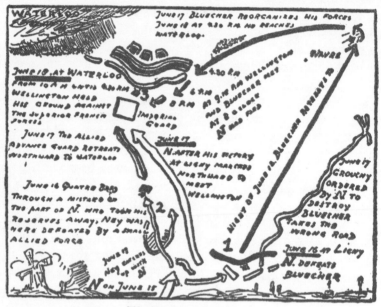

The Battle of Waterloo.

of Europe, Napoleon suddenly landed near Cannes. In less than a
week the French army had deserted the Bourbons and had rushed
southward to offer their swords and bayonets to the "Little Corpo-
ral." Napoleon marched straight to Paris, where he arrived on the
twentieth of March. This time he was more cautious. He offered
peace, but the allies insisted upon war. The whole of Europe arose
against the "perfidious Corsican." Rapidly the Emperor marched
northward that he might crush his enemies before they should be
able to unite their forces. But Napoleon was no longer his old self.
He felt sick. He got tired easily. He slept when he ought to have
been up directing the attack of his advance guard. Besides, he missed
many of his faithful old generals. They were dead.

Early in June his armies entered Belgium. On the 16th of that month he defeated the Prussians under Blücher. But a subordinate commander failed to destroy the retreating army as he had been ordered to do.

Two days later, Napoleon met Wellington near Waterloo. It was the 18th of June, a Sunday. At two o'clock of the afternoon, the battle seemed won for the French. At three a speck of dust appeared upon the eastern horizon. Napoleon believed that this meant the approach of his own cavalry who would now turn the English defeat into a rout. At four o'clock he knew better. Cursing and swearing, old Blücher drove his deathly tired troops into the heart of the fray. The shock broke the ranks of the guards. Napoleon had no further reserves. He told his men to save themselves as best they could, and he fled.

For a second time he abdicated in favor of his son. Just one hundred days after his escape from Elba, he was making for the coast. He intended to go to America. In the year 1803, for a mere song, he had sold the French colony of Louisiana (which was in great danger of being captured by the British) to the young American Republic. "The Americans," so he said, "will be grateful and will give me a little bit of land and a house where I may spend the last days of my life in peace and quiet." But the English fleet was watching all French harbors. Caught between the armies of the Allies and the ships of the British. Napoleon had no choice. The Prussians intended to shoot him. The English might be more generous. At Rochefort he waited in the hope that something might turn up. One month after Waterloo, he received orders from the new French government to leave French soil inside of twenty-four hours. Always the tragedian, he wrote a letter to the Prince Regent of England (George III, the king, was in an insane asylum) informing His Royal Highness of his intention to "throw himself upon the mercy of his enemies, and like Themistocles, to look for a welcome at the fireside of his foes . . . "

On the 15th of July he went on board the *Bellerophon,* and surrendered his sword to Admiral Hotham. At Plymouth he was transferred to the *Northumberland* which carried him to St. Helena.

There he spent the last seven years of his life. He tried to write his memoirs, he quarreled with his keepers and he dreamed of past times. Curiously enough he returned (at least in his imagination) to his original point of departure. He remembered the days when he had fought the battles of the Revolution. He tried to convince himself that he had always been the true friend of those great principles of "Liberty, Fraternity and Equality" which the ragged soldiers of the convention had carried to the ends of the earth. He liked to dwell upon his career as Commander-in-Chief and Consul. He rarely spoke of the Empire. Sometimes he thought of his son, the Duke of Reichstadt, the little eagle, who lived in Vienna, where he was treated as a "poor relation" by his young Habsburg cousins, whose fathers had trembled at the very mention of the name of Him. When the end came, he was leading his troops to victory. He ordered Ney to attack with the guards. Then he died.

But if you want an explanation of this strange career, if you really wish to know how one man could possibly rule so many people for so many years by the sheer force of his will, do not read the books that have been written about him. Their authors either hated the Emperor or loved him. You will learn many facts, but it is more important to "feel history" than to know it. Don't read, but wait until you have a chance to hear a good artist sing the song called "The Two Grenadiers." The words were written by Heine, the great German poet who lived through the Napoleonic era. The music was composed by Schumann, a German, who saw the Emperor, the enemy of his country, whenever he came to visit his imperial father-in-law. The song therefore is the work of two men who had every reason to hate the tyrant.

Go and hear it. Then you will understand what a thousand volumes could not possibly tell you.

THE TREE OF JADE

By CORNELIA MEIGS

FROM the time when they first went to the dame school to learn their letters, Jonathan Adams and Humphrey Reynolds spent most of their waking hours in each other's company. They looked for birds' nests together in the woods at the edge of the broad Susquehanna River, they paddled along its marshy banks, they played absorbing games in that busy, entrancing place, Jonathan's father's shipyard. Or they would stand side by side watching a great ship of war come sailing up the bay, a flying vision of square white sails and darkly outlined rigging, the vessel that was commanded by Captain Reynolds, Humphrey's father. The two boys talked much of what they would do when they were men; they would sit for long hours on the wharf, their legs dangling above the water, discussing the future.

"I am going into the Navy, like my father," Humphrey would say, "and I intend to sail in the finest and fastest ship of the whole fleet to the very ends of the world and back again. And I will have you for an executive officer, Jonathan."

"No," Jonathan would return seriously, "I get sick when I go to sea and I don't like hardtack and salt pork. No, I will stop at home in my father's yards and some day I will build a ship that is a real ship and not just tubs like these."

They parted when they were seventeen and did not meet again for years, for Humphrey went into the Navy as he had planned and Jonathan, with mallet and chisel in hand and with that sober, earnest air that always clung to him, was already at work in his father's shipyard. In time he became master of the entire business, while Humphrey was scouring the seas, sailing on just those far voyages of which he had so often dreamed. Jonathan had his dreams also, but he did not speak of them, only toiled away at building the heavy, sturdy vessels that carried America's trade overseas early in the last century. Honest ships they were and reliable, as sure of coming to port as though they had belonged to the age of steam, but oh, how long it took them to make a voyage! In the privacy of his dingy little office Jonathan, with the door fastened, would push aside the clutter of plans and drawings and would get out the model of a strange vessel, sharp, slender and graceful, with a hull like a racing yacht. He would set it upon the bench to carve a little here, to alter a curve by a hair's breadth there, or merely to stand staring at it sometimes for hours at a time, staring and thinking.

One day when he was so standing, utterly lost in some unspoken vision, there came a knock at the door, followed by an impatient second one and a thunderous third, all during the moment of time that it took the shipmaster to put out of sight his beloved model. When the door was opened there strode in a tall sunburned person in blue uniform, Humphrey Reynolds come at last to see his old comrade, bringing a roll of government documents under his arm.

"Congress has taken a sudden turn toward increasing the Navy," the young officer explained, "and the orders are going out to build twelve ships in haste. One of the contracts is to come to you, if you will take it. They are even in such need that they have not laid down the specifications to the last bolt and rope's end, so that the man who builds this ship and the officer who superintends the construction can really have something to say about the design."

He looked his old friend very steadily in the eye and saw a slow smile of deep, unspoken delight dawn upon the shipbuilder's face. Jonathan Adams' hard hands did not often tremble, but they shook a little now as he reached up to the shelf above the bench and brought down his model.

"I have been thinking about such a design since I was ten years old," he said, "and the chance to build it has come at last. We will make them a real ship, Humphrey, and the whole world will open its eyes when it sees you sail her."

She grew up quickly on the ways, that ship of their very hearts' desire, with her bowsprit standing far out over the neighboring street, and with people stopping in the lane to watch Jonathan's whole force of workmen toiling up and down her timbered sides. Old Navy officers who had seen, some of them, the ships of the

Revolution, and who had all fought in the War of Eighteen-twelve, would come to inspect her and would shake their heads.

"Look at that high, sharp bow," one would say; "such a craft will never be seaworthy in the world. Why can't these young fellows stick to the models we have tried out for them?"

"And see the spread of sail this drawing shows," another would comment, pointing fiercely with a stubby forefinger; "why, the whole ridiculous affair will capsize in the first good puff of wind! I'm thankful I don't have to go to sea in her."

But the two comrades closed their ears and sat, often far into the night, in the cramped little office, poring over drawings and comparing designs.

"You have her thought out to the last ring, block and halyard," Humphrey would say, "and you never even knew if you could build her. What a dreamer you are!"

"It takes dreaming to keep a man at his work," Jonathan would answer. "How do you think I would have had the patience, all these years, to drive wooden pins into cross-timbers, or to mend the rigging of limping coastwise schooners if I had not been thinking of just such a ship as this, and seen her, in my mind's eye, putting to sea under full sail, to smash every sailing record that has been known?"

The day of the launching came, then the stepping of the giant masts, the completing of the rigging and bending of the new sails.

"The *West Wind* will be ready for sea in two weeks now," Humphrey said, one morning at breakfast, to Miranda Reynolds—she was my great-grandmother and I was named for her. They had been married only a month and this would be his first cruise since their wedding. She drew her breath quickly, she had not known it was to be so soon.

"People say," she began hesitatingly, "old sailors and longshoremen and even the Naval officers that have been here, say that the *West Wind* will never stand a storm."

"They are the kind of men," Humphrey scoffed, "who would be sailing vessels of the model of the Ark, did not people like Jonathan Adams have the courage, sometimes, to build something new. No,

the *West Wind* is going to teach all the shipmasters something they
never knew before, when once she sets sail. And we expect to clear
for Gibraltar in less than a month. Why, Miranda, you're not crying?"

"No," declared Miranda, choking bravely, for tears have no place
in a sea captain's household. She even managed to muster a watery
smile. "I wonder what you will leave behind you in foreign parts
this time; your gold snuffbox, perhaps."

It was a longstanding joke that young Captain Reynolds was so
careless of his possessions that he never came home from a voyage
without having lost or mislaid by the way everything he had. But
the gold snuffbox had survived several cruises, since it was the most
valuable thing he owned. It had been presented to him by the citizens of his town when he had come home from sea some years ago,
after, so he expressed, "a miserable Algerine pirate lay alongside
him and insisted on being taken."

It is probably only a short paragraph in your history book and
possibly a very dull one that tells you how, a little more than a hundred years ago, the seas swarmed with pirates whose home ports
were the North African cities of Algiers, Tripoli and Tunis. The
great nations of Europe and, with them, the young United States,
used to buy safety from these lawless Barbary States by sending them
gifts and tribute. But when, finally, the Pasha of Tripoli sent word
to our President that his last gift was not large enough and that
more must be sent, the answer was a fleet of American warships and
the bombardment of the astonished monarch's seaports. There were
many spirited encounters during that little war, many feats of daring
seamanship of which history has lost sight among the greater events
that have followed. But for years after the struggle was over, the
United States Navy still policed that foreign sea with such thorough-
ness that the pirate craft that dared venture from port were bold
and desperate indeed.

It was thither that the *West Wind* was to sail, with dispatches for
the Commodore of the Mediterranean Fleet. At last the ship was
ready, a rare and beautiful sight with her slim hull, her rows of
guns and her towering reach of silvery new canvas.

She sailed with the early tide, at daybreak of a mid-April morning, a ghostly fairy-like thing, slipping away in the gray light and the mist of dawn. Miranda stood on the dock to watch her go, with Jonathan beside her staring fixedly after his winged dream, flying at last beyond the seas.

"There will be tales to tell when she comes back," he said at last, "and I look for her to cut down the sailing time by three, four, five days, perhaps. She has borne away the hearts of both of us but she is a good ship and she will bring them back again."

His stout faith in his ship was matched only by Humphrey's unwavering confidence. Others might have said that this maiden voyage of his first command was a heart-breaking one, for many of his men were untrained seamen, grumbling at their narrow quarters and heavy labor, while the art of handling the new vessel was, in itself, not easy to acquire. The weather was boisterous and the winds fitful, but the *West Wind* did not betray the two good friends who had brought her into being. The storms lent her wings so that, at last, anxiety and discontent gave way entirely to pride in the speed that she was making. There was a certain grizzled old sailor, however, who openly discredited all claims of the ship's prowess, and who even refused to believe the evidence of the day's reckoning.

"Twenty-three days is the best she will do," he vowed over and over again. "I will stake a year's pay on it that she can't make an hour less."

Yet, on the nineteenth day of their passage, a warm, gusty afternoon of early May, when the far horizon swam in haze, it was he who came himself to the captain and broke through all etiquette to report, round-eyed with amazement—

"There's land been sighted, sir, and I don't understand it at all. It—it looks like Gibraltar!"

So she came through the gates of the Mediterranean, a gentle breeze behind her, "sails all filled and asleep" as the seamen said, a swift slender hull under a cloud of snowy canvas. She pushed into the straits where had plied back and forth the daring Phœnician craft, the Roman galleys and the high-pooped ships of Venice and of

Spain, but she was no lesser vessel than any one of them, for she
was the first of the Yankee clipper ships!

I have never seen those North African cities, Tangier and Tunis
and the rest, and I have no doubt that today they are very little like
what Humphrey Reynolds saw. But his stories have come down to
me so clear and vivid, that I almost feel that I have known these
very places with their white houses, their tropical green, the confusion and chatter of foreign tongues in the narrow streets, the hushed
silence of the wide, walled gardens. For long months the American
warships would lie off these ports, keeping a watchful eye upon the
doings of the dusky potentates and archpirates who ruled them.
The officers and men would go ashore to stare at the strange sights
and to bargain for souvenirs among the street vendors, seemingly
oblivious of the scowling, hostile faces about them.

It was in Tripoli on a day when Captain Reynolds was walking
from one dark cupboard of a shop to another, looking for some fitting gift to take home to Miranda, that he was suddenly startled by
the sight of a paleface among all those dusky ones. It was not white,
but yellow, and belonged to an old Chinaman as dried up and withered as a mummy who had somehow wandered, a rare thing in those
days, to this African city and kept a little shop there among the
Moors, Arabs and Berbers of Tripoli. His wares were different from
the others and very new indeed to Humphrey's eyes, for just such
carvings and silks did not often find their way to America. The old
man invited the officer to come inside, where more articles stood
upon the narrow shelves and where Humphrey had almost decided
upon the purchase of a beautifully carved ivory box for Miranda
when he spied, in a niche opposite the tiny window, such a thing as
he had never seen before.

A little pine tree was growing in a pot, a real, living one, and
a miniature of just such a tree, bent and twisted by the sea winds,
that grew upon the hill above the Susquehanna at home. The art
of stunting and pruning these tiny trees, developed in Japan perhaps,
but known to some Chinese, was quite unheard of in the Western
world so that Humphrey could scarcely believe his eyes when they

told him it was green and growing and evidently kin to the giant ones in America.

"Miranda must have that," was his instant decision; "she will find that I can manage to bring home the gold snuffbox and something more besides."

His determined effort to buy the tree, however, had a strange effect. At first the old shopkeeper merely met all his offers with a determined shake of the head, but, as Humphrey insisted, he became more and more excited and at last, wringing his hands, burst into a torrent of jabbering explanation. Captain Reynolds had cruised along these shores long enough to have learned a little of the mixed dialect of French, Spanish and Moorish words by which foreigners and natives contrived to understand one another, so that he was able to gather from the Chinaman's flood of talk that the pine tree was the most precious of his possessions, that he had carried it himself all the way from Pekin, that it was a hundred years old and that he felt certain that the spirits of his ancestors loved to cluster about its twisted little branches. What had caused his banishment from his own land Humphrey could not make out, but he did gain some inkling of how the withered old man felt as he looked back upon some frail, small hut on the shore of one of China's muddy yellow rivers, upon some bit of land that he and his ancestors had tilled patiently for unnumbered generations, upon a tiny garden where the tree had grown.

No, it was quite plain that he would not sell it!

So the ivory box was bought for Miranda after all. As Humphrey prepared to go, a picturesque person came into the shop, a fat, black man, very richly dressed with the silk scarfs, satin cloak and gold embroidered garments of a high court official. The young American glanced at him curiously as he squeezed by in the semidarkness of the narrow place, and was conscious of the penetrating stare of two hard black eyes that he could almost feel boring into his back as he went out. Before he had gone far, he thought that he heard a queer, smothered cry of terror in the shop. But the street was so full of noises that, though he paused to listen, he could not be certain and so went on again. In the busy days on board ship that followed, the

Chinaman and his treasure presently passed completely from his mind.

Reports of the *West Wind's* quick passage had been going about all this time through the Mediterranean Fleet.

"But that was only a trial," Humphrey kept saying, "when we were learning how to handle her. On the voyage home we'll show you even more plainly what she can do."

That voyage was now soon to be, for the vessel had been selected to carry back the Commodore's dispatches and reports to Washington. On the day before she was to sail, a message came from the Pasha of Tripoli that he was sending his personal representative to make the ship a visit of ceremonious farewell. Captain Reynolds sighed deeply when he heard this news, for such overtures from a government elaborately friendly but secretly treacherous were uneasy occasions. When the stout, dusky minister of state came over the side, gorgeous in his jewels and satins, Humphrey, after a moment of doubt, recognized him as the man whom he had met in the old Chinaman's shop. The other gave no sign of recognition, however, but gravely went through the elaborate messages from his august master, inspected the ship with solemn interest and expressed not only surprise but some doubts when told of the time she had made between America and Gibraltar.

"Why, it cannot be done!" he cried. Not even pirate craft, it seemed, could fly on such swift wings. "There are favorable winds and chances for good luck on the eastern passage, but when your prow is turned toward home again, when you are obliged to go southward to get the trade winds that blow for all ships alike, then you will find that this is an ordinary craft, just like the rest."

"We will equal our record or better it," Humphrey replied obstinately, "although, as I own, the westward voyage is a longer and more difficult one. But the *West Wind,* sir, is a ship not like other ships."

After they had sat some time in the Captain's cabin, partaking of refreshment and exchanging polite assurances of good will, the black visitor, with great ceremony, produced an impressive gift from his master, a richly embroidered scarf which he presented with a long speech that Humphrey only half understood. He accepted it unwillingly and made such reply as he could, after which there came an awkward pause in the talk. Finally the Tripolitan minister, with smooth boldness, remarked that his illustrious master would be willing to accept in return some small gift, merely as a remembrance of the visit of Captain Reynolds and his beautiful ship. For a moment Humphrey was utterly at a loss, since the government that had filled his magazines with powder and shot in case of trouble had quite neglected to provide for any such occasion as this. Yet the beady eyes of the African, fixed so steadily upon him, seemed to hint that some present must be forthcoming or serious difficulties would follow. There seemed but one thing to do.

"How Miranda will laugh at me, after all," Humphrey sighed as he slowly brought out the gold snuffbox and placed it in the dark hand that was extended so quickly to receive it.

The exchange of gifts should have brought the visit to an end, but for some reason it did not. The African still sat, staring across the table at Humphrey, his eyes narrowed to black slits.

"The gift is of great beauty," he said at last, "but I might explain that the Pasha, my master, has especial love for his gardens and is most particularly delighted when he is given any—any small curiosity to add to the treasures he has already gathered there." Seeing Humphrey look blank, he explained more clearly. "You and I met, some days since, in the shop of that mad old Chinaman who owns, but will not sell, that little pine tree a hundred years old. The Pasha had taken a fancy to own it, so, since the old man would not part with it willingly, he sent some servants to—to fetch it. But they failed. I understand the tree is on board this ship after all."

"On board the *West Wind?*" echoed Humphrey amazed. "I give you my word that it is not here."

"The tree is on this ship," insisted the other steadily. "The Chinaman heard somehow of our coming and departed, treasure and all; he was seen fleeing through the town; he was seen making his way to this vessel. And the Pasha of Tripoli desires the little pine tree!"

There was a pause, but Humphrey said nothing. The dusky visitor shrugged his shoulders and slipped one sleek hand within his satin robe. "The American Captain wishes further persuasion," he said with a sly grin. "I have something here for himself alone, which will perhaps make him more generous."

He drew out a handful of gold coins and laid them upon the table, looked at Humphrey narrowly and, seeing no signs of yielding, sighed deeply and drew out another and another. He piled them up in little shining heaps and stood gazing with an expectant smile across at the American. But, since Humphrey did not put out a hand to take them he broke forth petulantly—

"In the name of the Prophet, is not that enough? You grasping Yankees would have everything! These are not African coins, man, but good English sovereigns, French louis d'or, Spanish doubloons, such as you can spend like water anywhere you go. And all in exchange for one small thing upon which my master has set his heart. Come, you drive a hard bargain."

"I drive no bargain for what does not belong to me, to be paid for in stolen coin," Humphrey answered hotly. "Do you think that I do not know that your pirate vessels have brought in this gold; that, for each of those heaps of coin, there has probably been a good ship sent to the bottom, English, French or Spanish? Have you not learned once what America thinks of piracy?"

The fat man shrugged his shoulders again.

"America is a forgetful land, and far away," he commented dryly. "News carries thither slowly and judgment comes even slower back again. It is twenty years since your country fought with mine; we believe America is ceasing to watch us. The Atlantic is a broad and windy sea!"

"You do not know," the young officer replied slowly, "that there is a wise man in my country, my comrade and dear friend, who has learned how to make the Atlantic a thousand miles less broad. He built this ship with which we have shortened the voyage by four days, and will, when we set sail again, lessen it by more than that. Your pirate craft are swift, but Yankee wits are swifter and presently your vessels will bring back a tale—for every seacoast will ring with it—that Jonathan Adams' ship the *West Wind* has crossed the ocean in eighteen days."

"Eighteen days," scoffed the other. "That is past any man's be-lief. Ships move by sails, not wings!"

"Eighteen days," repeated Humphrey sternly; "I promise you that you will hear of our voyage made in just that time. And when other vessels are built to match or to better her, our country will come a great stride nearer to you, a thousand miles nearer to traitors, mur-derers and thieves."

He brought his hand down upon the table with such force that the heaps of gold went rolling and tumbling to the floor, and the dignified Arab was forced to go groveling on his hands and knees to pick them up again. When he arose, Humphrey was standing by the door which he held open.

"I will send an officer," he said, "to go with you to search the ship. Since you believe that no man speaks the truth, you shall see with your own eyes that the Chinaman and his treasure are not here."

There was no doubt that the man who had the duty of escorting the foreigner over the ship took extreme delight in conducting him through the narrowest, dirtiest recesses of the hold, so that the court official's fat person was breathless and his silken garments much the worse for grease and tar when he finally expressed himself as satis-fied and came once more on deck. His farewells were less stately than his greetings had been, and he turned back for a last word be-fore he went over the side.

"If the *West Wind* sails away, after all, carrying my master's heart's desire, may every curse and every evil spirit known to good Mohammedans follow you upon your way. May every hardship that sailors can suffer fall upon you, may your voyage be such a one as never captain knew before!"

He departed in a great show of dignity and magnificence and was rowed ashore, while Humphrey, with a sigh of relief, turned himself to the preparations for getting under way. He had vowed a vow within himself that Jonathan Adams should not be disappointed and that, on the homeward voyage, they would shorten the passage by the five days for which he had hoped.

It was at daylight the next morning, when the *West Wind* had cleared the harbor of Tripoli and, leaving behind the palm-clad shore with its minarets and towers and its evil, hostile city, was standing out to sea, that Captain Reynolds sat down in his cabin to examine the log book which he had sent for, to make certain that wind and weather and the exact hour of weighing anchor had been correctly noted. He smiled as he glanced at the entry of the day before with its record of the visit of state.

"And he had the impudence, even, to curse me," he reflected, chuckling, "as though any one could hide on my ship without my knowing—"

He stopped abruptly, the page half-turned in his hand. For a strange sound was developing in the locker opposite his bunk, a scratching as though a rat were shut in behind the door, then the clicking of the latch as, out from the narrow space where no one would think a grown man could hide, came tumbling the China-man, half-smothered, but clutching unharmed his heart's treasure in its porcelain pot.

The Mohammedan's curse had been thorough and, so it began to seem as the voyage went on, of some effect, but he had forgotten one thing. Whatever went wrong, whatever accident, small or great, befell the ship on her race across the Atlantic, the wind never failed. The very sprites, afreets and genii known to Arab fancy seemed to sit in the hollow of the sail and lend strength with their blowing to the lusty trade winds. Lines parted, tackle jammed, and sails carried away, but still the wind held. The oldest but ablest seaman, he who had not believed in Gibraltar when he saw it, fell from a yard and was picked up with a broken knee. A falling block, dropping from a height to the deck below, crushed in its passage the shoulder of another sailor. But still the wind held and still the ship cut the South-Atlantic rollers like an arrow. Seven days, eight days, nine days—they were halfway across, and excitement had begun to run breathlessly high.

At the end of the ninth day, while the *West Wind* was wallowing in a cross sea, it was discovered that the water casks had broken loose from their lashings, that two of them were crushed, others

injured, and that the greater portion of their precious water had
leaked away.

"Then we have need to make port all the more quickly," Captain
Reynolds said grimly, and stood by in person while to each man
including himself the meager allowance for each day was measured
out.

The one who fared worst upon the voyage was the old Chinaman.
He suffered hideously from seasickness for the first few days, although he made shift to stagger on deck, to haul at ropes and to give
such service as his feeble strength allowed. When the water failed,
he seemed somehow to be suffering far more than any of the rest.
On the second day after the mishap to the casks, he came to the captain's cabin, utterly refusing to be driven away. With trembling
yellow hands he drew the pine tree from beneath his rags and set it
on the table.

"After I die," he requested calmly, "will you not in justice see that
my share of water still goes to keeping my ancestors' tree alive?"

It seemed that his whole allowance of drinking water had been
poured into the pot, since he preferred to perish himself rather than
permit his great treasure to droop and wither.

Humphrey argued and commanded, but to no purpose. The
Chinaman merely shook his head obstinately and vowed by all his
gods that he would not drink while his tree was thirsty. At last,
however, a compromise was made. The little pine was to remain on
the Captain's table and every day, in Humphrey's presence, the
Chinaman was to drink half his allowance of water and pour the
other half upon the dry roots.

"If you can keep alive on that, your tree should also," Humphrey
said; "there is no other way to do."

Still muttering protests that his tree would die, the old man
crawled away. Humphrey stood looking silently at the little pine
tree, so fresh and vigorous in spite of its hundred years. He took the
water that had been set upon his table and drank half of it at one
gulp, for he had just come below and the hot quarterdeck was a
thirsty place. Then he paused a moment, the half-empty cup in his
hand.

"I am a soft-hearted fool," he muttered, and poured what was left on the dry earth of the porcelain pot.

The days passed while the men grew weaker and more sluggish at their work, but still the breeze held and the speed of the *West Wind* did not falter. They passed no ship from which they could obtain water, their only hope lay in the making of port. They turned northward, lost the trade winds, seemed for a terrible moment to be hanging becalmed, but a stiff breeze caught them and bore them still toward home. The old Chinaman seemed to shrivel away like a dead leaf, but he came stumbling every day to share his mouthful of water with his precious tree. Captain Reynolds himself looked more worn and haggard than any of his men. Only the Chinaman, glancing sideways with his slanting, beady eyes at the lusty green of the little pine seemed to suspect why. They were like the flitting ghosts of a ship's crew that morning when the hot, glittering expanse of sea was broken by a wavering line on the horizon and the lookout's husky call of "Land-ho" announced the low green shore of Maryland. Eighteen days from Gibraltar and all records broken at last!

She came into the Susquehanna River for repairs, did the worn but triumphant *West Wind*, and Jonathan Adams came rowing out to board her, his sober face for once all wreathed in smiles.

"By five days you shortened the voyage," he said, "and I had not really hoped for more than four. I always said she was not a tub, but a real ship at last. There will be others like her, and her children's children will dare to spread such sail that they will cross the Atlantic in half your time."

As Humphrey came up the ladder to where Miranda was waiting on the wharf, his first words were—

"I left the snuffbox behind," while she, laughing shakily, answered—

"I knew you would."

The whole crew, down to the cabin boy, were hailed as heroes when they left the ship, but there was one who managed somehow to go ashore as mysteriously as he had come aboard. The old Chinaman with his treasured pine tree disappeared, no one knew whither, hiding himself, perhaps, lest some emissary from Africa should even yet seek him out and rob him. For more than a month Humphrey searched and inquired for him all up and down the shore of the bay, but no one had seen him and no one knew where he had gone.

Jonathan Adams' ship the *West Wind* sailed on many voyages and was the model for other vessels of her class, bigger and swifter even than herself—the great race of American clippers that once ruled the seas. They gave our country the highest place in the world's shipping, and they brought her, even as Humphrey had said, a thousand miles nearer to her neighbors across the Atlantic. But that is not all of the story of this famous voyage. The real end came seven years later, when Humphrey had risen to be Commodore Reynolds and when, between two cruises, he was spending a holiday at home. One summer afternoon, a small, bent figure toiled up the driveway of the big house above the Susquehanna. Humphrey, with Miranda, was sitting in the shade of the high-columned veranda and for a moment did not recognize the strange face, so covered with dust that the yellow skin and slanting eyes were scarcely visible. But the old Chinaman walked straight to Miranda and laid his offering on her lap.

"For you," he said. "He wanted to bring it to you from the very first!"

It was not the real pine tree, but one made of jade and enamel with tiny jewels set around the top of the pot. Humphrey and his wife exclaimed and admired and examined it on every side.

"But I do not understand," Humphrey kept saying. "How did you come to make it, and to bring it to us after seven years?"

"After seven years!"

The old Chinaman smiled patiently.

"You Americans are ever in such haste. How long, think you, it takes a true craftsman to carve a tree of jade?"

EMMELINE

By ELSIE SINGMASTER

I: THE SOUND OF BUGLES

FOR an hour at least Emmeline lay quietly curled up on the rear seat of the Willing surrey. This vehicle was very old and low and broad; it had been built in the days when people made long journeys in carriages and liked to have them comfortable. At present the surrey was not in motion, but in repose in the Willing wagon shed. Tranquillity was not characteristic of Emmeline. She was by nature a jumping jack. Although she was fifteen years old and very desirous of appearing much older, she had put few of the ways of childhood behind her.

This June day was hot, and Emmeline had been active since early morning. She had risen at six o'clock, eaten her breakfast, fed the chickens, washed the dishes, and picked the last of the red raspberries; then, while she sat by Sister Bertha's bed, she had raveled enough lint to fill a pint measure. After taking Sister Bertha her tray, she had gone downstairs to eat her own dinner hungrily. While she waited on Sister Bertha, or when she heard the neighbors talk about Sister Bertha, Emmeline's face was a blank mask. Of her sister —or rather, her sister-in-law—Emmeline was deeply ashamed.

Sister Bertha was, alas! a rebel. She had come from the South before the war had broken out to teach school in a village near Gettysburg; there young Henry Willing had seen her and had loved her, and nearly a year ago had married her. It was an act not hard to understand after you had seen Bertha. But it was war time, and between the two, in the opinion of Emmeline, there should have been undying hatred instead of love. Henry had already enlisted, and had gone away in his beautiful blue uniform to join his regiment. He cherished the comfortable conviction that his mother's home was still his, and thither he had brought his bride. To Emmeline the act was subversive of all order; it was contrary to the traditions of the world. Henry was, moreover, hers; he did not belong to this pale, dark-eyed creature to whom she had to carry trays.

To Emmelines' mother, Henry's marriage had brought great care. Soon after Bertha had come to the old home she had been taken ill with a slow fever, and had lain for weeks helpless in her bed. After a while she had got better, and had been able to walk to the window and to look out across the green fields toward the south, where two small hills lifted rounded heads above the undulating fields.

"One is called Big Round Top and one Little Round Top," Emmeline had explained in a rare moment of confidence. "There are queer rocks on Big Round Top. One is shaped like George Washington's head, hat and all, and there are two tremendous elephants, and there is Devil's Den. I climbed through Devil's Den once when we went for a picnic. When we go to grandfather's you can see it. At grandfather's there is a new calf, and there is Willoughby Run, where I go fishing. I—"

At that point, Emmeline, reminding herself that she was holding commerce with an enemy of her country, had stopped.

Emmeline's mother bore cheerfully the addition to her family. Bertha was Henry's—that was reason enough; she was helpless, and she was, besides, a very lovable person. Mrs. Willing had begun bravely to make quilts for Henry's setting up in housekeeping, and even poor Bertha had tried to lift a needle in her slim, white fingers. Bertha could pick lint, but she did not succeed in sewing. Now for two weeks she had lain once more quiet and pale in her bed. Her improvement had been inspired by Henry's letters; at the coming of one she had sat up; at the coming of the second she had walked to the window. Suddenly, alas! letters had ceased to arrive, and poor Bertha rose no more. The neighbors—Mrs. Schmidt across the street, Mrs. Bannon next door—were certain that Bertha could rise if she would. Mrs. Schmidt undertook to condole with Mrs. Willing upon the difficulties of her situation. In that Mrs. Schmidt was unwise. Mrs. Schmidt's husband was a sutler in the army; and she had a great fear of his enemies.

"Ach, I pity you!" she cried in her German way. "She is strange to you and a rebel to it yet!"

Mrs. Willing's eyes flashed. She was a stout, able person with a great deal of common sense.

"She is my daughter-in-law, Mrs. Schmidt," she answered sharply.

Mrs. Schmidt said no more to Mrs. Willing, but to Mrs. Bannon and to Emmeline she continued to express her pity for Mrs. Willing. Emmeline made no consenting answer, but her heart was meanly pleased.

Now, lying in the old carriage, Emmeline dreamed. She had a favorite vision, in which she saw herself an army nurse, bringing comfort to hundreds of wounded Union soldiers. At the end of a long career she became engaged to a young Union general. Of course she realized that there was little chance of such dreams coming true. The war could hardly last until she was old enough to be engaged, or wise enough to be a nurse. Indeed, as a practical nurse, she had already failed. Long and irksome were the hours she spent by Sister Bertha's bed—that fact was plain even to the poor invalid herself.

It is impossible to tell to what length Emmeline's dreaming might not have gone this hot, sleepy afternoon. But Emmeline heard, or thought she heard, a sound, and to her, dreaming was far less interesting than doing. She sprang up, tossed back the long braids of her hair, and climbed down out of the carriage. Here she shook herself thoroughly awake, and thus prepared for active life, ran out into the hot sunshine.

Standing still in the garden, Emmeline cocked her head. She had been certain that she heard shouting. Gettysburg, which was near the border, had often prepared itself for the arrival of the enemy, but now almost all the inhabitants except Emmeline had relinquished that fear. Emmeline still expected a battle. She went out by the side of the house and looked up and down the street, which lay bare and hot and quiet. She could hear her mother's voice as she talked in a low tone to Bertha; across the street the Schmidt baby whimpered. Emmeline, who loved babies, often took charge of the Schmidt baby.

Emmeline listened for a long minute, but heard nothing more. She shook one braid to the front of her shoulder, braided it tighter, and shook it back; then she examined the other, which proved to be still securely fastened.

Emmeline had long, thick hair and sparkling eyes. Her dress of blue and white striped calico was made with a skirt as full as a ruffle; her active legs were clothed in pantalets to match her dress; her arms and neck were bare, according to the fashion of '63. Having smoothed down her dress, Emmeline sauntered across the street, and went to the kitchen door of the Schmidt house. She realized uneasily that Bertha was crying and that her mother was trying to comfort her. "I'll take the baby down the street, Mrs. Schmidt," Emmeline offered. "I have to go to the store."

"Thanks to you," answered Mrs. Schmidt, whose dinner dishes were still on the table. "With these six, indeed, I don't know what to do, Emmy."

Emmeline took the baby with the condescending air of perfect capability to perfect incapability. She would never, she said to herself, suffer her house or her children to get into the condition in which Mrs. Schmidt's house and children were. When she had washed the baby's face and smoothed his hair, he stopped crying at once, and with a beaming smile settled himself into his little cart. Then, with "Get ups!" and with prancings, Emmeline took him through the gate and down the quiet street. At the corner she stopped to look up the hill toward the seminary building and out toward the college. Now that the boys had formed a company and had gone to war, the town and Emmeline were denied even the excitement of their presence.

Emmeline traveled more and more slowly. The air was hot and heavy. She had seen nothing that day of her bosom friend, Eliza Batterson; perhaps if she waited, Eliza might appear. Her other boon companion, Jessie Mullin, had long since been sent away from Gettysburg to visit friends in the country to the north, so much did her parents fear an invasion. Emmeline prayed that no such ignominious experience would be hers.

Presently old black Tom, who sold peanuts on the streets of

Gettysburg, stopped to inquire about Henry; and then Mrs. Peter, the ever-curious, asked about Bertha. To black Tom, Emmeline gave gracious response; to Mrs. Peter, Emmeline returned an answer so short and sharp as to be impertinent. Mrs. Bannon and Mrs. Schmidt were neighbors, and had a right to discuss Bertha; Mrs. Peter had none.

When Mrs. Peter had gone, Emmeline remembered uneasily that Bertha had been crying, and that there was constantly a strained, anxious look in her mother's eyes. But Henry would come back; there would probably be a letter from him in the evening mail. Not for an instant would Emmeline admit to her mind the possibility of anything else.

Presently Emmeline yawned. She could hear now unmistakably the sound of voices, but it was only the laughter of the pupils of the Young Ladies' Academy. Next year Emmeline would enter the academy; there was at present, however, between her and those young ladies a gulf as wide as the Atlantic. She nodded to them, and then took the handle of the baby cart and proceeded on her way to the village store.

But Emmeline did not reach the village store, neither then nor for a long time thereafter. She heard a new sound, and looked up. Men and women were running past her; the courthouse bell gave a single startling peal; she heard the clatter of galloping hoofs.

"What's the matter?" cried Emmeline to a passer-by. "What in the world is the matter?"

"The rebels are coming! You can see them from the corner!"

"I don't believe it!" cried Emmeline, with a throbbing heart.

Emmeline thought of the Schmidt baby. He was heavy, and could not be dragged, cart and all, through crowds; he would be an annoying encumbrance to a girl who liked to be in the forefront of everything. It was certainly not true that the rebels were coming; but something was coming, and Emmeline wished to be at hand to see. If she hurried up this alley and down that back street, she could reach her own yard and then the front street. She could leave the Schmidt baby, fast asleep by now, on the side porch of her house, or could thrust him, cart and all, into the kitchen.

Planning as she ran, Emmeline hurried down the alley and the back street, and at last reached her own garden. Leaving the baby in the kitchen, she came through the side yard to the gate. There she halted, with quaking knees.

It was not the rebels that had come, but some strange, tanned, half-clad creatures; they marched in good order, and looked steadily from their hollow eyes at astonished Gettysburg, which crowded, half fearful, at corners, and hung, curious, from windows. Many of the soldiers were barefooted; others wore shoes from which the soles had fallen; some had tied the soles to their shoes with strips of soiled and blackened rags. Emmeline stared with open mouth.

Half in fun and half in earnest, the strangers began to jeer at their amazed and paralyzed audience:

"We're not a parade, Yankees!"

"We've come to eat you up!"

One of them caught sight of Emmeline, with her ruffled dress, staring eyes, and open mouth. "Hello, sissy!" he called. "Look out that when you close your mouth you don't bite your tongue off!"

Emmeline did not realize the full measure of the insult, for as he spoke, she had caught sight of a flag that hitherto she had beheld only in pictures—a flag that she scorned and despised. She mounted at once to a higher bar on her mother's gate.

"'Oh, say, can you see by the dawn's early light,'" sang Emmeline; "'What so—'" Suddenly she felt some one seize her. She struggled, and cried, "Let me go! Let me go, I tell you!"

Then she realized that the hand on her shoulder was a familiar one.

"Emmeline," commanded her mother, "be still!"

"He insulted me! He's a rebel!"

"Emmeline," commanded Mrs. Willing again, "be still!" Then from her mother's lips came an incredible order: "Go and fill the water pail, and bring it here with a dipper."

"Mother!" gasped Emmeline. "Are we going to give them water?"

"Go, Emmeline!"

"They are the enemies of my country!"

"Go!" said Emmeline's mother.

When Mrs. Willing spoke in that tone, even Henry, who was a man, moved swiftly. Emmeline looked up into her mother's face, but her mother was not looking down at her. Her eyes were turned toward the street, toward that apparently unending line of weariness and raggedness and burning eyes. She saw only the men's hunger, their thirst, their need.

When Emmeline returned, her mother told her to put the pail under the tree at the edge of the pavement. As she stood there waiting, with her mother's hand on her shoulder, her eyes flamed and her heart fumed; but no soldier stopped to drink.

"Go offer them water, Emmeline."

"Mother!" protested Emmeline again.

Emmeline went and filled the dipper and stood holding it out; but no soldier left the line, although the lips of many were almost black. Some looked in Emmeline's direction, some passed grimly without a glance.

"They will not drink it, Mother!" cried Emmeline.

"You don't end our lives that way, sissy!" jeered a passing voice.

Emmeline dropped the dipper and fled back to her mother's side. Her mother had covered her face with her hands and stood shivering. Emmeline, watching her, was for the moment awed. For the first time something of the heavy horror of war penetrated her young heart.

"We are not really going to have a battle, Mother!"

Mrs. Willing shook her head. "They have come for money and supplies."

"Will they get them?"

"Not here, dear. We haven't them."

"Where will they get them?"

"At York, perhaps," her mother replied.

"May I go down to the square now, mother?"

With the passing of the soldiers, the feeling of horror had passed also. Emmeline felt secure here in her own quiet village.

"Why, no, of course not!" In Mrs. Willing's eyes was still that anxious, strained expression. "Where is your baby? Take him to his mother and come right back."

With a heavy heart Emmeline went to obey. She said to herself
that she never could see anything; she remembered all the pleasures
that had been denied her in her short life—the political meetings
and funerals she had been forbidden to attend, the parties for which
she was thought too youthful—and she felt sadly aggrieved. There
was nothing to do in this dreary town. Even picnics had ceased,
and home itself, devoted to the care of Sister Bertha, was home
no more.

The afternoon passed, and Emmeline was sadly aware of the stir
down the street. Presently, after burning a few cars on a siding,
the troops went on their way. Saturday brought no excitement to
brighten Emmeline's dull lot. On Sunday, when a body of Union
soldiers rode through the town, Emmeline was, alas! in church.
Once or twice troopers galloped through the streets, and people whispered that soldiers were riding about the fields with maps. Gettysburg was once more alert and frightened.

On Tuesday, Emmeline, sitting by the bedside of Bertha with her
patchwork in her hands, heard a thrilling sound—a bugle blast. Forgetting Bertha, and dropping her patchwork and workbasket, she
flew to the window and stood entranced. Fate was again directing
affairs in Emmeline's way. A great body of soldiers was coming
down the street. They were all mounted soldiers—dusty, tanned, and
weather-beaten, but well clad and well fed. Above them floated a
banner that Emmeline knew—stripes of crimson and of white, with
white stars on a blue ground, like the stars of heaven—Emmeline's
flag—Henry's flag.

For almost a minute Emmeline held herself in check; then a
black-slippered foot went over the window sill, and a blue-and-white-
pantaletted leg followed. Sitting on the sill, she raised her voice in
song.

"'Glory, glory, hallelujah!'" sang Emmeline, beginning with the
chorus. "'Glory, glory, hallelujah!'"

This time no one grasped Emmeline; there was no one near
enough to grasp her. The soldiers cheered her, and waved to her,
and saluted her. With her red cheeks, and her long braids, and her
ruffled dress, she was a quaint and lovely figure. After a long time

her mother called to her, and she clambered back into the room. The troops had passed, but huzzas still filled the air. Out through the town the soldiers went, and camped on Seminary Ridge.

To her keen disappointment Emmeline was not permitted to visit the camp, but from her room that night she could see the campfires glitter. It seemed to her that her heart would burst with excitement. What would she see tomorrow? A battle?

But such good fortune could not last. When Emmeline opened her eyes the next morning, she found her mother by her bed. Mrs. Willing looked as if she had not slept.

"Get up, Emmeline," said she.

To Emmeline's dismay, she saw a little satchel in her mother's hand. Emmeline's mind was quick.

"You are not—you are not going to send me *away,* mother!"

"You are to go out to grandfather's for a little visit."

"Oh, *Mother!*" wailed Emmeline.

"Yes, Emmeline. Get up and dress. Mrs. Schmidt is going to her brother's, and you are to ride with her." Mrs. Willing was firm.

"Is there to be a battle?"

"We do not know." Mrs. Willing turned away.

"Oh, Mother!" wailed Emmeline a second time.

But no "Oh, Mother!" availed. Slowly, with a bitter heart poor Emmeline gloomily but obediently put on her striped dress.

II

EMMELINE AND THE SCHMIDTS TAKE A JOURNEY

Mrs. Schmidt's brother lived on a lane that branched from the Emmitsburg Road, a mile beyond the road that led to the farm of Grandfather Willing. If Emmeline had not had to travel in Mrs. Schmidt's company, she would have been spared some of the ignominy of her departure. Not only was she going away from all excitement, all possibility of distinguishing herself, but she was journeying in Mrs. Schmidt's outrageous cart. She was accustomed to associate with the Schmidts, not as an equal, but as a superior. While she was dressing, she could see lame Mr. Bannon and Mrs. Schmidt putting the Schmidts' ancient horse between the shafts of the springless wagon. Into that wagon they had thrust already a feather bed, numerous chairs, a few of the six young Schmidts, and a quacking duck in a coop. Wildly Mrs. Schmidt flew about, frantically she commanded.

"Get the boondles, Mary! Sally, get the tarpet sack!" Thus did Mrs. Schmidt's tongue trip in its haste. "Hurry yourself, Peter!"

Emmeline wept as she braided her hair. "Oh, Mother!" she wailed again.

But her mother was not at hand to hear. With swift steps Mrs. Willing went about the house, now waiting on Bertha, now packing a luncheon for Emmeline.

In the lower hall Emmeline burst once more into tears. Across the street the pyramid on the Schmidt wagon was growing higher and higher. Mrs. Schmidt evidently expected the utter destruction of Gettysburg. Several soldiers had come to her aid. They helped to stow her goods on the wagon; they teased her with all sorts of predictions, to which she could reply only with a feeble "Ach!"

"If the rebs get you, they'll eat you, lady!"

"Ach!" cried Mrs. Schmidt.

"Yes, sir! Now Johnnie, give me your hand and climb up here. Whoa, there!"

The soldier leaped frantically to the drooping and motionless head of Whitey.

"Ach!" cried Mrs. Schmidt. "I am a poor, poor woman!"

"Some of the rebs are looking for sweethearts, missis."

To that Mrs. Schmidt was not even able to say "Ach." She tried to explain that she was married, and that she considered such a remark insulting; but before she could make her meaning plain, the soldiers had hoisted her aboard and had put the reins into her hands. Then a bright light flashed in the eyes of Mrs. Schmidt.

"Ach, Emmy, you are going with!"

To her mother Emmeline cast one more piteous glance.

"Oh, Mother," begged Emmeline earnestly, "do not make me go!"

Mrs. Willing turned from the soldier with whom she had been

talking and looked down upon Emmeline. It was evident that her glance rested upon the most precious creature in the world. Her tears had fallen into the satchel that she had packed for Emmeline. It was with an anxious heart that she was sending her away. The soldier had answered her questions kindly, and had advised her to get the sick person away also; but it was impossible to get Bertha away. Then, said the soldier, she should be moved to the cellar as soon as the shooting began. Mrs. Willing, in a voice too low for Emmeline to hear, said something to the soldier, to which he answered, "God help her, lady!" Emmeline's mother was not able to suppress a groan.

"Oh, Mother," said Emmeline again, "do let me stay here!"

For answer, Emmeline's mother led her across the street and helped her to climb into the wagon.

"I am in great trouble, Emmeline," said she earnestly, "and this is the way you can help me. Go and take care of Mrs. Schmidt and the baby. Grandfather will bring you back as soon as it is safe. Pray for us all, Emmeline."

Awed by her mother's expression, Emmeline tried to gulp down her tears. As the wagon gave a preparatory jerk before getting under way, she lifted the Schmidt baby from Mrs. Schmidt's knee to her own, and was rewarded by a little brightening of her mother's face.

Mrs. Schmidt chirruped to her horse, and they were finally off. Few persons except the soldiers noticed them, for each house along the street had its own anxiety. Other horses were being harnessed, other families stood about in fright. Once a group of soldiers rode toward Emmeline and her friends. Their warlike appearance terrified Mrs. Schmidt.

"Now we will be killed at last!" she cried.

"We will be nothing of the kind," answered Emmeline. "Please try to drive straight, Mrs. Schmidt."

As the soldiers passed, they advised Mrs. Schmidt in a friendly way to tie her children in, at which Mrs. Schmidt at once began to crane her neck backward to count her offspring. The soldiers seemed as gay as if they were on a journey of pleasure. Riding from house to house, they rapped on the doors with their swords; their petted horses sometimes put their noses in at the windows. The soldiers ordered people to stay in their cellars. If only Emmeline could stay in a cellar—an adventure in itself unspeakably delightful.

"Ach, Emmy," cried Mrs. Schmidt, "will we ever get to your gran'pop and my brother?"

"I hope not," answered Emmeline, at which cryptic remark Mrs. Schmidt sank into silent gloom.

Just before they reached the Evergreen Cemetery, with its tall pine trees, Mrs. Schmidt turned old Whitey aside, and drove into a country road that ran between pleasant fields. Some were cultivated, and others were carpeted with daisies; on all the fences wild roses bloomed. It was now eight o'clock, and the July sun shone hotter and hotter. Mrs. Schmidt panted, and grew red in the face, and tried to fan herself with her old sunbonnet.

At any other time Emmeline would have enjoyed the excursion. Before her, but still several miles away, the two Round Tops rose against the hazy horizon. The Emmitsburg Road which they traveled lay between two long ridges of varying height, named Cemetery Ridge and Seminary Ridge. Presently they would turn to the west, and cross Seminary Ridge. Beyond it, about half a mile, lay Emmeline's grandfather's farm, where she was always welcomed with great joy, and where there was good fishing, and a little calf, and a litter of new kittens, and the companionship of a venturesome girl, Ellen Watson by name, from the next farm.

But Emmeline did not want to go to Round Top, and she did not care to see the kittens and the calf; she wanted to stay in Gettysburg. Eliza Batterson would stay, and would have a hundred boastful things to tell her. It was bitterly disappointing to be sent away. If Bertha had not been there to be taken care of she might have stayed. She agreed with Mrs. Bannon that Bertha could rise if she would.

The little Schmidts made no sound on the journey. Terrified by their mother's fright, they huddled in their various uncomfortable positions in the body of the wagon. Once Emmeline, hearing a gentle whimper, looked round, and saw that a chair had fallen upon Betsy, and that she looked out from between the rungs as if from a cage. Scrambling back to rescue her, Emmeline observed a long line of wagons like their own coming from Gettysburg.

Giving the sleeping Carl to his mother, Emmeline now took the reins herself, and in the pleasure of managing old Whitey forgot that she was an aggrieved and disappointed person. She clucked sharply to him and switched him with the reins. When all methods of hurrying his lagging gait proved futile, she proposed that she and the older children should walk and thus relieve him for a while of their weight. Only Mrs. Schmidt remained in the cart, with Carl in her arms.

"We are emigrants," said Emmeline, forgetting her disappointment for a moment. "We are emigrants marching o'er the plains, We—" Then Emmeline stopped, and all the little Schmidts stopped, and old Whitey lifted his head.

"What is that noise over there, say?" asked Mrs. Schmidt.

"Listen!" commanded Emmeline.

"What is that noise?" demanded Mrs. Schmidt in a louder tone.

"Listen!" commanded Emmeline more sharply.

Old Whitey lifted his head a little higher. Away to the north, beyond the seminary building, toward the dim line of blue hills on the horizon, there was a sharp crack! crack! crack!

"Somebody is gunning," said Mrs. Schmidt with conviction. "I wonder what they are gunning?"

"They are shooting men!" cried Emmeline excitedly. "Our soldiers are shooting down the rebels! I—"

A deeper, heavier sound crashed upon the air and interrupted Emmeline's sentence. The first great boom of cannon lengthened into a rumble—long, low, echoing, ominous. Whitey shivered and gave a strange snort; with a cry, Mrs. Schmidt seized the reins in both hands. But Whitey would not advance.

"Get in by me, Emmy!" cried Mrs Schmidt. "Children, get in! Emmy, get in!"

Emmeline helped the numerous little Schmidts into the wagon, and then, climbing in after them, took the reins from Mrs. Schmidt. She assured herself that there was nothing to be afraid of. The shooting, loud as it sounded, was far away.

"We will hurry, Mrs. Schmidt. We will soon be there. Get up, Whitey! Get up, I say!"

With strange, jerky motions, Whitey started; but Whitey's efforts were exerted more in an upward than a forward direction. He pranced, if the word can be used to describe a motion so stiff; he tossed his head, he snorted again. His progress became even slower than before. The heat seemed to grow each moment more intense, but the travelers did not dare to stop in the shade.

To the north there now appeared puffs of white smoke and flashes of light. The roar became continuous; before one rolling echo was more than well begun, another hollow boom had started other echoes. Mrs. Schmidt grew pale and the baby began to cry. Emmeline became impatient with the Schmidts, impatient with the dancing horse, impatient with the rough road. They had now come to a region which had recently been drenched with heavy rains. The wheels sank deep into the mud. Several times the travelers had to dismount while Whitey pulled the wagon out of a hole. Still the booming grew heavier and the white clouds thicker; but they were far away—far beyond the seminary building.

Emmeline and her party gazed so intently in the direction of the sound that they neglected to look ahead. At a sudden turn in the road, Emmeline gave a cry and pulled at Whitey's reins, although Whitey had already stopped, paralyzed. The road before them was no longer open; it was filled from fence to fence with marching troops. To Emmeline they numbered millions. Whitey snorted again; Mrs. Schmidt and her children almost ceased to breathe. To Emmeline it seemed that she and Mrs. Schmidt and the children and the duck faced the combined armies of the world.

The approaching troops made no amused comments, as the soldiers in Gettysburg had done. They were marching swiftly; some one shouted to the travelers to get out of the way, and Mrs. Schmidt tugged first at the right rein and then at the left, thinking that if Whitey would not go in one direction, he might in the other. But vainly she tugged, and vainly she adjured her steed with weeping and with strange German exclamations. At last Emmeline had to lead him to the roadside.

A corps of soldiers marched past, tramping with even, hasty step; caissons rattled by; great cannon rumbled along; huge wagons drawn by mules lumbered through the mud. On and on marched the thousands of men, with eyes fixed before them, as those deeper, wilder eyes of the enemy had been.

Emmeline shrank behind the broad body of Mrs. Schmidt. These were Emmeline's own soldiers, but they seemed grim and terrible. Surely they could whip all the other soldiers in the world! When they were almost past, Emmeline thought of Henry, and looked after them in dismay. Then she realized that, even if Henry had been among them, he could not have spoken to her. She suddenly began to long for the shelter of her grandfather's house.

When the corps had passed, Whitey was with difficulty restored to the road—a horrible road, in which the ruts were now much deeper and the stones more protruding. At a snail's pace he crept. Stragglers following the soldiers passed constantly—here a man leading a string of lame horses, there a man in charge of a line of ambulances or a damaged cannon. These stragglers were not so set upon advancing that they did not have a word for Mrs. Schmidt and her children and her duck.

Finally, when the sun was almost directly overhead, Whitey stopped at the entrance of the byroad on which the elder Willings lived. Mrs. Schmidt must drive on another half mile, and then leave the Emmitsburg Road in the opposite direction. She wept at parting from Emmeline, and the children wept, and Emmeline kissed the sleeping baby. The road was now clear; the house of Emmeline's grandparents was in sight, half a mile away.

Carrying the little satchel, Emmeline started to run. She was hungry, for she had forgotten to eat the luncheon her mother had put up for her, and she was anxious to tell her grandparents, who always listened to her with close attention, of the condition of affairs in Gettysburg. The booming sound had ceased; the battle was certainly over. Perhaps this afternoon her grandfather would drive into Gettysburg with her. That would be glorious indeed!

She opened the gate at the foot of the lane, and then, swinging it shut behind her with a slam, waved her hand toward the porch. Her grandmother knew that slam; it always brought her hurrying out to greet her darling. Emmeline hastened toward the house.

"Hello!" she called eagerly. "Where are you?"

When no one answered she called a little louder:

"Grandmother!"

Still there was no response. Emmeline stopped in the grassy lane, startled.

"Grandmother!" she called again. Still there was no answer. Emmeline approached the door with hesitation. Here the dog and the cat usually met her; but now no friendly animals were to be seen. Moreover, the shutters were closed and there were no familiar crocks sunning themselves on the fence.

"Grandmother!" called Emmeline again, as she put her hand on the latch. "Grandmother, where are you?"

The latch did not yield. The door was locked! Emmeline shook it, pressed her body against it, and called again. It seemed to her suddenly that everything was mysteriously still, that the woods beyond the house were strangely dark, and that the sky was very far above her.

"Where are you?" she called. When no answer came, she ran down the slope to the barn.

The horse and the old-fashioned buggy were gone. Returning to the house, Emmeline sat down on the bench outside the door and thought.

"They are over at the Watsons'," she said aloud, with great relief. "They drove over for something. They will soon be back again."

At that moment Emmeline remembered her luncheon. When she had eaten the last crumb, she felt better. She rose and started across the fields to the Watsons'. But there only deaf Grandmother Watson was at home. She had seen nothing of Emmeline's grandparents, and had evidently heard no unusual sound. Emmeline started back across the fields. It seemed to her much later than it was. Surely they would have to come back before night! The cows would have to be milked, the chickens fed. Probably they would be back by now!

Then on a rising bit of land, Emmeline stood still. The Emmits-

burg Road was again filled with troops. Apparently all the armies of
the world were once more gathered there; but these were new
troops, marching in the same direction as the others had gone. She
could distinguish the mounted officers, the boxlike caissons, the
great cannon, all moving swiftly.

Across the fields drifted urgent cries. With trembling, Emmeline
ran on.

But the farmhouse was still deserted. Again Emmeline tried the
door. There was a window above the shed into which she could
climb, but she was afraid to enter alone. Again she heard the booming of cannon. It grew heavier, more ominous.

Perhaps her grandparents had gone to the Hollingers', to the
south. She could reach the Hollingers' by a circuitous route through
the fields.

Again she set forth. She was now too tired to walk rapidly, and
her journey consumed almost an hour. But the Hollinger house was
also deserted. Too frightened to cry, Emmeline started back once
more to her grandfather's farm. She was footsore and exhausted by
the heat; she gasped with weariness. The heavy roaring sound of
the cannon filled the air and deafened her. She remembered those
fixed, staring eyes of the soldiers who had marched by.

Suddenly fear of the enemy oppressed her. She remembered
stories she had heard about the cruelty in prisons, about the burning
of houses, the torturing of women and children. She thought with
aching heart of her mother and her home. How patiently she would
sit by Bertha's bed, how obedient she would be!

Again she started to run. If the cows were at home in the stable
or the pasture, then her grandparents must surely return. But Emmeline remembered that she had seen nothing of the cows either
in the stable or in the pasture! Down near the woodland the
chickens had been busily scratching, but there had been no other
sound or sign of animal life on the place. Perhaps the cows were
down near Willoughby Run. In this great heat they would naturally have sought the shade and the cooling waters of the stream.
They must surely be there!

The path lay partly in the thick woodland above the farmhouse.

Coming out of it, with the farmhouse and garden immediately before her, Emmeline gave a cry of joy. The house was no longer deserted; there was a man on the porch; there was some one opening the doors of the barn.

"Grandfather!" called Emmeline. "Where have you been?"

Then Emmeline stood still. So did the man on the porch. So did other men down by the lane, by the gate, in the road. They were strangers, and there were scores of them, multitudes of them. They were soldiers in worn uniforms.

Of soldiers, as soldiers, Emmeline was not afraid; but the color of these soldiers' uniforms was gray!

III

EMMELINE MEETS THE ENEMIES OF HER COUNTRY

It seemed to Emmeline, as she stood at the outlet of the wood road, that an hour passed before any one spoke or moved. She herself was too much confused to speak. How had these men come up so quietly? Porch and dooryard and fields were thronged. The ridge that cut off Gettysburg from her view, the road down which she had run after she had left Mrs. Schmidt—they, too, were filled with men, and horses, caissons, cannon, and huge wagons. And the soldiers were clad, not in friendly blue, but in hateful gray.

Only in Emmeline's immediate neighborhood was silence. Beyond, men were shouting, horses were neighing, and wheels were creaking. Yonder, a body of troops advanced to the music of a fife; here a bugler was playing. Men were laying fires with little piles of sticks; men were going to Willoughby Run for water; men were leading horses down to drink. The throng seemed to be thickening every moment.

One man, tall and lean and brown, lifted his hand from the latch of Grandfather Willing's door and came to the edge of the porch. He had only one arm; under his coat were the bandages that still bound a recent wound. He had quiet gray eyes, which smiled at Emmeline.

He and his friends could have been to Emmeline no more startling an apparition that she was to them. The dust of travel had soiled somewhat her blue-and-white dress and her white stockings, but she seemed to the soldiers immaculate and fairylike. Some exclaimed sharply; into the eyes of others came a sudden smarting and burning. In their minds they saw, far away, other little girls with dark braids and ruffled dresses. But Emmeline did not see their tears; these were her enemies.

The tall man with the kindly face crossed the dooryard and approached Emmeline.

"Well, sissy," he drawled, "and who may you be?"

A variety of emotions almost suffocated Emmeline. Uppermost was hatred of that particular form of address.

"I am Emmeline Willing," said she, with dignity.

Men left their piles of sticks and crowded to the fence; others, who were going on errands, made a detour in order to come a little nearer to the group.

"And who," drawled the tall man, "who may Emmyline Willing be?"

Emmeline saw the thickening crowd and remembered the dull roar that had ceased only a little while ago. She grew pale, but she answered bravely:

"I am the granddaughter of the owner of this place."

"So-o-o! And where may the owner of this place be?"

"He has gone away." Emmeline's courage was failing. She felt the cooler air of evening and saw the shadows lengthening as the sun sank behind the woodland. "My grandfather would not wish you to be here. You ought to go away."

"Now, sissy," drawled the tall man, in a distressed voice, "don't cry!"

"I am not crying," protested Emmeline, in spite of good evidence to the contrary. "I want you to go away!"

"Well, sissy,"—the tall man seemed actually to be considering Emmeline's command—"we couldn't very well do that."

"You will have to!" cried Emmeline. "Our soldiers are here by the million! They will make you go!"

The tall man made no answer to Emmeline's assertion. "You come here to the porch, sissy. Nobody's going to hurt a leetle gal."

"I am going home," announced Emmeline. "I am going home to my mother. The battle is over." In spite of her brave words, Emmeline moved a little nearer to the porch. "Isn't the battle over?" she said.

"Not exactly," said the tall soldier.

As he mounted the porch, the others moved away. Busy men could not stand forever looking at a little girl in a striped dress. The tall soldier laid his hand on the latch.

"Sissy, do you know any way to get this door open short of breaking it in?"

"You can't get in!" cried Emmeline. "It isn't your house! You—"

"Look here," interrupted a rough voice, "get this door open! Stop your crying and keep out of the way!"

The newcomer set his shoulder against the door. The old latch held for an instant, and then, as the soldier gave another sharper thrust, the hasp tore from the wood. Emmeline grew still paler. From the porch she could see farther over the country; on hills and fields men were still marching, horses were still being led or driven, cannon and caissons were rumbling along.

The soldier who had burst open the door was now in Grandmother Willing's kitchen. He threw wide the shutters, and rattled the lids of the stove, and opened the doors of the cupboard.

Once more little Emmeline protested furiously:

"You can't touch those things!"

The soldier lifted a handful of kindling from the box by the stove, and heaping it into the fire box, lighted it.

"Can you bake?" he demanded rudely.

Emmeline did not answer. Could she bake? She had been taught here in this very kitchen, she had mixed her dough in that very bowl on the table, and had set her rising in that old-fashioned bread trough in the pantry. Would she bake? Never while breath was in her body!

Men were now crowding in at the door; an army wagon had stopped at the gate, and rough soldiers were bringing in great coffeepots and cans. One of them brought Grandmother Willing's hens and roosters, headless, plucked, ready for the pot. Emmeline backed farther and farther into the corner, speechless and tearful.

"If I were you, I'd go upstairs, sissy," the tall man said. "Set at the window and look out. There'll be a lot going on that you can see."

Blindly Emmeline turned to obey. Crying bitterly, she climbed to her own little room, and there sat down on a chair by the window.

Where were those thousands of blue-coated soldiers? Why did they permit this great army to camp on these hills, to occupy her grandfather's house, and his fields, and the other fields round about? The enemy were now chopping down trees and tearing down fences; they had already ruined her grandfather's wheat and killed her grandmother's chickens. Why did not the blue-coated soldiers come and drive them away?

At the sound of galloping hoofs, Emmeline looked out of the window. She saw that a man on horseback had stopped at the gate and was talking with the tall soldier. His voice rose exultantly:

"We drove 'em like sheep through the town! We have thousands of prisoners! Tomorrow we'll settle them!"

"There's a leetle gal here," the tall soldier answered in his slow way. "She came to see her gran'paw, but he had gone. She lives in Gettysburg.

"She'll be safer here than in Gettysburg. Tell her to stay indoors. There'll be hotter work tomorrow."

"So they say!" drawled the tall soldier.

Presently the aroma of chickens boiling in the pot began to spread through the house. It seemed to spread to an amazing distance, for from all directions men came crowding into Grandmother Willing's kitchen. The surly cook swore at them and at the stove, whereupon a drawling voice reminded him that there was "a leetle gal" within hearing. The cook's tones sank to a rumble.

But Emmeline paid no heed to the loud voices of the hungry men; she did not even smell the delicious odor of the cooking chickens. She heard only those dreadful, exultant words from the lips of the mounted soldier:

" 'We drove 'em like sheep through the town! We have thousands of prisoners! Tomorrow we'll settle them!' "

So that was why no Northern troops had come to her rescue and the rescue of her grandfather's house!

Emmeline ceased to cry; alarm and terror dried her tears. She thought of her mother and of Bertha. She recalled the deep earnestness of her mother's eyes.

Had there been fighting in quiet, peaceful Gettysburg? Emmeline had picked lint for padding, had wound muslin strips for bandaging, and had seen Gettysburg soldiers who had returned with a leg or an arm missing; but of actual battle Emmeline had no clear idea. She had thought of bugle blasts, of banners flying, of loud, inspiring commands; beyond that her imagination had failed. Now for the first time it became clear to her that actual danger of death threatened those whom she loved.

Where was her mother? Had Bertha been taken into the cellar as the soldier advised? Vague recollections of the details of Bertha's illness came to her, scraps of conversation between her mother and Bertha that she had heard as she passed the door of the sick room. A vague, half-formed suspicion flashed into her mind. At this moment Emmeline began suddenly to grow up. But the first speech of her adult life was childish.

"I must go home!" she cried, as she sprang from her chair.

She ran down the steps and out to the porch. Darkness had come; soldiers lay about on the grass, and the murmur of their voices spread in all directions. The moon was rising; in its first oblique rays all things looked queer and distorted.

There were many sounds: the click of pickaxes against stones, the crash of trees that were being felled, the hoarse shouts of officers giving orders. Emmeline rushed to the side of the tall soldier, who was sitting on the steps.

"I must go home!" she declared again. "I *must* go home!"

"Now, you're just frightened," the tall soldier said. "There ain't no reason for you to be skeered. No harm'll come to you. We ain't wild beasts, sissy."

"I must see my mother!"

"You'll see her soon, sissy."

"My sister-in-law is sick and my brother is away." Emmeline forgot for an instant that this was an enemy of her country. "We haven't heard from him for weeks. He's in the reserves; he—" Remembering the character of her audience, Emmeline paused. Then she added, "I *must* go home!"

The tall soldier changed the subject.

"I got a leetle gal like you; Bessie is her name—Bessie Christy. I haven't seen her for two years."

"Why not?" asked Emmeline, curious in spite of herself.

"On account of war. Now, Emmyline, 'tisn't every leetle gal can watch the sappers at work before a battle. They're the folks that build the breastworks. Look at them up there! You might see great things if you watched, 'stead of crying. You might see General Lee ride by."

"I hate him!"

"Now, sissy!"

"I hate you all!"

Private Christy looked at Emmeline for a moment with a smile on his lips.

"I'll explain the army to you, Emmyline," said he. "It's a wonderful thing, an army. If you begin at the top, there's the commander-in-chief, and next below him—" Private Christy went on and on in his pleasant, drawling voice. The duty of a private was this, he explained, the duty of a sutler was that. Presently Emmeline asked him what he did. Her voice was no longer sharp; it was soft and drowsy and gentle. After a long time, when Private Christy said, "I have my work too, Emmyline," without saying what that work was, Emmeline did not hear. Feeling a light touch on his arm, Private Christy looked down and beheld Emmeline's head resting upon it.

"Well, I vum!" said he softly.

For a long time Private Christy sat still; presently slow tears rolled down his tanned cheeks. He called to one of the men:

"Say, you, Mallon!"

The soldier approached.

"Well, I'll be switched!" he said.

"You take her upstairs, Mallon."

It may have been that Mallon, too, had a "leetle gal" at home; at any rate, he seemed to know how to lift a sleeping person of Emmeline's size.

"The pore leetle gal!" said one-armed Christy, as he led the way.

"I'm sick of this war!" answered Private Mallon soberly.

Through the hot kitchen, where the cook had ceased his work, up the narrow stairs, they carried Emmeline to her room, and there, without waking her, laid her gently upon her bed.

"Couldn't she be got out of this?" asked Private Mallon.

Private Christy shook his head. "Not nohow," said he.

Private Mallon returned to his sleep on the grass, Private Christy to his seat on the porch steps. Far away to the west there was a sudden, indefinable suggestion of a great body of men marching. Private Christy heard it and shook his head; Private Mallon nudged his neighbor.

"More coming," he said, and turned on his side.

All about on the daisies of the field lay the great carpet of sleeping men. Everyone got some sleep that night. Those who dug pits in which to lie half hidden on the morrow, or who threw up semicircular walls of earth or timber to shelter the great cannon, gave pick and shovel after a while to others roused from sleep, and threw themselves down near where they had been working.

Later in the night Private Christy lay down on the porch floor and slept heavily and comfortably.

Meanwhile to the rear of the great army pressed on another great army, which, being assigned its place, lay down also. The time between sunset and sunrise in early July is short enough even for those who are not exhausted by long marches.

On the ridge, officers riding back and forth in the bright moonlight marked positions and looked speculatively across at that other parallel ridge, which takes its name from the Evergreen Cemetery near one end. Far to the north, where the heavy cannonading had been, ambulances traveled the fields, guided by a whimper or a groan of pain. The greatest general of all, whom Private Christy had promised Emmeline she might see, rode about on his white horse studying the victory won, planning fresh victory for tomorrow. Thus, rapidly enough, the night waned.

When the sun rose on July 2, the thousands of soldiers in gray stirred and woke. In the Willing kitchen the surly cook began to bake his miserable biscuit; on the porch Private Christy rose and yawned, and persuaded the cook to give him place on the stove for his coffee-pot. All about in the fields and woods the thousands rose and prepared their simple breakfast. Emmeline slept and slept. Five o'clock yesterday had found her awake and dressed; but today five o'clock passed, then six, then seven, then eight.

Along the lines of battle all was peace; it was almost as quiet as on any other summer morning. Cannon were moved without noise under cover of the woodland, as if each great army wished to hide from the other.

Emmeline, waking, lay still and stretched out her arms. Where was she? Why was she still dressed? How had she got to bed? She sat up and looked out of the window. Then it was not a dream, after all! Round her were still the thousands of Confederate soldiers; below her on the porch she heard Private Christy's voice.

"'Bout time to begin, ain't it?" he queried.

A voice answered that it had been time long ago. Emmeline saw the sun high in the sky; she smoothed her dress and braided her hair, and ran down the steps. There was no battle; it was the middle of the morning, and still there was no battle. Surely she could go home!

In the kitchen the surly cook gave her one of his soggy biscuits. It was nine o'clock, according to the stubby hands of Grandmother Willing's clock, which ticked on the mantelshelf.

Emmeline's tall friend was on the porch.

"Good morning, Emmyline!" said he cheerfully.

Emmeline's war code, which she remembered clearly this morning, did not permit her to say "Good morning" to the enemy.

"There is no battle," she announced. "I want to go home."

"Oh, but you can't do that!"

"I must!" Emmeline looked about her. Still all was peaceful. "Just up that road! I walked almost all the way yesterday."

Private Christy shook his head.

"No, Emmyline. 'Twouldn't do."

"You are an enemy of my country!" cried Emmeline. "You have no right to keep me! I am going home!

When Emmeline reached the gate, Private Christy called to her. "Come back, sissy!" he said.

Emmeline obeyed, weeping.

"Aren't you afraid that there biscuit'll p'isen you?" he asked. "Seems to me if I was a woman and could bake, I couldn't swallow that biscuit. You wouldn't bake me a real biscuit, I suppose?"

"No," answered Emmeline with decision, "I wouldn't."

"Well," drawled the quiet voice, "you don't have to."

Emmeline, standing with one foot on the step of the porch, considered. She had taken one bite of the biscuit. Although she was wretchedly hungry, she could eat no more.

"Will you let me go if I bake you some?" Emmeline asked.

"I'll see," answered Private Christy.

The cook had left his stove, and Emmeline went to work with the familiar utensils—the yellow bowl, the wooden spoon. When the biscuits were in the oven, she looked up to find the doorway crowded with soldiers; some of them were bandaged like Private Christy; all of them were thin and deeply tanned.

"Are you going to give we-all some of them real biscuit?" asked an eager voice.

Emmeline's face flushed crimson; the position of almsgiver to her enemy was not altogether unhappy.

"I'll see," she answered.

When one pan was taken from the oven, Emmeline had another ready and then another and another. Emmeline grew warmer and warmer and her cheeks rosier and rosier.

"Now," said Emmeline, "you can watch that last pan. I am going home."

"But I haven't had any!" cried Private Christy. "Nobody here knows anything about baking and turning 'em! Oh, please, sissy, bake me a pan!" Private Christy brought in fresh fuel for the fire. A half-hour passed, another half-hour.

"Now," said Emmeline, "I am going."

Private Christy made no answer. The hungry crowd in the yard had faded away; the very atmosphere seemed charged with suspense. Emmeline looked out of the door. Was the army still here?

The army was still here; but the army was formed, massed. It was like a great animal, alive, awake, crouching for a spring.

Then Emmeline screamed, and whirled round on the step. Near at hand—almost, it seemed to her, in the very house itself—the cannon roared.

IV

THE SECOND DAY OF BATTLE

AT the sound of the cannon shot, Private Christy, still sitting calmly on the step, looked up.

"No call to be—"

Another roar cut short Private Christy's speech. Emmeline fled into the kitchen, and Christy rose and followed her.

"No call to be skeered, sissy," he said, speaking loudly into her ear. "The shooting ain't *here.*"

Emmeline covered her ears with her hands. Another fearful detonation shook the old farmhouse to its foundations. The windows trembled in their frames, the floor seemed to rock. Emmeline sank into a chair by the kitchen table, hid her face in her arms, and screamed hysterically.

"Sissy," cried Private Christy, "stop it! Don't ye dare to cry like that!" Private Christy's face was drawn. "It's an awful thing to have to hear a woman cry like that! Listen to me! The shooting ain't this way; it's that way. Them guns is half a mile off and pointing the other way. Noise can't hurt ye, don't ye know that? You've got to get used to it, for it's going to last some time. Do you hear me?" Private Christy bent his head until it was near Emmeline's. "You're the only one among all these thousands that's safe, sissy. Now stop it!"

Emmeline checked her sobs. "I can't stand it!" she cried.

"But you've got to stand it. Now dry your tears. You can sit here, or you can go down cellar, or up attic under the eaves, or you can come out on the porch and sit with me. It ain't everyone can watch troops going into battle. I wish *I* could hold a gun again!" he added, with longing in his voice.

Thus admonished and encouraged, Emmeline rose slowly and dried her tears. Private Christy put his hand on her shoulder, and they returned to the porch.

There was little confusion to be seen. The long morning's work had put all in readiness for the engagement. Round the farmhouse regiments waited in line. Other troops had moved from their posts farther to the south, across the ridge, and down into the valley between the ridge and the two Round Tops. In that direction, and hidden from the farmhouse, were the cannon from which issued the thunderous roar. Now the sharp crack of musketry and confused shouts and yells accompanied the deep boom of the cannon. Clouds of white smoke, growing thicker every moment, rose from the valley.

Near the farmhouse, regiments waited motionless beneath their banners. Officers were already in the saddle; men stood at attention. It was as if the great commotion were no concern of theirs. But suddenly a quiver passed through them. Swords flashed in the air, commands were shouted, bugles blew; to the music of fife and drum the troops mounted the slope toward the ridge.

"There they go!" cried Private Christy. "That's my company, and they're goin' without me!"

The troops topped the ridge and vanished under the white, thick blanket of smoke. As if fresh fuel had been added to a great flame, the smoke thickened, the cannonading grew heavier, the crack! crack! of musketry more incessant.

Emmeline stood with her arms clasped round the pillar of the porch. With each great detonation she grasped the pillar more tightly, as if she feared that the waves of sound might wash her away. Sometimes she closed her eyes and drew in deep breaths of air. Between her gasps of fright she stared, awed and fascinated. She saw the last troops cross the hill and the smoke clouds thicken. Presently she saw black missiles hurtle through the air and bright flashes from beyond the hill divide the low-lying cloud. Suddenly she screamed. A dark object, passing over the ridge with a shrill, whistling sound, had plunged into Grandfather Willing's potato patch. Private Christy took Emmeline by the arm and led her round the corner of the house.

"Nothing but a stray shot, sissy; but if I was you, I believe I'd stay here. Nothing can hurt you through these stone walls."

He led her to a seat on the grass close to the west wall of the house. There she sat dazed. Sometimes she blinked; sometimes she smoothed absently the wrinkled, soiled fabric of her blue and white dress; otherwise she did not move. She could not think or reason; she could only listen.

Private Christy went back to his seat on the porch. Presently he returned and smiled at Emmeline, and then went into the house. There in the hot kitchen, working slowly with his single hand, he made a fresh fire, and set upon the stove Grandmother Willing's washboiler and filled it with water. Then he went upstairs and looked round. Emmeline vaguely wondered again what his business was as a member of the army. Thus far he had done nothing.

Still Emmeline sat on the grassy bank by the house. Before her was the sloping field leading to Willoughby Run. Down that field she had often raced. Under the trees by the side of the stream horses were tethered, and nearby were hundreds of wagons. The sun was getting low.

Emmeline rose stiffly. It seemed to her that the roar of cannon had grown a little less thunderous. She would go round the house and out to Private Christy. Private Christy, although an enemy, was comforting. As night drew near, her longing for home grew keener, but she had begun to realize that she could not return now.

Emmeline did not find Private Christy on the porch; he was apparently running away from her. She saw his long legs carrying him up the slope; presently he broke into a run. He was not going into the battle; he was meeting those who were returning. That is, he was meeting a few—those who, although wounded, could still drag themselves along. They had left behind them thousands of their comrades, who could not join even such a halting, pitiful procession as theirs. Hundreds who had started with the procession had fallen by the way.

In the forefront of the straggling line was Private Mallon, who had carried Emmeline up to bed. His arm hung limp and his hair was clotted with blood; he fell heavily against Private Christy as they met.

Again Emmeline's arm encircled the porch pillar. In some dim, long-past existence Emmeline had dreamed of binding wounds, of smoothing fevered brows, of lifting her voice in song for the comfort of the suffering! Now Emmeline wished that the earth would open and swallow her.

While she stood with her arm clasping the pillar, Private Christy and Private Mallon entered the gate. Private Christy's work was now before him; for this task had he remained with the army, while in Georgia his little Bessie grew beyond his recollection.

"Leetle Emmyline," he shouted, "you get some warm water in a basin and some old cloths, will you, Emmyline?"

Emmeline grew paler and paler; the first shocking sight of wounds seemed to paralyze her. Private Mallon, tottering in upon the arm of his comrade, fixed apologetic, tortured eyes upon her.

"It ain't no place for a leetle gal!" he muttered.

Then Emmeline took another great step toward womanhood.

"I will try," she said, weeping.

When she had filled her basin with water, and had gathered the worn fragments of homespun linen that Grandmother Willing had laid away for emergencies, she took them with trembling hands into the parlor. Other wounded, blackened forms had crept in and had laid themselves down on the parlor carpet —the treasured carpet that was the pride of Grandmother Willing's life.

"Put wood in the stove, Emmyline," commanded Private Christy cheerfully, "and bring more of these rags. You'll make a fine nurse, Emmyline!"

As she turned to obey, Emmeline glanced out of the door. Creeping and crawling, the procession continued to arrive. They came through the gate one by one; they crossed the yard and the porch.

A man fell heavily on the steps, and involuntarily Emmeline took her enemy by the arm and helped him up.

"I'm looking for Christy," he said in a dazed voice.

Private Christy and his work were evidently well known.

"I am to keep the boiler filled," repeated Emmeline, as she went back to the kitchen. "I am to bring warm water and towels and cloths. I am not to cry or scream. I am not to cry or scream!"

Into the house still came the wounded, into Grandmother Willing's parlor, and into Grandmother Willing's sitting room, and up the stairs into the bedchambers, and out to the kitchen.

"Keep the kitchen clear!" commanded Private Christy. "Keep the room above clear! Nobody in there!"

Someone answered roughly that the room above was to be filled.

Private Christy's voice did not always drawl; he raised it now so that it could be heard above the slackening crash of musketry:

"There's a leetle gal in this house, gentlemen. That is her room above the kitchen."

"A little girl!" repeated a weary voice somewhere. "I'd like to see a little girl!"

Moving about deftly, Private Christy helped this man to lie down and that one to find a more comfortable position. He seemed like a mother getting her brood together for the night; they looked up to him like children who found in him their only hope.

"Emmyline," he said gently, when she brought him the things for which he had asked, "do you suppose you could help me?"

"I could try," said Emmeline.

Private Christy passed her the end of one of the long strips of cloth.

"There, Emmyline, you take that and wind it round and round."

With a gasp, Emmeline obeyed; together she and Private Christy bound the wounded arm of Private Mallon.

The sun had vanished behind the woodland and the fleecy clouds above were golden; the cooler air of evening had begun to breathe through the old farmhouse. The sound of firing near by had ceased entirely. The battle was surely over; surely, thought Emmeline, these men would go away and Gettysburg could have peace. Perhaps she could still go home tonight! There were many wagons standing idle down by Willoughby Run; perhaps one could be spared to take her. If she could only go home and see here mother she would ask for nothing more in the world. Perhaps Henry had come back. If Henry was wounded like these men, her mother could not take care of him and Bertha, too. She *must* go home. Then Emmeline gave a great cry. Deliverance had come! She sprang to the window and began to call to some one outside. Private Christy, who was on his knees near the window, turned and looked out quickly.

"They are Union soldiers!" cried Emmeline. "We have won! They will take me home! Here I am! Here I am!" she waved her arms as she called.

Private Christy looked down at the company of blue-coated soldiers. He saw what Emmeline did not see: that their progress was directed and hastened by soldiers in gray who carried muskets.

"They are prisoners, Emmyline."

"Prisoners!" cried Emmeline.

"Yes, sissy."

"Didn't we win?"

"Not exactly, Emmyline."

"What will they do with them?"

"They'll take 'em down to that woods and guard 'em."

Leaning suddenly out of the window, Emmeline began to scream. Among the prisoners was a slender soldier to whom she called.

"There is my brother! Henry, Henry, dear, dear Henry! Here I am, Henry, here I am!"

"Be quiet, sissy," commanded Private Christy.

Emmeline stepped across a soldier on the floor, and then across another. In frantic excitement she sought the door.

Private Christy caught and held her. "Where are you going, Emmyline?" he asked.

"I'm going to my brother."

"You don't know if it was your brother. It was too dark to see."

"It was my brother! I'm going to find him!"

"No, Emmyline."

"What will they do to him?"

"Nothing."

"I haven't seen him for months and months. He is my only brother. He had a bandage round his head. Oh, please, please let me go!"

"No," said Private Christy. "Come, Emmyline, I need you."

Emmeline went back to her work, and her tears dropped on the face of the soldier by whom she knelt.

"It's too bad, sissy," said he, weakly. "I wish I could help you."

Emmeline gulped back her tears. It was Henry; of that she was certain. Where had they taken him? Was he lying wounded, bleeding, alone? But Emmeline had mercifully no time for speculation. She continued to help with the bandaging and to run up and down the stairs.

About the house confusion thickened. Troops returned, powder-blackened, exhausted, famished. Many of the soldiers bound up their own wounds, or let their comrades perform that service for them. From the dark fields rose again the aroma of boiling coffee and frying bacon. The troops in the fields near at hand seemed to have moved closer together, but Emmeline did not understand the significance of the maneuver. Every few minutes she went to the window and strained her eyes into the dusk. Even in the brightening moonlight her gaze could not penetrate into the woodland where the prisoners had vanished.

Presently, when she turned from the window with a sob, Private Christy was looking down upon her. "Emmyline," said he, in his pleasant drawl, "how about them biscuit?"

"I could bake some," answered Emmeline, suddenly realizing that perhaps hunger was one of the causes of her own misery.

"Biscuits, boys!" cried one pale soldier to another. "She's going to bake biscuits!"

Feeble cheers answered.

"You won't go out of the kitchen, will you, sissy?"

"No," Emmeline promised, and went wearily down the stairs.

The joy with which her first batch of biscuits was received roused her once more. There were many who could not eat, and who called only for water. As the time passed, those cries grew louder and more frequent.

Presently, lantern in hand, a doctor entered and made his way from patient to patient. His clothes had dark stains upon them, and in the dim light he looked white and worn; he moved quickly from one patient to the next, as if other work awaited him. Several quiet forms he turned over, and those were presently taken away.

Emmeline baked her biscuits and spread them with apple butter from her grandmother's crocks, and carried them from room to room. There were by this time dark stains also on her striped dress. Private Christy, saying a word here, changing a position there, moved about the house like a great gray ghost.

A little later, when Private Christy found his assistant asleep by the kitchen table, he took her last pans from the oven and sat down opposite her. The night was quiet, and again there came to the ear of the listener the strange, half-defined suggestion of men marching. Private Christy ate quickly; once he interrupted his feast to go upstairs in answer to a groan. His return woke Emmeline, who lifted her head from the table and looked at him sleepily from blinking, dark-rimmed eyes.

"We've got 'em all fixed up pretty comfortable," said Private Christy softly, as if he and Emmeline had succeeded in some common task. "Now, Emmyline, it's time for you to go to bed."

"Is the battle over?" asked Emmeline.

"No, sissy."

Emmeline's mouth quivered. "Do men like to fight?" she asked, blinking drowsily.

"Like to fight?" repeated Private Christy. "Like to fight, Emmyline? Like layin' up there with arms and legs ruined? Like livin' their days without half a body? Of course they don't like it!"

"Will there be more wounds tomorrow?" asked Emmeline stupidly.

"Where's there's fighting, there's wounds."

"Will it last after tomorrow?"

"God help us, no!" said Private Christy.

V

PRIVATE CHRISTY SAYS FAREWELL

On the morning of July 3, Emmeline got up earlier than she had on the morning of July 2. Disturbed by dreams and oppressed by the heat, she had slept restlessly. She had waked once in the night, and had gone to the window to look down upon the woods into which the Union prisoners had vanished. There, except for the stamping of restless horses, all was quiet; but beyond, toward the west, there was incessant movement. Fresh troops were arriving and were settling down for a few hours of heavy sleep. Emmeline could hear Private Christy making his rounds in the farmhouse. Now he was in the kitchen; now he brought fresh water from the pump; now he spoke soothingly to one of his comrades.

When Emmeline woke again, daylight had come, and the great host was already astir. Men laughed; even in this house of pain the soldiers were merry. Downstairs Private Christy had built a fire in the stove; Emmeline could hear the crackling flames. Stiff and sore, she rose, and, after braiding her long hair and contemplating the stained untidiness of her limp ruffles, she went down the steps. She was very tired; her mouth drooped and her eyelids seemed to have weights upon them.

Downstairs the wounded soldiers were trying to sit up; some even tried to stand. One man proclaimed his intention of joining his company as soon as he had eaten. Almost immediately, as if in answer to his boasting, his knees gave way and he sank to the floor.

Private Christy greeted Emmeline cheerfully:

"Here's hot coffee for you. You look a leetle droopy. Drink this and you'll feel like a two-year-old."

Choking back her tears, which seemed to flow without any excuse, Emmeline took the cup of coffee and sat down. She lifted the cup to her lips, and then put it back into the saucer.

"I hear a noise!" she cried. "They're shooting again!"

"That's way off," answered Private Christy. "That's miles off."

"It's near Gettysburg!" Emmeline now wept outright. "I have so many troubles I can't count them all. My mother is in danger and my brother is a prisoner—I am sure it was my brother! Perhaps my home is destroyed!"

"Oh, no, sissy!"

"Can I go down to the woods to find my brother?"

"I ain't in charge of that woods, Emmyline."

"Will they take him away?"

"I don't know."

"You don't know anything!" stormed Emmeline.

Private Christy's gray eyes twinkled. It was much better to hear Emmeline storm than to have to watch her cry.

Again Emmeline made biscuit and spread apple butter and carried her tray about the house; again she brought water and bathed hot faces. There was nothing else for her to do. If she cast a longing glance toward the woodland, Private Christy was beside her with his "Now, Emmyline!" In the middle of the morning Private Christy called her to the door and pointed to the ridge.

"Can you see up there some mounted officers?"

"Yes."

"Do you see the white horse?"

"Yes."

"That's General Lee, Emmyline." Private Christy spoke in a solemn tone. "That's something for you to remember all your life."

"I'd rather see General Meade," said Emmeline defiantly.

"But you don't mind lookin' at my general," answered Private Christy good-naturedly.

Presently there began again another general movement of the troops about Grandfather Willing's house. They marched forward toward the ridge and passed over it, and disappeared into the valley where yesterday the cannon had roared. Now, except for the distant rumble, there was no sound.

"Where have they gone?" asked Emmeline.

"Over there," Private Christy replied noncommittally.

"What are they doing?"

"Just waiting. Now, Emmyline, you get some water for them poor souls upstairs. I have an errand to do."

When Emmeline was out of sight, Private Christy went down
across the fields to the woodland and looked about. On the far side
near the open land were the Union prisoners, well guarded. Many
of them were wounded, and lay about on the ground or sat propped
against the trees. In their direction Private Christy made his way.
War brought about strange meetings. It was improbable but not impossible that the little girl's brother was among the prisoners.

"Goin' to pull out?" he asked a guard.

"No orders yet. I think we move with the army."

"Got a man here by the name of Willing?"

"I don't know their names."

"Can I ask?"

"No."

"Well, you find out for me, will you, Sam? His leetle sister's up
here, and she thought she saw him. I suppose she couldn't come
down and talk to him?"

"No, she couldn't."

Until eleven o'clock the distant roar continued; then followed
complete silence; but the silence did not rest the ear or ease the heart.
The heavy, hot atmosphere was weighted with mystery. Emmeline,
moving about nervously, asked a hundred questions of Private
Christy. The wounded soldiers dragged themselves to windows;
from there they could see nothing except the scattered remnants of
the command, the trampled fields, the ridge with its bristling cannon and its barricades. From the troops who had gone over the hill,
nothing had been heard; it seemed as if they had been swallowed up.
Emmeline made biscuit and coffee, and went to the front door and
then to the attic window, and looked first toward Gettysburg and
then toward Willoughby Run. She grew more and more nervous
and excited.

"If it is not over, I don't understand why they don't begin! If it is
over, I don't see why I cannot go home! I don't see why I have to be
kept here! I don't—" Two clear, distinct shots ended the mysterious
silence. Emmeline lifted her head like a startled rabbit. It seemed
that no matter how much cannonading she had heard, she could
never grow accustomed to the hideous sound.

Those two clear shots were answered by all the thunders of heaven. From the ridge that Emmeline watched sped forth the fiery charge. She saw the puff of white smoke, the blinding flash, heard the great detonation. From the opposite ridge came back an equally furious answer. Then thunder and roar and blast filled the world.

Again, as yesterday, Emmeline screamed, and then at once was silent. There was no use in screaming when Private Christy across the room could not hear her, when, indeed, she could not hear herself! For hours to come Emmeline forgot her home, her mother, Sister Bertha, Henry. The terrible sound dulled her senses and paralyzed her mind.

Standing at the kitchen table, she could look through the hall and out of the front door. There, framed as in a picture, she saw a strange sight. A dark missile descended upon the ridge. That was no chance, stray shot, as yesterday's missile had been; it was well aimed, and it struck its mark—a caisson filled with explosives. At once caisson, horses, men, were lifted into the air. Then, a little distance away, another caisson was struck.

Soon yesterday's sad spectacle was repeated. Once more the procession of wounded crept down the slope. From the ridge to the farmhouse, and to all other farmhouses and places of refuge—and few and scattered they were—proceeded the wounded. No longer was the Willing farmhouse the refuge of those only who were able to walk. Thither hastened the lumbering ambulances; thither stretchers were carried; thither the wounded, supporting each other, crept inch by inch. Emmeline watched them come; Private Christy ran to help them in. In distraction Emmeline began once more to heat water and to make coffee and biscuit. That she could do! It was well that she had had yesterday's experience before today's!

Wounds from fragments of shell are worse than wounds from bullets; the advancing throng, alas! were wounded as terribly as they could be wounded and still live. For some, Private Christy did nothing except to help them lie down and to cover them with one of Grandmother Willing's blankets. A doctor and a nurse, who had been assigned to the Willing house, tried to do the work of twenty doctors and nurses. They put Emmeline to work. They gave her hard and terrible tasks, but she accomplished them bravely, receiving an immediate reward in many blessings from those she tended. She wrote down addresses and messages, and comforted the men as best she could, and wept.

"It will make them take it easier, little girl, if you write them about me."

"Perhaps you would go to see them sometime, when the war is over."

It was amazing to hear how many had daughters or little sisters like Emmeline. As she listened to one after the other, and tried to fix their requests in her mind, her dark eyes grew wider and her face paler. Still the two hundred cannon roared. That sound unnerved even the hardened soldier and the general trained by long experience in battles, who began to ask themselves whether human spirit could endure more. The like of that sound the world had till then never heard.

In midafternoon came peace. As suddenly as it had begun, it seemed to Emmeline, the thunder stopped. Emmeline burst into tears, and then, not knowing that she had cried, went on with her work.

"It is over," Emmeline assured herself. "Now it is certainly over."

But Emmeline knew nothing of the tactics of war. There were still those thousands of infantry who had marched over the hill and who had as yet given no account of themselves. Where were they? They still had work to do. A few minutes they waited, until the last echo had died away, and then, in magnificent array, they marched forward across the fields to the opposite ridge, marched straight in the face of the enemy's cannon, which they supposed had run short of ammunition. Of those brave thousands, few returned whole across the wide fields; many did not return at all. Emmeline, watching them in the morning, had thought them wonderful; but Emmeline could not judge how glorious they were. Now they would march no more. If Emmeline had listened, she could have heard, borne upon the wind, rapturous shouts from that opposite ridge; but she heard only the broken words and gasps of the men about her. Private Christy heard with haggard, white face; the generals heard

—those who survived. The greatest general of all, whom Emmeline had watched upon his white horse, listened with a breaking heart.

Gradually the clouds of smoke lifted, gradually the odor of smoke was carried away. The sun set in a stormy sky, and once more the air cooled. The battle was over; upon the wide field peace descended, but it was the peace of death and woe. From Round Top to Gettysburg and far beyond lay strewn those who a few hours before had moved in strength and pride.

Gettysburg, hearing the result of the battle, breathed a long sigh of great relief. Citizens appeared from the places where they had taken shelter; women and children came out upon the streets again, and stared at house walls torn by shells and at barricades thrown across streets. At Emmeline Willing's house men and women and children gazed in awe. The house had been strangely protected; it stood among its fellows unharmed. There, to Emmeline's Sister Bertha, had been sent a little child. There Bertha herself lay sleeping in the bed to which she had been restored. One by one men and women and children tiptoed into the kitchen to behold with their own eyes the little baby lying in his cradle.

Mrs. Willing moved quietly about her house and attended to her charges. All the cruelty and horror of war weighed upon Mrs. Willing. No word had come from her boy. And where was Emmeline, her darling, her little girl, whom she had unwittingly sent into greater danger? Where were the elder Willings?

Meanwhile Emmeline worked on. She had ceased to be partisan; she asked no question either about victory or defeat. As night advanced, a great uneasiness seemed to spread. Troops were moved, trees were felled, and new breastworks erected. Emmeline's room was occupied now; a young officer lay upon the bed, and less important patients upon the floor. With his single arm, Private Christy continued to accomplish wonders.

"You are my other arm, Emmyline," he said in his drawling voice. "You mustn't forget me, Emmyline."

Emmeline looked up, startled.

"Are you going away?"

"We can't stay here."

"What shall I do then?"

"Without *me?* Are you going to miss *me?*" said Private Christy in astonishment. "Why, you will go home, Emmyline."

"Home!" repeated Emmeline, as if the word were strange.

That night Emmeline slept on a chair by the kitchen table. Private Christy, who did not sleep at all, put a folded coat under her head and stood for a moment smoothing her dark hair; then he went on with his sad work.

Once or twice the moon showed for an instant, only to vanish; the sights upon which it looked were best shrouded in darkness. When morning dawned, troops were still massing behind the protecting breastworks. As soon as it was light, Private Christy made his way down the slope to Willoughby Run, and addressed himself once more to the soldier who guarded the prisoners:

"Any orders?"

"Orders to be ready to move."

"Did you find Willing?"

"He's the man with his head tied up, there by the tree."

"Where's the colonel?"

"Over yonder."

Private Christy saluted the colonel and stood waiting. The colonel had a map spread out on his knee; on it he was tracing with his finger the path to the west which had been laid out for him. It was evident from the colonel's eyes that he, too, had passed a sleepless night. Presently he looked up at Private Christy, and with a nod gave him permission to speak.

"There's a prisoner in the woods, sir, by the name of Willing. This is his grandfather's place, and his leetle sister's up there in the house. She's worked bakin' and nursin' till she's almost dead on her feet. She's a sweet leetle gal, sir. Could you leave her brother here? She's far from home and alone."

The colonel looked absently at Private Christy. Private Christy seldom asked favors; moreover, if it had not been for his self-assigned work, Private Christy might long ago have been at his home in Georgia.

"I'll see, Christy," he said, and returned to his map.

Six o'clock passed, seven o'clock, eight o'clock, and now the great wounded army seemed to breathe deeply and to turn a little and to think about rising. It was beaten, sore, but it could not pause here. It was still in the country of its enemy; it must be up and away lest worse harm befall it. Opposite lay the victor, who, although wounded also, was better furnished with the munitions of war. The beaten army must set forth on the weary march by which it had come.

All the forenoon men were marching. From the woods near by, wagons, rough, springless and uncovered, drawn by thin, jaded horses, approached over the fields to the doors of farmhouses and barns. Into them were lifted the wounded from the houses and from the open fields. They were not lifted carefully; there was not time to be careful. Across the fields toward the west to the nearest road the wagons went and took their places in the great line.

The skies lowered more and more, and presently from the east a chilling wind began to blow. Standing in the doorway, Emmeline felt it on her bare arms and neck, and shivered. When a wagon stopped at Grandfather Willing's door and the bearers entered, Emmeline went weeping to bid farewell to these her enemies. Private Christy had lifted his knapsack to his shoulder and had taken in his hand a staff, as if he were preparing for a long journey.

The officer in charge of the wagon ordered all men who were wounded only in the arms or head or shoulders to walk beside it; others were lifted in upon the board floors of the wagon; others were left where they lay.

Emmeline clung to Private Christy's hand.

"Why don't they take them, too?" she asked.

"They're too sick, Emmyline."

"What will become of them?"

"I don't know, Emmyline. You give 'em water."

"Are you really going away from me?"

"I've got to go, Emmyline!" said Private Christy. "Marchin' orders are marchin' orders. You stay in the house, mind! You write to me sometime, and when the war is over you've got to get acquainted with my Bessie."

"Does this end the war?" asked Emmeline.

"I don't know, sissy, but I'm afraid not. Emmyline, would you"—
Private Christy blushed like a boy—"would you give me a kiss?"

"I will give you a dozen!" cried Emmeline.

Then, beside the lumbering wagon, Private Christy marched away.
A soldier leaned on his arm before he left the porch; before he had
left the gate he had given his staff to another. Bereft, Emmeline
watched him go. Once he turned and nodded his head to her, and
then marched on.

Private Christy looked up at the lowering sky. In a moment he
felt on his cheek the first drop of the advancing torrent. Then the
heavens opened on the great generals and the marching soldiers and
the wounded in their open wagons.

Emmeline stood upon the step until the tall, gray figure with his
wagon and his wounded had vanished in the mist. She was
drenched, but she dared not go inside. She guessed why those suffer-
ers had been left behind! And night was coming and all would be
dark and dreadful. Emmeline could hear the ticking of Grandmother Willing's clock on the kitchen shelf and the sound of deep,
anguished breathing.

Then she heard footsteps, and turned in fright. Not one of those
sick men could even raise his head—who was it who came upon her
so stealthily and so suddenly? Through the kitchen approached a
tall figure in a blue suit, with a bandaged head. Private Christy had
not left his "arm" without protection.

"Henry!" cried Emmeline.

"Little Emmeline!" said Henry.

Into the outstretched arms flew Emmeline.

"I knew it was you! Oh, Henry, Henry, Henry!"

VI

THE TERROR PAST

ALTHOUGH Emmeline Willing's grandparents were well on in
years, they were young in spirit. They liked to make excursions in

their old-fashioned buggy pulled by their faithful Dandy. They had not intentionally deserted their home on the eve of battle. Grandmother Willing would have been as little likely to fly from excitement as Emmeline.

A few days before the battle Grandfather and Grandmother Willing had gone on a visit to their daughter Sally, who lived on an isolated farm to the west. Grandmother Willing had taken Tiger, the cat, with her in a basket, and Rover had trotted beneath the buggy. Before they had started they had driven their two cows, Molly and Betsy, over to the Hollingers', who had promised to care for them. When the enemy had approached, the Hollingers had fled, driving their own cattle and Molly and Betsy before them.

Early on the morning of July 1, the two elder Willings bade their daughter farewell, and with no thought of what awaited them, started to return home. When Emmeline and Mrs. Schmidt were startled by the first crack of musketry, Grandfather and Grandmother Willing were even more amazed and frightened as they approached from the other direction. Suddenly soldiers appeared—it seemed to Mrs. Willing—from the ground itself, and sprang to Dandy's bridle. The soldiers turned the horse and buggy sharply round, and Dandy dashed for the shelter of the stable he had recently left. "A battle after all!" cried Grandfather Willing, his ruddy face paling. "A battle in Gettysburg!"

Grandmother Willing said nothing for a long time. She grasped Tiger's basket tightly with one hand and with the other clutched the side of the carriage. Tears ran down her cheeks and she drew long, gasping breaths.

"A battle in Gettysburg!" she repeated at last. "Mary is there, and Emmeline is there, and that poor young woman of Henry's is there! Like as not poor Henry is dead. What shall we do?"

"There is only one thing we can do, Mother; that is go back to Sally's. The town will be protected."

"I want to go home!" sobbed Grandmother Willing, much as Emmeline had sobbed. "They might get out as far as our house, and they might do damage."

"The fighting is three miles from our house, Mother."

When they reached their daughter's farm, Sally came running to meet them.

"Oh, I have been so worried about you! Get down, Mother. Come in. Oh, this dreadful noise! Look, Father!"

Old Mr. Willing's eyes followed her pointing finger. On the main road, a few rods from the farmhouse, thousands of soldiers were marching rapidly toward Gettysburg. Their line extended back for at least a mile. From the porch and windows of the farmhouse terrified faces watched them.

Grandmother Willing wept again.

"Perhaps our dear Henry is among them!"

"Henry, Mother! Why, these are the rebels!"

"Oh, dear! Oh, dear!" wailed Grandmother Willing. "What shall we do?"

"We will do two things, Mother," answered Grandfather Willing solemnly. "We will wait and we will pray."

A hill shut out from the farmhouse a view of the first day's battlefield. When Grandfather Willing and his son-in-law proposed to make their way to higher ground, such a loud outcry rose from the women and children that they abandoned the plan. Gathering the family about him, Grandfather Willing prayed that the engagement might be short and victorious for the arms of righteousness. When toward evening the noise of battle ceased, grandfather hoped that his prayers had been answered.

On Wednesday morning, Grandmother Willing rose early from her bed. Toward the southwest she could see the Round Tops; before her the plain was clear and beautiful. Her heart rejoiced.

"Look, Father, now we can go home!"

Grandfather Willing came to the window and looked out. He saw the clear, beautiful plain, but he saw also another and a startling sight. From the west approached fresh troops. The main road, where it left the woodland, was crowded. Rapidly the throng drew near; officers shouted, drivers urged their horses, wagons rattled.

"Is there going to be *more?*" asked Grandmother Willing.

All morning the family in the farmhouse watched the road and the distant plain. The troops vanished from sight as they approached

Gettysburg. When by noon there had been no further sound of shooting, Grandmother Willing suggested that they start.

"We can surely go now, Father!"

Just then a boy came from a farm a mile across the fields with news that made Grandmother Willing change her mind. There had been yesterday, he said, a terrible battle; Gettysburg was now in the possession of the Confederates. Troops were gathering from all directions; there was going to be worse fighting before the day was over.

It was not until late afternoon that the firing on the second day began. Then it was that Emmeline, in her grandmother's kitchen, had first screamed and whirled round, and that Private Christy had told her to be still. To the watchers at the farmhouse on the hillside the time passed more slowly than it did to Emmeline. From the upper windows they could see the clouds of smoke, and could tell exactly where the cannon stood; it was clear to the Willings that the battle raged near their house.

On Friday, the third day of the battle, Grandmother Willing made no request to be taken home. She woke to the sound of cannon, dull and distant; she listened with blanched face until noon. At one o'clock, when it began once more in its final and most terrible fury, Grandmother Willing covered her ears, so that she might hear less and pray more. From hundreds of terrified hearts in Gettysburg and round Gettysburg rose petitions for relief from the torture of the sound.

When silence finally came, the family on the hillside did not dare to rejoice, but waited fearfully for another roar.

But no roar came. Twilight faded to dusk, dusk to night, and silence persisted. From the direction of Gettysburg came no sound. If troops moved on the Cashtown Road, the Willing family did not know. They slept heavily and woke later than was their custom.

When they rose, the bright sun of other mornings was not shining. The day was cloudy, the air heavy. In the direction of Gettysburg all was dim and hazy.

"And now," said Grandmother Willing, "we can go home."

Grandfather was as patient as Private Christy. He shook his head with a gentle, "No, Mother." Between them and home lay thousands of troops; until they departed silence signified nothing.

All the morning the clouds thickened and the air grew heavier. At noon horsemen, riding toward the west, appeared on the main road. At the first crossroad they turned toward the south. They rode slowly, with bent heads on tired horses. Presently wagons followed. Then to the ears of the little family on the hillside there rose from that unending line of rough ambulances a strange sound. The women and children could not understand it, but their cheeks grew still whiter and tears gathered in their eyes.

"What is it?" they cried. "What can it be?"

"The wounded are being taken away," explained Grandfather Willing solemnly. "Hark, how the drivers hurry the horses! They are afraid! They are retreating! Thank God! Thank God!"

The storm drove the Willings indoors, but the sound followed them. Through the long afternoon, through the long night, the Willings heard those wailing cries and those anguished commands to hasten.

When Sunday morning dawned, those cries were startling other farmhouses and villages miles away. They never faded entirely from the recollection of those who heard them.

Soon the boy from the next farmhouse crossed the fields again. The battle was over, the Northern arms were victorious, Gettysburg was safe.

"Now," said Grandmother Willing, "I want to go home."

Grandfather Willing pondered. He had been studying a route that he thought they could safely follow. He knew all the byroads and all the farmers' lanes across the fields.

"You stay here, Mother. I wish you would stay here."

Grandmother Willing gave her husband one look, and then lifted her cat, Tiger, into his basket.

In the mysterious dusky light of the Willing farmhouse, Emmeline and her brother Henry had stood for a long moment in each other's arms. They dared not accept with too much enthusiasm this sudden joy. The rain was beating on the roof and the windows. The delirious mutterings of the other inhabitants of the house had died away.

"Oh, Emmeline!" said Henry again. "Little Emmeline, is it you?"

"Yes," said Emmeline, with a long sigh, "it is."

"How are they at home?"

"Mother is well, but Sister Bertha is sick."

"When did you come out here?"

"On Tuesday."

"Where"—Henry looked about, startled—"where are Grandfather and Grandmother?"

"I imagine they went to Aunt Sally's."

"And you have been here *alone!*"

"No." Emmeline laughed feebly. "No, not alone."

Henry started again. Over his sister's shoulder he saw a man lying on the floor in the parlor.

"There are wounded men in this house!"

"Oh, yes!" said Emmeline.

"You have been taking care of these men!"

"I gave them water and biscuit, and I talked to them."

Henry went a step nearer the parlor door.

"That man is—is dead, Emmeline! And you've been here alone!"

"I wasn't alone," protested Emmeline. Between her and yesterday, even between her and this morning, there was falling a haze, gray and concealing as the low-lying clouds outside. She began to weep. "There was someone here to take care of me. I have been safe all the time. And he is gone away forever!"

Henry looked into the parlor and the sitting room, and then went upstairs. Emmeline heard him exclaim. When he came down again, he went to the kitchen door and looked out. The trampled fields were already sodden. At the foot of the garden was a trench, begun for a well and abandoned. It was not deep, but it was deep enough. There, shrouded in Grandmother Willing's comforters, were laid those who, in this house, had given their lives for their convictions. One of the Watson boys, coming to see how his neighbors had fared, saved Emmeline a share in the last sad ceremony of battle.

Presently night fell upon the little farmhouse. Henry and Emmeline slept side by side on Grandmother Willing's kitchen floor. Often Henry rose and went about the house to minister to the wounded in Grandmother Willing's beds. When he returned, he laid a protecting arm across his little sister and so fell asleep once more. The mystery of his release was now clear to him. The humanity of the act, the helplessness of his enemy, combined to create in his heart a bitter hatred of war, a hatred felt by all who had anything to do with that sad battlefield.

The broadening light of Sunday morning wakened brother and sister. Across the wide valley between the two battle lines, great wagons were traveling swiftly. For friend and foe alike, doctors and nurses of the victorious army had begun their work of mercy. To the door of the Willing farmhouse came at noon an ambulance. Some houses the attendants had found deserted except for their suffering guests. In others were women who had performed incredible and uncounted deeds of mercy. Each house had its epic of heroism and danger and sorrow. A charm seemed to have been laid upon these heroic ministers; it was as if an angel standing before them had protected them in their ways. Of them all, only one had perished.

In the Willing house there was little for doctors or nurses to do. The house was orderly once more; the surviving soldiers asked feebly about the result of the battle, and when they heard, turned their faces away even from Emmeline.

The homeward journey of Grandmother and Grandfather Willing ended in the middle of Sunday afternoon. It had been much more roundabout than Grandfather Willing had planned, more awful than he had dreamed. As they drew near the scene of battle and beheld on every side its sad destruction, their hearts failed them utterly. Where was Mary? How was poor Bertha? Where was Emmeline, Emmeline who was forever getting into mischief of some kind? Above all, where was Henry?

Grandmother Willing was thinking of him as they drew near the farmhouse. Then looking up, she saw him standing on the porch, and behind him, in the doorway, Emmeline. Grandmother Willing made no motion to alight from the wagon. She sat still with Tiger on her lap.

"How did *you* get here?" she asked in a trembling voice.

"We have been here all the time," said Emmeline. There came into the eyes of Emmeline a sudden sparkle. What a tale she had to tell Eliza Batterson!

Grandmother Willing allowed herself to be helped out of the carriage. She came rapidly through the gate and across the dooryard, which was now trampled into a muddy slough. From the doorway she could see into her parlor with its stained carpet. She looked from it to the stains of the same color on her granddaughter's dress. In spite of all that Grandmother Willing had seen, she did not yet realize the full meaning of a battle.

"Has blood been shed here?" she asked in an awed tone.

With an arm round her, Henry said, "Yes, Grandmother."

Grandmother Willing's gaze still rested upon Emmeline.

"Did you see this?" she demanded, as if Emmeline were to blame for having got herself once more into mischief. "Were you in the battle, Emmeline?"

"Yes."

"Did you have wounded rebels here?"

"Yes. There are some upstairs now!" cried Emmeline.

"In my house!" exclaimed Grandmother Willing. "In my beds!" Grandmother Willing's youthfulness was apparent in the speed with which she started up the stairs. "I'll 'rebel' them!"

Those below waited. They could trust her to do nothing violent.

"Oh, you poor, poor souls!" cried Grandmother Willing abovestairs.

An ambulance driver who was making a journey to Gettysburg now offered to take Henry and Emmeline home. Henry must join his company as soon as possible, and the best way to find them was to go to Gettysburg, where he could doubtless get information about their position. He was heavily oppressed by anxiety and alarm, and could hardly wait until the driver received his orders to start.

Along the wooded ridge the ambulance traveled; Henry sat in the seat with the driver, Emmeline in the body of the wagon. There was no road; they made their way round shattered cannon, wrecked caissons, and far sadder remnants of the great battle. They passed close by the seminary building, where the Union soldiers had first camped. It was five o'clock on Sunday afternoon, the most peaceful hour of the week; but Gettysburg's streets were thronged with soldiers, mounted and on foot. Citizens were on their doorsteps. This Sunday was a day not of rest, but of rejoicing.

Suddenly Emmeline saw twinkling in the breeze before her a bit of color, and her pale cheeks flushed. From windows and doorposts floated once more Gettysburg's flag—the stars of white on a field of blue, the stripes of red and white.

Unobserved, Henry and Emmeline passed down the street. In the back of the wagon, Emmeline could not be seen, and as for Henry —no one looked twice at a Union soldier with a bandaged head. No one noticed them, in fact, until Mr. Bannon, who was sitting on his porch with his pipe, saw them; he lifted his arms with a shout and hurried forward in his lame way to greet them. He shouted some wild sentence at them, but they could not wait to be greeted by lame Mr. Bannon. Hand in hand they went along the house and to the kitchen porch. There, at the open door, they paused.

"Well, Mother," said Henry.

Mrs. Willing did not move. She was sitting by the opposite window shelling peas that had been planted, it seemed to her, a generation ago. She sat with a half-opened pod between her fingers and looked at her children. Mrs. Schmidt's brother, driving into town an hour ago from his farm beyond the battlefield, had reported the safety of his sister and her brood, but had brought no news of Emmeline. Mrs. Willing could not at first quite believe that here, in flesh and blood, were the two children who lay so heavily upon her heart.

"Is Bertha safe, Mother?" asked Henry. Still Henry and Emmeline did not move, and Mrs. Willing did not rise to meet them.

"Yes," answered Mrs. Willing. "Bertha is asleep upstairs."

"Is—" began Henry, and then he repeated that single meaningless word. "Is—"

Now Emmeline had begun to move. She pursued, however, a strange course. She took a step toward her mother, then a step toward the corner of the room, then a step toward her mother, then another away from her mother. Mrs. Willing rose; the peas and their pods rolled in all directions.

"Mother!" cried Emmeline. "Mother! Mother!"

The first exclamation shocked Mrs. Willing. It was hoarse, and in its sharp tones was all the misery through which Emmeline had lived. The second "Mother!" expressed pure astonishment and nothing else. But in the third was all Emmeline's youth restored.

Henry had seen the object toward which his sister's erratic steps were turned and had finished his sentence, "Is it mine, Mother?" He now took his mother into his arms and put his head on her shoulder as if he himself were not a very long way from the cradle in which his son reposed.

But for Emmeline, tears were past. She knelt upon the floor, enchanted, enslaved, a happy servitor of the sister who, sleeping in her quiet bed, knew nothing of the new joy that awaited her.

"Oh, Mother!" cried Emmeline. "It *is* a baby!"

ABE LINCOLN'S BOOKS

By CARL SANDBURG
Illustration by James Daugherty

THE farm boys in their evenings at Jones's store in Gentryville talked about how Abe Lincoln was always reading, digging into books, stretching out flat on his stomach in front of the fireplace, studying till midnight and past midnight, picking a piece of charcoal to write on the fire shovel, shaving off what he wrote, and then writing more—till midnight and past midnight. The next thing Abe would be reading books between the plow handles, it seemed to them. And once trying to speak a last word, Dennis Hanks said, "There's suthin' peculiarsome about Abe."

He wanted to learn, to know, to live, to reach out; he wanted to satisfy hungers and thirsts he couldn't tell about, this big boy of the backwoods. And some of what he wanted so much, so deep down, seemed to be in the books. Maybe in books he would find the answers to dark questions pushing around in the pools of his thoughts and the drifts of his mind. He told Dennis and other people, "The things I want to know are in books; my best friend is the man who'll git me a book I ain't read." And sometimes friends answered, "Well, books ain't as plenty as wildcats in these parts o' Indianny."

This was one thing meant by Dennis when he said there was "suthin' peculiarsome" about Abe. It seemed that Abe made the books tell him more than they told other people. All the other farm boys had gone to school and read "The Kentucky Preceptor," but Abe picked out questions from it, such as, "Who has the most right to complain, the Indian or the negro?" and Abe would talk about it, up one way and down the other, while they were in the cornfield putting up fodder for the winter. When Abe got hold of a storybook and read about a boat that came near a magnetic rock, and how the magnets in the rock pulled all the nails out of the boat so it went to pieces and the people in the boat found themselves floundering in water, Abe thought it was funny and told it to other people. After Abe read poetry, especially Bobby Burns's poems, Abe began writing rhymes himself. When Abe sat with a girl, with their bare feet in the creek water, and she spoke of the moon rising, he explained to her it was the earth moving and not the moon—the moon only seemed to rise.

John Hanks, who worked in the fields barefooted with Abe, grubbing stumps, plowing, mowing, said: "When Abe and I came back to the house from work, he used to go to the cupboard, snatch a piece of cornbread, sit down, take a book, cock his legs up high as his head, and read. Whenever Abe had a chance in the field while at work, or at the house, he would stop and read." He liked to explain to other people what he was getting from books; explaining an idea to someone else made it clearer to him. The habit was growing on him of reading out loud; words came more real if picked from the silent page of the book and pronounced on the tongue; new balances and values of words stood out as if spoken aloud. When writing letters for his father or the neighbors, he read the words out loud as they got written. Before writing a letter he asked questions such as: "What do you want to say in the letter? How do you want to say it? Are you sure that's the best way to say it? Or do you think we can fix up a better way to say it?"

As he studied his books his lower lip stuck out; Josiah Crawford noticed it was a habit and joked Abe about the "stuck-out lip." This habit too stayed with him.

He wrote in his Sum Book, or arithmetic, that Compound Division was "When several numbers of Divers Denominations are given to be divided by 1 common divisor," and worked on the exercise in multiplication; "If 1 foot contains 12 inches I demand how many there are in 126 feet." Thus the schoolboy.

What he got in the schools didn't satisfy him. He went to three different schools in Indiana, besides two in Kentucky—altogether about four months of school. He learned his A B C, how to spell, read, write. And he had been with the other barefoot boys in butternut jeans learning "manners" under the school teacher, Andrew Crawford, who had them open a door, walk in, and say, "Howdy do?" Yet what he tasted of books in school was only a beginning, only made him hungry and thirsty, shook him with a wanting of more and more of what was hidden between the covers of books.

He kept on saying, "The things I want to know are in books; my best friend is the man who'll git me a book I ain't read." He said that to Pitcher, the lawyer over at Rockport, nearly twenty miles away, one fall afternoon, when he walked from Pigeon Creek to Rockport and borrowed a book from Pitcher. Then when fodder-pulling time came a few days later, he shucked corn from early daylight till sundown along with his father and Dennis Hanks and John Hanks, but after supper he read the book till midnight, and at noon he hardly knew the taste of his corn bread because he had the book in front of him. It was a hundred little things like these which made Dennis Hanks say there was "suthin' peculiarsome" about Abe.

Besides reading the family Bible and figuring his way all through the old arithmetic they had at home, he got hold of "Æsop's Fables," "Pilgrim's Progress," "Robinson Crusoe," and Weems's "The Life of Francis Marion." The book of fables, written or collected thousands of years ago by the Greek slave known as Æsop, sank deep in his mind. As he read through the book a second and third time, he had a feeling there were fables all around him, that everything he touched and handled, everything he saw and learned had a fable wrapped in it somewhere. One fable was about a bundle of sticks and a farmer whose sons were quarreling and fighting.

There was a fable in two sentences which read, "A coachman, hearing one of the wheels of his coach make a great noise, and perceiving that it was the worst one of the four, asked how it came to take such a liberty. The wheel answered that from the beginning of time, creaking had always been the privilege of the weak." And there were shrewd, brief incidents of foolery such as this: "A waggish, idle fellow in a country town, being desirous of playing a trick on the simplicity of his neighbors and at the same time putting a little money in his pocket at their cost, advertised that he would on a certain day show a wheel carriage that should be so contrived as to go without horses. By silly curiosity the rustics were taken in, and each succeeding group who came out from the show were ashamed

to confess to their neighbors that they had seen nothing but a wheelbarrow."

The style of the Bible, of Æsop's fables, the hearts and minds back of those books, were much in his thoughts. His favorite pages in them he read over and over. Behind such proverbs as, "Muzzle not the ox that treadeth out the corn," and "He that ruleth his own spirit is greater than he that taketh a city," there was a music of simple wisdom and a mystery of common everyday life that touched deep spots in him, while out of the fables of the ancient Greek slave he came to see that cats, rats, dogs, horses, plows, hammers, fingers, toes, people all had fables connected with their lives, characters, places. There was, perhaps, an outside for each thing as it stood alone, while inside of it was its fable.

One book came, titled, "The Life of George Washington, with Curious Anecdotes, Equally Honorable to Himself and Exemplary to His Young Countrymen. Embellished with Six Steel Engravings, by M. L. Weems, formerly Rector of Mt. Vernon Parish." It pictured men of passion and proud ignorance in the government of England driving their country into war on the American colonies. It quoted the far-visioned warning of Chatham to the British parliament, "For God's sake, then, my lords, let the way be instantly opened for reconciliation. I say instantly; or it will be too late forever."

The book told of war, as at Saratoga. "Hoarse as a mastiff of true British breed, Lord Balcarras was heard from rank to rank, loud-animating his troops; while on the other hand, fierce as a hungry Bengal tiger, the impetuous Arnold precipitated heroes on the stubborn foe. Shrill and terrible, from rank to rank, resounds the clash of bayonets—frequent and sad the groans of the dying. Pairs on pairs, Britons and Americans, with each his bayonet at his brother's breast, fall forward together faint-shrieking in death, and mingle their smoking blood." Washington, the man, stood out, as when he wrote, "These things so harassed my heart with grief, that I solemnly declared to God, if I know myself, I would gladly offer myself a sacrifice to the butchering enemy, if I could thereby insure the safety of these my poor distressed countrymen."

The Weems book reached some deep spots in the boy. He asked

himself what it meant that men should march, fight, bleed, go cold and hungry for the sake of what they called "freedom."

"Few great men are great in everything," said the book. And there was a cool sap in the passage: "His delight was in that of the manliest sort, which, by stringing the limbs and swelling the muscles, promotes the kindliest flow of blood and spirits. At jumping with a long pole, or heaving heavy weights, for his years he hardly had an equal."

Such book talk was a comfort against the same thing over again, day after day; so many mornings the same kind of water from the same spring, the same fried pork and corn meal to eat, the same drizzles of rain, spring plowing, summer weeds, fall fodder-pulling, each coming every year, with the same tired feeling at the end of the day, so many days alone in the woods or the fields or else the same people to talk with, people from whom he had learned all they could teach him. Yet there ran through his head the stories and sayings of other people, the stories and sayings of books, the learning his eyes had caught from books; they were a comfort; they were good to have because they were good by themselves; and they were still better to have because they broke the chill of the lonesome feeling.

He was thankful to the writer of Æsop's fables because that writer stood by him and walked with him, an invisible companion, when he pulled fodder or chopped wood. Books lighted lamps in the dark rooms of his gloomy hours ... Well—he would live on; maybe the time would come when he would be free from work for a few weeks, or a few months, with books, and then he would read. . . . God, then he would read. . . . Then he would go and get at the proud secrets of his books.

His father—would he be like his father when he grew up? He hoped not. Why should his father knock him off a fence rail when he was asking a neighbor, passing by, a question? Even if it was a smart question, too pert and too quick, it was no way to handle a boy in front of a neighbor. No, he was going to be a man different from his father. The books—his father hated the books. His father talked about "too much eddication"; after readin', writin', 'rithmetic, that was enough, his father said. He, Abe Lincoln, the boy, wanted to know more than the father, Tom Lincoln, wanted to know. Already Abe knew more than his father; he was writing letters for the

Illustration by James Daugherty.

neighbors; they hunted out the Lincoln farm to get young Abe to find his bottle of ink with blackberry brier root and copperas in it, and his pen made from a turkey buzzard feather, and write letters. Abe had a suspicion sometimes his father was a little proud to have a boy that could write letters, and tell about things in books, and outrun and outwrestle and rough-and-tumble any boy or man in

Spencer County. Yes, he would be different from his father; he was already so; it couldn't be helped.

In growing up from boyhood to young manhood he had survived against lonesome, gnawing monotony and against floods, forest and prairie fires, snake bites, horse kicks, ague, chills, fever, malaria, "milk-sick."

A comic outline against the sky he was, hiking along the roads of Spencer and other counties in southern Indiana in those years when he read all the books within a fifty-mile circuit of his home. Stretching up on the long legs that ran from his moccasins to the body frame with its long, gangling arms, covered with linsey-woolsey then the lean neck that carried the head with its surmounting coonskin cap or straw hat—it was, again, a comic outline—yet with a portent in its shadow. His laughing "Howdy," his yarns and drollery, opened the doors of men's hearts.

Starting along in his eleventh year came spells of abstraction. When he was spoken to, no answer came from him. "He might be a thousand miles away." The roaming, fathoming, searching, questioning operations of the minds and hearts of poets, inventors, beginners who take facts stark, these were at work in him. This was one sort of abstraction he knew; there was another: the blues took him; coils of multiplied melancholies wrapped their blue frustrations inside him, all that Hamlet, Koheleth, Schopenhauer have uttered, in a mesh of foiled hopes. "There was absolutely nothing to excite ambition for education," he wrote later of that Indiana region. Against these "blues," he found the best warfare was to find people and trade with them his yarns and drolleries. John Baldwin, the blacksmith, with many stories and odd talk and eyeslants, was a help and a light.

Days came when he sank deep in the stream of human life and felt himself kin of all that swam in it, whether the waters were crystal or mud.

He learned how suddenly life can spring a surprise. One day in the woods, as he was sharpening a wedge on a log, the ax glanced, nearly took his thumb off, and left a white scar after healing.

"You never cuss a good ax," was a saying in those timbers.

LOUISA ALCOTT, WAR NURSE

By CORNELIA MEIGS

Illustration by Warren Chappell

THE city of Washington lay silent in the raw cold of a cloudy December day, silent and listening. It was almost as if the people walking to and fro in the broad streets were afraid to speak aloud; it was as though they were all straining their ears for a sound just too far off to be actually heard. A great battle was going forward. That was official news, brought to the tall, gaunt man in the White House, who was even now walking up and down the long office room, waiting and listening just as was everyone else. Rumors were flocking in—General Burnside, the Union commander, was splendidly victorious—General Burnside was in utter rout with all his forces. Rumors of a battle always contradict one another for a little while, until finally the truth comes drifting in. The truth came at last. It was news of a signal defeat of the Union troops at Fredericksburg. Close behind it came the rumble of heavy wheels, as the ambulances brought the thousands of wounded to the hospitals of Washington.

Louisa Alcott's new life as a nurse had just begun. She had not learned very much about her duties as yet, only which ward was to be hers, how the meals of fat pork and dishwater coffee were served, how many different people must be applied to before an order for bandages and medicine could be filled. The hospital to which she had been sent was in Georgetown, on high ground just outside Washington. The building had once been a large hotel, wherein slatternly housekeeping with lazy, casual servants had held sway for years. Upon the accumulation of dirt and dilapidation, there had been poured the hastily gathered equipment of a hospital—flimsy iron cots, dingy mattresses, hard pillows, bedding and crockery and surgeons' supplies in all the necessarily enormous quantities.

It had looked, nevertheless, like an imposing place to Louisa as she drove up in the dark, saw the rows of lighted windows and the guards at the door. The recollection of her travels was still like a great adventure upon her, so unused was she to even so modestly brief a journey as this. May and Julian to see her off in Concord, the night spent in Boston with Cousin Lizzie Wells, a few last pangs of wonder and foreboding, then Anna and John Pratt saying good-bye before the puffing train bore her southward! To go from Boston to Washington was an elaborate process in 1862; one journeyed by train to New London, by boat to New York, took another inexpressably early train from Jersey City and reached Washington long after dark. She had studied her traveling companions with edification; she had chuckled delightedly over the tribulations of hoop-skirted ladies trying to go to bed in the narrow cabin berths of the steamer.

As Philadelphia went past the car windows she pressed her nose to the pane and wished that she could stop a little to see more of her "native city." When she came at last to her journey's end, was carried in a bumping cab over the long drive to Georgetown, when she finally dismounted, stiff with lengthy, uncomfortable traveling, the first sensation which came over her was a wave of terrific shyness. All these strange people, a crowd of men about the doors—how was she to face them; what was she supposed to do first? She walked forward boldly, was admitted, welcomed and taken to her room.

A tiny apartment it was, for which the words bare and dreary would give too rich a description. Two inhospitable iron beds told her that she was to share it with another nurse. Half the window panes were broken, and, opposite the curtainless opening, the innumerable windows of a great hospital in a church across the way, stared in upon her. It was inadequately warmed by a narrow fireplace, in which a pair of bricks supported one end of a log, which, too big for the aperture, extended out into the room and had to be pushed into the fireplace by degrees as the wood burned away. The closet was tiny, full of cockroaches and loud with the scampering of rats. She was warned at once to leave nothing of value lying about, as both the colored and the white hospital attendants were rapacious thieves.

When she was introduced to her duties in the ward, she looked about in dismay at the rows of sagging beds, the dirty floors, the unwashed windows, and the long corridors haunted with evil smells. The comfortable, plain neatness of the house in Concord seemed a thing of which she had dreamed, so remote it appeared to be from this vast dismal place. But she had come to work and, no matter what the circumstances were, work she would do. There was no lack of it. A nurse had just given out, ill, and her place was thrust upon Louisa, so that, with no training and with insufficient knowledge, she found herself immediately superintendent of a ward containing forty beds. Those who occupied them were suffering variously from measles, diphtheria and typhoid.

The hospital nevertheless was not crowded just then; most of the patients were recovering to a certain degree, so that the pressure for the first three days was not unendurable. She began to get acquainted with her fellow workers, with the faces on the pillows, faces which very soon learned to brighten as she came near. Even without surgical skill or proper knowledge, Louisa was a rare nurse. She might be shy, weary or sick at heart, but even here she always remained good company.

Like the others, she had waited through the long dark day for news from Fredericksburg and had gone to bed, worn out with apprehension. At three o'clock in the morning she was awakened by the general summons—

"The wounded are coming."

They came streaming in, filling every vacant bed and cot, waiting in the halls, laid on pallets on the floor. Those who could walk stood in dismal groups about the stoves, cold, wet and dirty. They had been fighting in the rain and mud for three days, and, when they were hurt, were bundled into the ambulances with only the briefest of emergency treatment. Louisa, who thought that she was used to sickness and nursing, had no experience of anything like this.

"What do I do first?" she asked desperately of a superior, hurrying past.

"Wash them," was the brief reply.

So, armed with a tin basin, a towel so rough that it might be made of sandpaper, and a cake of brown soap which, at home, she would have used only for scrubbing the floor, she advanced upon

her task. She began with the man in the bed nearest her, a person
so covered with dirt that his own family might not have known him.
She commenced to draw off his ragged uniform, working easily and
gently as she knew how to do, holding her breath for fear a groan
of pain would reproach her efforts.

"May your bed above be aisy, darlin', for the day's work you
are doin'," said a rich, cheerful voice. Louisa, hearing it, laughed
aloud with relief. Faces on the long row of pillows turned and
smiled and the Irish soldier laughed with her. It was a good beginning.

During the days and nights which followed she was nothing
but a bundle of tired aches, driven somehow by a determined will
and a cool head. How much there was to do and what aimless confusion and lack of management there were to hinder the doing of it!
There were calls for her in every direction and need for help even
amongst those who had no strength to call. At first all those gray,
worn faces looked alike to her; but little by little she began to know
her horde of new patients, the cheery Irishman, the querulous, com-
plaining man with a little wound, the big, patient Virginia blacksmith with a mortal one. It was on her first turn of night duty that
she became acquainted with the little drummer boy and his friend
Kit.

As she walked between the beds through the great candlelit cave
which had once been the hotel ballroom, she caught the noise of a
stifled crying, a strange sound in that heroic company where even
groans were comparatively rare. In the last bed was the smallest
patient in the hospital, Billy, the drummer boy, aged only twelve.
As Louisa bent over him, he broke into open, little-boy weeping.

"I dreamed that Kit was here and when I waked up he wasn't."
He shook with sobs, as well as with the terrific chill which had
waked him.

She quieted him as only Louisa really could have known how to
do, and presently got his story from him, spoken softly lest the rest
of the ward be disturbed. The yellow candle shone down upon his
white, drawn, pitifully small face as he looked up at her and told her
everything that had happened. Men were so badly needed in the

army that the Government was obliged to accept boys to beat the rolling drums and blow the bugles. Billy had been the object of envy of all his young friends when he marched away with the regiment, thumping gloriously as they went down the road. He had drummed for long, weary marches, in the hot sun, in the rain and the snow; he had never lagged, though his legs were short and his strength only half that of a real soldier's. He fell ill with fever during the Fredericksburg campaign and was burning and shivering in his tent when the command came to go into battle.

He lay under the wavering canvas, hearkening to the boom of the guns, hearing the cheer of his comrades as they went into action. He could not move, he could only wait and wonder. He thought of each one whom he knew, the one who liked to tease him, the one who gave him good advice and Kit, splendid Kit, who was his chief friend and the object of his adoration. Would the battle bring harm to Kit? That was his chief thought, as he lay there and watched the tent canvas shiver and tremble in the cold wind.

What was this he heard now, the sound of feet, thousands of feet going by the tent, not with the measured tread of marching, but with haste, with running panic?

"Was this a retreat? Could it possibly be that Kit—that General Burnside's army, had been forced back by the Johnny Rebs?"

There was a voice at the tent door. Some one was standing against the light. It was Kit with the kindly face and the strong arms who gathered him up from his bed of blankets on the ground. Too weak to ask questions, Billy lay against his friend's shoulder and was carried away in that vast, dreary river of defeat which flowed down all the roads that led from Fredericksburg.

More than one voice said near them, "You're hurt yourself, Kit; let me take him."

But his comrade would not give him up. The endless shuffle of weary feet changed finally to the rumble of ambulance wheels, but still the two traveled on, still Kit's arm was around him. Billy fell into a long sleep of complete exhaustion and wakened only at the hospital door. He was being lifted, but by whose hands? Where was Kit? A battered soldier near him told him as gently as he could that

Kit had—had gone. Billy would have cried out in anguish, but soldiers did not do that. He was one of the regiment; he must take this blow without whimpering. He did.

In the hospital he lay, silent and wide-eyed, facing his grief with unwavering spirit. It was the dream which betrayed him. He dreamed that Kit was with him again, that they were sitting together by the bivouac fire, laughing and joking as they had so often done Kit's warm hand was on his shoulder, his strong voice was speaking just beside him—and suddenly he awoke to the shadowy ward, to the flickering lights from the candles and the glowing stove, to the rows of silent beds. Grief took him unawares and he wept, stifling the great sobs in the pillow as best he could. It was so that Louisa found him. It was into her ear that he poured out the whole story. For a whole hour she listened and comforted. At last he was cheered and quieted; at last he was dropping to sleep.

Louisa leaned back in her chair, to rest a minute and draw her breath; for it had taken all her strength and spirit to help the desolate little boy. How tired she was and how long the night! But she could be still for a little now, she thought, and gather courage again.

A step behind her made her start and turn about. A long rifleman from Pennsylvania had risen from his bed and was tramping down the ward, walking in the sleep of pain-ridden fever. She rushed to him and seized him by the arm, protesting and commanding. It was dangerous for him to be walking about with a serious wound; he must get back to bed at once.

"I'm going home," he announced, and tramped on. He would neither wake nor listen. Tall Louisa hanging on his arm was as nothing to his gigantic strength as he strode onward, repeating steadily, "I'm going home."

A huge fellow at the end of the ward, less seriously hurt than some of the others, rose from his blankets and came to her rescue. His powerful arms accomplished what her remonstrances could not; so that finally he led the wanderer back to his own place. Quiet settled down again; Billy was asleep, the lank Pennsylvanian was drifting into more peaceful dreams, muttering still, now and then, that he was going home.

That was what they all dreamed about in that crowded, ill-smelling place—home. Louisa knew it, for her own thoughts, at the back of her mind, were always on the clean perfume of pine-covered hills, on the glint of the river between green meadows, on the lighted windows in the friendly houses all along the road.

In the brief free hour between the night watch and the day, she wrote letters to her family of whom she thought so incessantly. The place that she was in was squalid and dreary; there was no romance in the sights she was seeing now, so she thought. But she was bound that they at home should see it all, just as she was always seeing them in the inner vision of her mind. As the days went by, she wrote and wrote, whenever she could snatch a minute, so that they too would become acquainted with the blacksmith John Sulie and jolly little Sergeant Bain, with Billy and Kit. She herself had learned to know Kit as well as though he were actually there, even though the knowledge came entirely through the chatter of Billy, who had taken her for his confidante. She was often so tired that the writing wavered in the page; but the picture that she drew in words was always clear.

She did not feel as strong and undaunted as she had intended to be. Although she did not know it, she was actually perishing for want of the fresh, bracing air which she had always breathed, of the spare, wholesome food which she was used to eating. She could have courage to steel her heart against the onslaughts of homesickness and the sight of suffering all about; but she could not steel her body against the poisons of that unhealthy place. She grew daily more thin and pale, but everyone around her was far too busy to notice such a thing.

In spite of all she felt, Louisa could be nothing other than herself. The ward which she had in charge resounded with laughter, just as the old house in Concord had done. Here was suffering everywhere; but there were jokes everywhere also, since there is no place where something comic cannot be discovered. Some people thought the mirth unseemly; but the men laughed and loved her. The windows were nailed down; but she wrenched them loose and threw them open for a time every day, quite deaf to the dire prophesies of what the consequences might be. She made beds, carried trays, and dressed wounds, and left her patients chuckling whenever she turned away to a new task. How she managed it she could not have told anyone. She did it by being Louisa.

While she was on night duty, she slept half the day and spent the other half going about Washington. She knew that she must have some fresh air and, in spite of weariness, always managed to find enough enterprise for roaming abroad. She had seen so little of the world that she felt she must make the most of this chance. Washington in war time was a strange, crowded, thrilling place. The endless lines of army wagons crawled through the streets, each drawn by its team of six mules. Louisa loved animals and found mules fascinating, they were so unfamiliar and so extraordinarily clever. She would see an astute old beast, tired of pulling, deliberately lie down in the street, as though to die, straightway bringing about a traffic jam of profane and enraged proportions. A crowd would gather; remedies would be applied, strong remedies such as mule drivers know. The big, black animal would lie inert, evidently come to the last of his pulling. Every one would offer advice; the other mules would stand patiently waiting, watching their fallen comrade with expressions of mild reproach and surprise. At last, after blocking the activities of the United States Government for half an hour, the recumbent mule would change his mind, arise with awkward scramblings, and go cheerfully on his way, as though no small unpleasantness of any kind had occurred.

The streets were filled with strolling soldiers, garbed in the bright parti-colored uniforms which have no place in war of the present day, white breeches, red fezzes, gold-embroidered coats, little blue jackets which swung over the shoulders. Different regiments had different costumes, each vying with the other for brilliant effect. There would be columns of marching troops in blue-gray, caped overcoats, rifles on shoulders, faces set and grim with the memory of what the men had so recently seen. If she did not see him herself, she heard people talking everywhere of the President, who used to go about Washington on horseback amidst all this hurry and bustle, incongruously dressed in his long black coat, black, ill-fitting trousers

and tall hat, a queer, ungainly figure against the background of all
this pomp and circumstance of war. The guard which he was forced
to have and to which he was so indifferent would come clattering
behind, very magnificent, to make up for the shabbiness of that
tall man with the dark, lined, deeply absorbed face who rode
ahead.

She visited the Capitol, finding it of special interest for a fantastic
reason. She had seen a picture of it when she was small and had
always, in her mind's eye, taken it for the model of a fairy palace.
Cinderella, so she imagined, went to housekeeping with the Prince,
after the glass slipper episode, in just such a mansion. She climbed
the broad stairs and went in—to be greatly disillusioned. It was big
and impressive; but to her eyes there was no romance here. Congress
was not sitting nor the Senate, so that the place was given over to
colored janitors who stood about and gossiped and idly plied, here
and there, an intermittent broom. There was an unexpected smell
of fresh bread through the whole building, from the huge bakery in
the cellar where loaves were baked for the troops stationed about
Washington. The crowded streets were more interesting, where
through the mud or the dust or the snow and amid the casual
groups of strolling pigs, there toiled ever forward the long, picturesque, relentless procession of the war.

She was changed finally to day duty, where the routine went on
always in set order and always with infinite variations. Breakfast
came first, with its innumerable trays and teapots, then bed-making,
then the dressing of wounds. There would be no bandages; she
would rush all over the building to get an order signed for more.
Adhesive tape would be lacking; the orderly who had charge of the
supplies would have to be found, would be discovered after long
search, drunk in the lower regions, and would have to be told, in no
uncertain terms, to return to his duty. Stout-hearted Louisa could
perform this part of her office rather well and the man would go
shambling back to his place with promises of no further backsliding.
Some patients would get better, would begin to be spoiled and demand incessant attention; some would be worse and have to be
watched over constantly. One woman came every day to see her hus-

band, who, as everyone knew but herself, had not long to live. He
passed in the night, so suddenly that no one had time to send warning to her, and she came in to see him, just as usual, in the morning.

"Why, where's Emanuel?" she cried out in terror, as she saw the
empty cot. Men turned their heads, nurses stood still; who was to
tell her? The limping Irish orderly came up and took her gently by
the arm.

"Sure, they've moved him to a better bed. Come with me, dear,
while I show you." And he led her away.

There were a few others who were regular visitors and one woman
who insisted, against all the rules, on staying to care for her sick son.
She was a thorn in the flesh of the hospital staff; for her sharp, scold-
ing voice could be heard all day, finding fault of every kind with
institution and nurses, food and management, since nothing afforded
proper service for George. In spite of her small-spirited complain-
ing, however, she showed courage and indefatigable devotion. There
was no bed for her, so she slept upon the floor beside her boy's cot
and rose up in the morning, more acid and irritable than before.
The men made all manner of game of her, some of it of no delicate
nature, but she paid no attention and continued with her ministra-
tions. She did some good, for she was a constant joke in the ward;
she was an example, though rather an odd one, of persevering
loyalty. It was with mixed feelings that they all saw her gather up
the convalescent George, finally, and take him elsewhere. The ward
was more peaceful after she was gone; but there was something missing which had been of use, at least, to break the monotony.

A languishing lady came to volunteer her services for taking care
of the dear boys and was put through a severe catechism within
Louisa's hearing. Could she work hard? No, she was always greatly
fatigued after an hour or two of effort. Did she find it easy to keep
awake at night? Oh, dear, she could not do night duty, she was
afraid to watch alone and was all in a tremble at the very thought of
a delirious patient. Could she help dress wounds and bathe feverish
patients? No, she was very much afraid of infection. She also
dropped the fact that she fainted at the sight of blood. There could
be little hope that she could eat the food, the salt beef, the bread

which seemed to be made of straw and sawdust, the sloppy coffee. Her services were not accepted.

There was one man of whom the others talked much even before he arrived. It was John Sulie, the giant blacksmith from Virginia. His comrades on the battlefield all told of how John had insisted that others be picked up and cared for before himself, and so did not come with the first consignment of wounded. They wondered and worried lest he should not be brought to the same place. Louisa went in to look at him, asleep, the evening after he finally arrived, a man so tall that his bed had to be lengthened to hold him. His face was splendid and serene, "like a great statesman's," she said afterwards. She came to know him well; for her presence seemed to help him bear the pain of having his wounds dressed. He was tremendously strong, with a body which had been magnificent before the shells of war had torn it almost to pieces. The surgeon in charge took Louisa aside and laid a duty upon her. It was she who, when the time came, must tell this man that he was to die.

She did. A nurse must do as she is told. She sat beside him, wrote his last letters to that family which he had been supporting before the conviction came upon him that he must go to the war. A mother, a younger brother and sisters—he was taking care of them all. The young brother would have to do it now. He dictated the messages and as she wrote them down, said only to her, "I hope the answer will come in time for me to see it."

They called her in the night to tell her that he was going and that he wanted her. She stood by while his dearest comrade of march and battle and camp fire said good-bye to him. War makes some terrible things and some beautiful ones; the most beautiful is the regard of one hard, scarred soldier for another. She felt that she, also, had lost a beloved friend when suffering at last relaxed its hold and let him go.

She made other friends; she could not fail to make many in this strangely assorted company. One was little Sergeant Bain who was apt to get into mischief in the ward, like an idle small boy. His right arm was disabled, but he insisted on writing certain letters himself, with his left hand, blushing all the while and beginning them, as she could not help seeing, "My dearest Jane." She heard all about Jane finally, and nursed that young lady's adorer back to sufficient health for him to go home to lay his heart before her. She used to tell him stories out of Dickens when the pain was unendurable, and he could always laugh. There was a big German of elaborate manners and enormous heart, who was a great help to her in the ward, who comforted Billy when he was longing for Kit. Billy got well, the German got well, many got well and went away. All of them bade her the most grateful of good-byes. Some of them kissed her.

In spite of all the good that she was doing, things were not going well with Louisa. That feeble lady who admitted to fainting at the sight of blood was right in one thing, impotent and silly as she was. She did well to be afraid of infection. It was everywhere in that crowded, unclean place. The vile smells proclaimed it, the close air, the dirt-sodden floors and the dingy walls. With no respect for persons, it attacked the sick and the wounded, the nurses and the doctors alike. On the first day that she came, Louisa had cared for measles, diphtheria, typhoid and pneumonia, all in the same room. She was put in charge of her first ward because another nurse "had been taken ill." Louisa presently developed such a cold that it seemed as though she were to have pneumonia. That, however, was merely by the way. What she did have was typhoid.

The illness came on slowly. Her feet became heavier and heavier; she coughed so that she had to stop and hold to things until the paroxysm was over. She took a walk one day up to the Georgetown Heights above the hospital, where there were woods and paths and a far view over the Potomac. She stood beside a clear, bright-running brook and could hardly believe that this peace and beauty were so near to all that was crowded with pain and terror. It was the last time that she walked abroad. The next day was cold and stormy and her own strength was at an end. The doctors at last took notice of her state and ordered her to keep her room.

Even now she was not willing to give in. She sat at the window, sewing and writing her letters home. She still wanted those at home to know of the further fortunes of John and the Sergeant and Billy. Most of all she seemed to want them to understand about Kit, whom she had never seen. He had died at the hospital door, but he seemed, none the less, to be the real hero of all that heroic company. She did not speak of how ill she was.

Although the weeks had seemed so full and so long, she had only been at the hospital a little more than a month. The first of January passed and with it a tremendous event. Back in September, Abraham Lincoln, amid much criticism and a storm of protest, had issued his preliminary Emancipation Proclamation, declaring that when the New Year began, all slaves in the United States should be "forever free." Louisa saw that "forever" begin. With the stroke of midnight, freedom descended upon those thousands who had never dreamed of anything but toiling servitude. Bells rang, jubilant Negroes marched through the streets, shouting, weeping, singing "Glory Hallelujah." Louisa flung up her window and leaned out to cheer with the rest. The face of that fugitive, of whom she had thought ever since her childhood, was a ghost in her memory which could now be laid—forever.

She became more and more ill and finally could not rise from her bed. Her room was cold and raw, with the chill and fog coming in through the broken windows. She could hear the rats scurrying in the wall, while all the evil smells of the vast, unsanitary place came pouring in upon her. She lay there thinking about the work which she could do no more, about the hospital days, about the barren Sundays. Occasionally, a dull, uninterested chaplain preached a hurried sermon to men, every one of them in need of religion, some of them on the edge of eternity, all of them with hearts opened by pain and the ghastly memories of battle. What would it be, she wondered, if Theodore Parker should suddenly be there; how would his strong voice sound ringing through the crowded, pain-filled room; what if his great knowledge of God could minister to these groping ones? Theodore Parker had been dead nearly three years; but she knew, still, every word he had ever said to help her in her own need. He had given her courage to face some hard things; she could face this.

One night she woke suddenly, coughing and cold to the very bones. If the fire had gone completely out, she was helpless to rekindle it. The chilliness meant much misery; perhaps it might even mean death. She sat up in bed and saw a figure kneeling before the fireplace. It was the surgeon, busy and hard-worked all day, but come now to see that she was safe. He had brought an armload of kindling, which he had split himself downstairs, and was whittling shavings for fuel to start the dead fire. He looked about and saw her sitting up against the thin pillow with the inadequate blankets wrapped about her. "You will have to go home," he asserted peremptorily.

She shook her head. She had enlisted for three months; she could not give up after only one. She hardly remembered, now, how she had nursed as her first cases men with typhoid in that stifling and dirty place. The matron of the hospital was ill with typhoid also, was thought to be at the point of death, although Louisa did not know it. The Mays were an obstinate race. Louisa would not go. But home—beautiful and delicious word. She lay down and went to sleep thinking of it.

A week later she heard that word spoken again. The world around her was a dizzy blur now, through which figures came and went, tending her, bringing her food which she could not eat and water which she could drink unendingly. The matron had issued from her bed the peremptory order that Miss Alcott must be taken where she could have better care. Suddenly, to Louisa's bewildered surprise, a face leaned over her, a thin, fine-cut countenance which even now had not lost its look of peaceful and serene dignity. How could her father possibly be there? But it surely was he; this was his own voice saying: "I have come to take you home."

Even now she still refused to go, held by the unreasonable obstinacy of illness. For five days Bronson stayed and nursed her. He was a good nurse, with an inexhaustible fund of gentleness and untroubled patience. It did not seem wise to take Louisa away against her will.

She tossed and fretted and worried over the work which she had come to do, which now must go on without her. The men would miss her, she lamented. Just when she had come to know how best to take care of them, she had surrendered to weakness. Another matter troubled her. There was a rule of the hospital that the rough work of the wards was done by such men as were enough recovered to be up and about. With the lack of system and of any wise management, these convalescents were often ordered to do totally improper tasks. The nurses who had labored to get the wounded really set upon the road to recovery could not endure seeing their good work undone by some blundering order which laid upon a half-well man labor far too hard for him. One soldier, with such a bad heart that he should never have been taken into the army at all, was given heavy trays to carry, made to lift ponderous, helpless men until the work brought him suddenly into far worse illness than that with which he had first come. Another young boy, with a badly injured back, was put to the duty of scrubbing floors, in spite of the visible agony which it cost him. When this injustice was practised in her ward, Louisa had a simple remedy. She herself lifted and carried, and got down on her knees to scrub the floor, often after twelve hours of intensive, all-night duty. As she lay helpless, however, she worried continually over these unfortunates and feared no one would care for them. The days passed; the matron of the hospital, ill with the same malady, died. At last Louisa was too weak to resist longer; they prepared to take her away.

Everyone came out to see her go, her fellow nurses with comforts, the "boys" with small presents, a head nurse with a shawl, a Bible and a final list of sharp, imperious admonitions such as had been, for Louisa, a source of mirth and despair ever since she came. All of what was going on about her was nothing to Louisa now, as she was taken down to the waiting carriage, was accompanied to the station by a crowd of friends and was got, somehow, upon the train. It is probable that Bronson remembered that journey, every hour of it, as long as he lived, but upon Louisa it made no impression. Occasionally she would rouse herself to see faces staring at her, curious, or shocked, or horrified countenances, taking in her disheveled hair, her flushed cheeks, and her rumpled clothes. There was a pause and some uncomfortable changing about; that was Boston. Another effort followed, a sight of an agonized, terrified face which looked like her mother's, then a bed, a comfortable bed with cool sheets and a white soft pillow, upon which she could at last lay down her aching head. That was home.

In her room looking out above the Lexington and Concord high-way, Louisa lay for weeks, wrapped in the cloud of delirium, hearing

Warren Chappell.

The Alcott Home.

vaguely the sounds which came up from without, as the long battle went on within. She heard sleigh bells at first, then crows cawing, then robins singing. The fields were all white with deep drifts the day that she was brought into the house; the Mayflowers were in bloom on the hillside the morning when she came weakly to the door again and looked abroad upon the world. Thin, shaky, and with shorn hair, she was scarcely recognizable, even to herself when she looked into the glass. The days between her home-coming and that staggering walk to the door were like a bad dream; but they were over. She need never think of them again.

THE DEVIL AND DANIEL WEBSTER

By STEPHEN VINCENT BENET

Illustration by Tom Hall

I

ITS a story they tell in the border country, where Massachusetts joins Vermont and New Hampshire.

Yes, Dan'l Webster's dead—or, at least, they buried him. But everytime there's a thunderstorm around Marshfield, they say you can hear his rolling voice in the hollows of the sky. And they say that if you go to his grave and speak loud and clear, "Dan'l Webster—Dan'l Webster!" the ground'll begin to shiver and the trees begin to shake. And after a while you'll hear a deep voice saying, "Neighbor, how stands the Union?" Then you better answer the Union stands as she stood, rock-bottomed and copper-sheathed, one and indivisible, or he's liable to rear right out of the ground. At least, that's what I was told when I was a youngster.

You see, for a while, he was the biggest man in the country. He never got to be President, but he was the biggest man. There were thousands who trusted in him right next to God Almighty, and they told stories about him and all the things that belonged to him that were like the stories of patriarchs and such. They said, when he stood up to speak, stars and stripes came right out in the sky, and once he spoke against a river and made it sink into the ground. They said, when he walked the woods with his fishing rod, Killall, the trout would jump out of the stream right into his pockets, for they knew it was no use putting up a fight against him; and when he argued a case, he could turn on the harps of the blessed and the shaking of the earth underground. That was the kind of man he was, and his big farm up at Marshfield was suitable to him. The chickens he raised were all white meat down through the drumsticks, the cows were tended like children, and the big ram he called

Goliath had horns with a curl like a morning-glory vine and could butt through an iron door. But Dan'l wasn't one of your gentlemen farmers; he knew all the ways of the land, and he'd be up by candlelight to see that the chores got done. A man with a mouth like a mastiff, a brow like a mountain and eyes like burning anthracite—that was Dan'l Webster in his prime. And the biggest case he argued never got written down in the books, for he argued it against the devil, nip and tuck and no holds barred. And this is the way I used to hear it told.

There was a man named Jabez Stone, lived at Cross Corners, New Hampshire. He wasn't a bad man to start with, but he was an unlucky man. If he planted corn, he got borers; if he planted potatoes, he got blight. He had good-enough land, but it didn't prosper him; he had a decent wife and children, but the more children he had, the less there was to feed them. If stones cropped up in his neighbor's fields, boulders boiled up in his; if he had a horse with the spavins, he'd trade it for one with the staggers and give something extra. There's some folks bound to be like that, apparently. But one day Jabez Stone got sick of the whole business.

He'd been plowing that morning and he'd just broke the plowshare on a rock that he could have sworn hadn't been there yesterday. And, as he stood looking at the plowshare, the off horse began to cough—that ropy kind of cough that means sickness and horse doctors. There were two children down with measles, his wife was ailing, and he had a whitlow on his thumb. It was about the last straw for Jabez Stone. "I vow,' he said, and he looked around him kind of desperate—"I vow it's enough to make a man want to sell his soul to the devil! And I would, too, for two cents!"

Then he felt a kind of queerness come over him at having said what he'd said; though, naturally, being a New Hampshireman, he wouldn't take it back. But, all the same, when it got to be evening and, as far as he could see, no notice had been taken, he felt relieved in his mind, for he was a religious man. But notice is always taken, sooner or later, just like the Good Book says. And, sure enough, next day, about supper-time, a soft spoken, dark-dressed stranger drove up in a handsome buggy and asked for Jabez Stone.

Well, Jabez told his family it was a lawyer, come to see him about a legacy. But he knew who it was. He didn't like the looks of the stranger, nor the way he smiled with his teeth. They were white teeth, and plentiful—some say they were filed to a point, but I wouldn't vouch for that. And he didn't like it when the dog took one look at the stranger and ran howling, with his tail between his legs. But having passed his word, more or less, he stuck to it, and they went out behind the barn and made their bargain. Jabez Stone had to prick his finger to sign, and the stranger lent him a silver pin. The wound healed clean, but it left a little white scar.

II

After that, all of a sudden, things began to pick up and prosper for Jabez Stone. His cows got fat and his horses sleek, his crops were the envy of the neighborhood, and lightning might strike all over the valley, but it wouldn't strike his barn. Pretty soon, he was one of the prosperous people of the county; they asked him to stand for selectman, and he stood for it; there began to be talk of running him for state senate. All in all, you might say the Stone family was as happy and contented as cats in a dairy. And so they were, except for Jabez Stone.

He'd been contented enough, the first few years. It's a great thing when bad luck turns; it drives most other things out of your head. True, every now and then, especially in rainy weather, the little white scar on his finger would give him a twinge. And once a year, punctual as clockwork, the stranger with the handsome buggy would come driving by. But the sixth year, the stranger lighted, and, after that, his peace was over for Jabez Stone.

The stranger came up through the lower field, switching his boots with a cane—they were handsome black boots, but Jabez Stone never liked the look of them, particularly the toes. And, after he'd passed the time of day, he said, "Well, Mr. Stone, you're a hummer! It's a very pretty property you've got here, Mr. Stone."

"Well, some might favor it and others might not," said Jabez Stone, for he was a New Hampshireman.

"Oh, no need to decry your industry!" said the stranger, very easy, showing his teeth in a smile. "After all, we know what's been done, and it's been according to contract and specifications. So when—ahem—the mortgage falls due next year, you shouldn't have any regrets."

"Speaking of that mortgage, mister," said Jabez Stone, and he looked around for help to the earth and the sky. "I'm beginning to have one or two doubts about it."

"Doubts?" said the stranger, not quite so pleasantly.

"Why, yes," said Jabez Stone. "This being the U. S. A. and me always having been a religious man." He cleared his throat and got bolder. "Yes, sir," he said, "I'm beginning to have considerable doubts as to that mortgage holding in court."

"There's courts and courts," said the stranger, clicking his teeth. "Still, we might as well have a look at the original document." And he hauled out a big black pocketbook, full of papers. "Sherwin, Slater, Stevens, Stone," he muttered. "I, Jabez Stone, for a term of seven years—Oh, it's quite in order, I think."

But Jabez Stone wasn't listening, for he saw something else flutter out of the black pocketbook. It was something that looked like a moth, but it wasn't a moth. And as Jabez Stone stared at it, it seemed to speak to him in a small sort of piping voice, terrible small and thin, but terrible human.

"Neighbor Stone!" it squeaked. "Neighbor Stone! Help me! For God's sake, help me!"

But before Jabez Stone could stir hand or foot, the stranger whipped out a big bandanna handkerchief, caught the creature in it, just like a butterfly, and started tying up the ends of the bandanna.

"Sorry for the interruption," he said. "As I was saying—"

But Jabez Stone was shaking all over like a scared horse.

"That's Miser Stevens' voice!" he said, in a croak. "And you've got him in your handkerchief?"

The stranger looked a little embarrassed.

"Yes, I really should have transferred him to the collecting box," he said with a simper. "But there were some rather unusual specimens there and I didn't want them crowded. Well, well, these little contretemps will occur."

"I don't know what you mean by contertan," said Jabez Stone, "but that was Miser Stevens' voice! And he ain't dead! You can't tell me he is! He was just as spry and mean as a woodchuck, Tuesday!"

"In the midst of life—" said the stranger, kind of pious. "Listen!" Then a bell began to toll in the valley and Jabez Stone listened, with the sweat running down his face. For he knew it was tolled for Miser Stevens and that he was dead.

"These long-standing accounts," said the stranger with a sigh; "one really hates to close them. But business is business."

He still had the bandanna in his hand, and Jabez Stone felt sick as he saw the cloth struggle and flutter.

"Are they all as small as that?" he asked hoarsely.

"Small?" said the stranger. "Oh, I see what you mean. Why, they vary." He measured Jabez Stone with his eyes and his teeth showed. "Don't worry, Mr. Stone," he said. "You'll go with a very good grade. I wouldn't trust you outside the collecting box. Now, a man like Dan'l Webster, of course—well, we'd have to build a special box for him, and even at that, I imagine the wing spread would astonish you. He'd certainly be a prize. I wish we could see our way clear to him. But, in your case, as I was saying—"

"Put that handkerchief away!" said Jabez Stone, and he began to beg and to pray. But the best he could get at the end was a three years' extension, with conditions.

But till you make a bargain like that, you've got no idea of how fast four years can run. By the last months of those years, Jabez Stone's known all over the state and there's talk of running him for governor—and it's dust and ashes in his mouth. For every day, when he gets up, he thinks, "There's one more night gone," and every night when he lies down, he thinks of the black pocketbook and the soul of Miser Stevens, and it makes him sick at heart. Till, finally, he can't bear it any longer, and, in the last days of the last year, he hitches up his horse and drives off to seek Dan'l Webster. For Dan'l was born in New Hampshire, only a few miles from

Cross Corners, and it's well known that he has a particular soft spot for old neighbors.

III

It was early in the morning when he got to Marshfield, but Dan'l was up already, talking Latin to the farm hands and wrestling with the ram, Goliath, and trying out a new trotter and working up speeches to make against John C. Calhoun. But when he heard a New Hampshireman had come to see him, he dropped everything else he was doing, for that was Dan'l's way. He gave Jabez Stone a breakfast that five men couldn't eat, went into the living history of every man and woman in Cross Corners, and finally asked him how he could serve him.

Jabez Stone allowed that it was a kind of mortgage case.

"Well, I haven't pleaded a mortgage case in a long time, and I don't generally plead now, except before the Supreme Court," said Dan'l, "but if I can, I'll help you."

"Then I've got hope for the first time in ten years," said Jabez Stone, and told him the details.

Dan'l walked up and down as he listened, hands behind his back, now and then asking a question, now and then plunging his eyes at the floor, as if they'd bore through it like gimlets. When Jabez Stone had finished, Dan'l puffed out his cheeks and blew. Then he turned to Jabez Stone and a smile broke over his face like the sunrise over Monadnock.

"You've certainly given yourself the devil's own row to hoe, Neighbor Stone," he said, "but I'll take your case."

"You'll take it?" said Jabez Stone, hardly daring to believe.

"Yes," said Dan'l Webster, "I've got about seventy-five other things to do and the Missouri Compromise to straighten out, but I'll take your case. For if two New Hampshiremen aren't a match for the devil, we might as well give the country back to the Indians."

Then he shook Jabez Stone by the hand and said, "Did you come down here in a hurry?"

"Well, I admit I made time," said Jabez Stone.

"You'll go back faster," said Dan'l Webster, and he told 'em hitch up Constitution and Constellation to the carriage. They were matched grays with one white forefoot, and they stepped like greased lightning.

Well, I won't describe how excited and pleased the whole Stone family was to have the great Dan'l Webster for a guest, when they finally got there. Jabez Stone had lost his hat on the way, blown off when they overtook a wind, but he didn't take much account of that. But after supper he sent the family off to bed, for he had most particular business with Mr. Webster. Mrs. Stone wanted them to sit in the front parlor, but Dan'l Webster knew front parlors and said he preferred the kitchen. So it was there they sat, waiting for the stranger, with a jug on the table between them and a bright fire on the hearth—the stranger being scheduled to show up on the stroke of midnight, according to specification.

Well, most men wouldn't have asked for better company than Dan'l Webster and a jug. But with every tick of the clock Jabez Stone got sadder and sadder. His eyes roved around, and though he sampled the jug you could see he couldn't taste it. Finally, on the stroke of 11:30 he reached over and grabbed Dan'l Webster by the arm.

"Mr. Webster, Mr. Webster!" he said, and his voice was shaking with fear and a desperate courage. "For God's sake, Mr. Webster, harness your horses and get away from this place while you can!"

"You've brought me a long way, neighbor, to tell me you don't like my company," said Dan'l Webster, quite peaceable, pulling at the jug.

"Miserable wretch that I am!" groaned Jabez Stone. "I've brought you a devilish way, and now I see my folly. Let him take me if he wills. I don't hanker after it, I must say, but I can stand it. But you're the Union's stay and New Hampshire's pride! He mustn't get you, Mr. Webster! He mustn't get you!"

Dan'l Webster looked at the distracted man, all gray and shaking in the firelight, and laid a hand on his shoulder.

"I'm obliged to you, Neighbor Stone," he said gently. "It's kindly thought of. But there's a jug on the table and a case in hand. And I never left a jug or a case half finished in my life."

And just at that moment there was a sharp rap on the door.

"Ah," said Dan'l Webster, very coolly. "I thought your clock was a trifle slow, Neighbor Stone." He stepped to the door and opened it. "Come in!" he said.

The stranger came in—very dark and tall he looked in the firelight. He was carrying a box under his arm—a black, japanned box with little air holes in the lid. At the sight of the box, Jabez Stone gave a low cry and shrank into a corner of the room.

"Mr. Webster, I presume," said the stranger, very polite, but with his eyes glowing like a fox's deep in the woods.

"Attorney of record for Jabez Stone," said Dan'l Webster, but his eyes were glowing, too. "Might I ask your name?"

"I've gone by a good many," said the stranger carelessly. "Perhaps Scratch will do for the evening. I'm often called that in these regions."

Then he sat down at the table and poured himself a drink from the jug. The liquor was cold in the jug, but it came steaming into the glass.

"And now," said the stranger, smiling and showing his teeth. "I shall call upon you, as a law-abiding citizen, to assist me in taking possession of my property."

Well, with that the argument began—and it went on hot and heavy. At first, Jabez Stone had a flicker of hope, but when he saw Dan'l Webster being forced back at point after point, he just sat scrunched in his corner, with his eyes on that japanned box. For there wasn't any doubt as to the deed of the signature—that was the worst of it. Dan'l Webster twisted and turned and thumped his fist on the table, but he couldn't get away from that. He offered to compromise the case; the stranger wouldn't hear of it. He pointed out the property had increased in value, and state senators ought to be worth more; the stranger stuck to the letter of the law. He was a great lawyer, Dan'l Webster, but we know who's the King of Lawyers, as the Good Book tells us, and it seemed as if, for the first time, Dan'l Webster had met his match.

Finally, the stranger yawned a little. "Your spirited efforts on behalf of your client do you credit, Mr. Webster," he said, "but if you have no more arguments to adduce, I'm rather pressed for time—" and Jabez Stone shuddered.

Dan'l Webster's brow looked dark as a thundercloud. "Pressed or not, you shall not have this man!" he thundered. "Mr. Stone is an American citizen, and no American citizen may be forced into the service of a foreign prince. We fought England for that in '12 and we'll fight all hell for it again!"

"Foreign?" said the stranger. "And who calls me a foreigner?"

"Well, I never yet heard of the dev— of your claiming American citizenship," said Dan'l Webster with surprise.

"And who with better right?" said the stranger, with one of his terrible smiles. "When the first wrong was done to the first Indian, I was there. When the first slaver put out for the Congo, I stood on her deck. Am I not in your books and stories and beliefs, from the first settlements on? Am I not spoken of, still, in every church in New England? 'Tis true the North claims me for a Southerner, and the South for a Northerner, but I am neither. I am merely an honest American like yourself—of the best descent—for, to tell the truth, Mr. Webster, though I don't like to boast of it, my name is older in this country than yours."

"Aha!" said Dan'l Webster, with the veins standing out in his forehead. "Then I stand on the Constitution! I demand a trial for my client!"

"The case is hardly one for an ordinary court," said the stranger, his eyes flickering. "And, indeed, the lateness of the hour—"

"Let it be any court you choose, so it is an American judge and an American jury!" said Dan'l Webster in his pride. "Let it be the quick or the dead; I'll abide the issue!"

"You have said it," said the stranger, and pointed his finger at the door.

And with that, and all of a sudden, there was a rushing of wind outside and a noise of footsteps. They came, clear and distinct, through the night. And yet, they were not like the footsteps of living men.

"In God's name, who comes by so late?" cried Jabez Stone, in an ague of fear.

"The jury Mr. Webster demands," said the stranger, sipping at his boiling glass. "You must pardon the rough appearance of one or two; they will have come a long way."

IV

And with that the fire burned blue and the door blew open and twelve men entered, one by one.

If Jabez Stone had been sick with terror before, he was blind with terror now. For there was Walter Butler, the loyalist, who spread fire and horror through the Mohawk Valley in the time of the Revolution; and there was Simon Girty, the renegade, who saw white men burned at the stake and whooped with the Indians to see them burn. His eyes were green, like a catamount's, and the stains on his hunting shirt did not come from the blood of the deer. King Philip was there, wild and proud as he had been in life, with the great gash in his head that gave him his death wound, and cruel Governor Dale, who broke men on the wheel. There was Morton of Merry Mount, who so vexed the Plymouth Colony, with his flushed, loose, handsome face and his hate of the godly. There was Teach, the bloody pirate, with his black beard curling on his breast. The Reverend John Smeet, with his strangler's hands and his Geneva gown, walked as daintily as he had to the gallows. The red print of the rope was still around his neck, but he carried a perfumed handkerchief in one hand. One and all, they came into the room with the fires of hell still upon them, and the stranger named their names and their deeds as they came, till the tale of twelve was told. Yet the stranger had told the truth—they had all played a part in America.

"Are you satisfied with the jury, Mr. Webster?" said the stranger mockingly, when they had taken their places.

The sweat stood upon Dan'l Webster's brow, but his voice was clear.

"Quite satisfied," he said. "Though I miss General Arnold from the company."

Tom Hall

"Justice Hathorne is a jurist of experience. He presided at certain witch trials once held in Salem."

"Benedict Arnold is engaged upon other business," said the stranger, with a glower. "Ah, you asked for a justice, I believe."

He pointed his finger once more, and a tall man, soberly clad in Puritan garb, with the burning gaze of a fanatic stalked into the room and took his judge's place.

"Justice Hathorne is a jurist of experience," said the stranger. "He presided at certain witch trials once held in Salem. There were others who repented of the business later, but not he."

"Repent of such notable wonders and undertakings?" said the stern old justice. "Nay, hang them—hang them all!" And he muttered to himself in a way that struck ice into the soul of Jabez Stone.

Then the trial began, and, as you might expect, it didn't look anyways good for the defense. And Jabez Stone didn't make much of a witness in his own behalf. He took one look at Simon Girty and screeched, and they had to put him back in his corner in a kind of swoon.

It didn't halt the trial, though; the trial went on, as trials do. Dan'l Webster had faced some hard juries and hanging judges in his time, but this was the hardest he'd ever faced, and he knew it. They sat there with a kind of glitter in their eyes, and the stranger's smooth voice went on and on. Every time he'd raise an objection, it'd be "Objection sustained," but whenever Dan'l objected, it'd be "Objection denied." Well, you couldn't expect fair play from a fellow like Mr. Scratch.

It got to Dan'l Webster in the end, and he began to heat, like iron in the forge. When he got up to speak he was going to flay the stranger with every trick known to law, and the judge and jury, too. He didn't care if it was contempt of court or what would happen to him for it. He didn't care any more what happened to Jabez Stone. He just got madder and madder, thinking of what he'd say. And yet, curiously enough, the more he thought about it, the less he was able to arrange his speech in his mind.

Till, finally, it was time for him to get up on his feet, and he did so, all ready to bust out with lightnings and denunciations. But before he started he looked over the judge and jury for a moment, such being his custom. And he noticed the glitter in their eyes was twice as strong as before, and they all leaned forward. Like hounds just before they get the fox, they looked, and the blue mist of evil in the room thickened as he watched them. Then he saw what he'd been about to do, and he wiped his forehead, as a man might who'd just escaped falling into a pit in the dark.

For it was him they'd come for, not only Jabez Stone. He read it in the glitter of their eyes and in the way the stranger hid his mouth with one hand. And if he fought them with their own weapons, he'd fall into their power; he knew that, though he couldn't have told you how. It was his own anger and horror that burned in their eyes; and he'd have to wipe that out or the case was lost. He stood there for a moment, his black eyes burning like anthracite. And then he began to speak.

He started off in a low voice, though you could hear every word. They say he could call on the harps of the blessed when he chose. And this was just as simple and easy as a man could talk. But he didn't start out by condemning or reviling. He was talking about the things that make a country a country, and a man a man.

And then he began with the simple things that everybody's known and felt—the freshness of a fine morning when you're young, and the taste of food when you're hungry, and the new day that's every day when you're a child. He took them up and turned them in his hands. They were good things for any man. But without freedom, they sickened. And when he talked of those enslaved, and the sorrows of slavery, his voice got like a big bell. He talked of the early days of America and the men who had made those days. It wasn't a spread-eagle speech, but he made you see it. He admitted all the wrong that had ever been done. But he showed how, out of the wrong and the right, the suffering and the starvations, something new had come. And everybody had played a part in it, even the traitors.

Then he turned to Jabez Stone and showed him as he was—an ordinary man who'd had hard luck and wanted to change it. And, because he'd wanted to change it, now he was going to be punished

for all eternity. And yet there was good in Jabez Stone, and he
showed that good. He was hard and mean in some ways, but he was
a man. There was sadness in being a man, but it was a proud thing,
too. And he showed what the pride of it was till you couldn't help
feeling it. Yes, even in hell, if a man was a man, you'd know it.
And he wasn't pleading for any one person any more, though his
voice rang like an organ. He was telling the story and the failures
and the endless journey of mankind. They got tricked and trapped
and bamboozled, but it was a great journey. And no demon that
ever foaled could know the inwardness of it—it took a man to do
that.

V

The fire began to die on the hearth and the wind before morning
to blow. The light was getting gray in the room when Dan'l Webster finished. And his words came back at the end to New Hampshire ground, and the spot of land that each man loves and clings
to. He painted a picture of that, and to each one of that jury he
spoke of things long forgotten. For his voice could search the heart,
and that was his gift and his strength. And to one, his voice was
like the forest and its secrecy, and to another like the sea and the
storm of the sea; and one heard the cry of his lost nation in it, and
another saw a little harmless scene he hadn't remembered for years.
But each saw something. And when Dan'l Webster finished he
didn't know whether or not he'd saved Jabez Stone. But he knew
he'd done a miracle. For the glitter was gone from the eyes of judge
and jury, and, for the moment, they were men again, and knew
they were men.

"The defense rests," said Dan'l Webster, and stood there like a
mountain. His ears were still ringing with his speech, and he didn't
hear anything else till he heard Judge Hathorne say, "The jury will
retire to consider its verdict."

Walter Butler rose in his place and his face had a dark, gay pride
on it.

"The jury has considered its verdict," he said, and looked the stranger full in the eye. "We find for the defendant, Jabez Stone."

With that, the smile left the stranger's face, but Walter Butler did not flinch.

"Perhaps 'tis not strictly in accordance with the evidence," he said, "but even the damned may salute the eloquence of Mr. Webster."

With that the long crow of a rooster split the gray morning sky, and judge and jury were gone from the room like a puff of smoke and as if they had never been there. The stranger turned to Dan'l Webster, smiling wryly. "Major Butler was always a bold man," he said. "I had not thought him quite so bold. Nevertheless, my congratulations, as between two gentlemen."

"I'll have that paper first, if you please," said Dan'l Webster, and he took it and tore it into four pieces. It was queerly warm to the touch. "And now," he said, "I'll have you!" and his hand came down like a bear trap on the stranger's arm. For he knew that once you bested anybody like Mr. Scratch in fair fight, his power on you was gone. And he could see that Mr. Scratch knew it, too.

The stranger twisted and wriggled, but he couldn't get out of that grip. "Come, come, Mr. Webster," he said, smiling palely. "This sort of thing is ridic—ouch!—is ridiculous. If you're worried about the costs of the case, naturally, I'd be glad to pay—"

"And so you shall!" said Dan'l Webster, shaking him till his teeth rattled. "For you'll sit right down at that table and draw up a document, promising never to bother Jabez Stone nor his heirs or assigns nor any other New Hampshireman till doomsday! For any hades we want to raise in this state, we can raise ourselves, without assistance from strangers."

"Ouch!" said the stranger. "Ouch! Well, they never did run very big to the barrel, but—ouch!—I agree!"

So he sat down and drew up the document. But Dan'l Webster kept his hand on his coat collar all the time.

"And, now, may I go?" said the stranger, quite humble, when Dan'l'd seen the document was in proper and legal form.

"Go?" said Dan'l, giving him another shake. "I'm still trying to figure out what I'll do with you. For you've settled the costs of the case, but you haven't settled with me. I think I'll take you back to

Marshfield," he said, kind of reflective. "I've got a ram there named Goliath that can butt through an iron door. I'd kind of like to turn you loose in his field and see what he'd do."

Well, with that the stranger began to beg and to plead. And he begged and he pled so humble that finally Dan'l, who was naturally kind-hearted, agreed to let him go. The stranger seemed terrible grateful for that and said, just to show they were friends, he'd tell Dan'l's fortune before leaving. So Dan'l agreed to that, though he didn't take much stock in fortune-tellers ordinarily.

But, naturally, the stranger was a little different. Well, he pried and he peered at the lines in Dan'l's hands. And he told him one thing and another that was quite remarkable. But they were all in the past.

"Yes, all that's true, and it happened," said Dan'l Webster. "But what's to come in the future?"

The stranger grinned, kind of happily, and shook his head. "The future's not as you think it," he said. "It's dark. You have a great ambition, Mr. Webster."

"I have," said Dan'l firmly, for everybody knew he wanted to be President.

"It seems almost within your grasp," said the stranger, "but you will not attain it. Lesser men will be made President and you will be passed over."

"And, if I am, I'll still be Daniel Webster," said Dan'l. "Say on."

"You have two strong sons," said the stranger, shaking his head. "You look to found a line. But each will die in war and neither reach greatness."

"Live or die, they are still my sons," said Dan'l Webster. "Say on."

"You have made great speeches," said the stranger. "You will make more."

"Ah," said Dan'l Webster.

"But the last great speech you make will turn many of your own against you," said the stranger. "They will call you Ichabod; they will call you by other names. Even in New England some will say you have turned your coat and sold your country, and their voices will be loud against you till you die."

"So it is an honest speech, it does not matter what men say," said Dan'l Webster. Then he looked at the stranger and their glances locked.

"One question," he said. "I have fought for the Union all my life. Will I see that fight won against those who tear it apart?"

"Not while you live," said the stranger, grimly, "but it will be won. And after you are dead, there are thousands who will fight for your cause, because of words that you spoke."

"Why, then, you long-barreled, slab-sided, lantern-jawed, fortune-telling note shaver!" said Dan'l Webster, with a roar of laughter, "be off with you to your own place before I put my mark on you! For, by the thirteen original colonies, I'd go to the Pit itself to save the Union!"

And with that he drew back his foot for a kick that would have stunned a horse. It was only the tip of his shoe that caught the stranger, but he went flying out of the door with his collecting box under his arm.

"And now," said Dan'l Webster, seeing Jabez Stone beginning to rouse from his swoon, "let's see what's left in this jug, for it's dry work talking all night. I hope there's pie for breakfast, Neighbor Stone."

But they say that whenever the devil comes near Marshfield, even now, he gives it a wide berth. And he hasn't been seen in the state of New Hampshire from that day to this. I'm not talking about Massachusetts or Vermont.

THUNDERBIRD LIMPS HOME

FROM "THIS IS YOUR WAR"

By ERNIE PYLE

I T WAS late afternoon at our desert airdrome. The sun was lazy, the air was warm, and a faint haze of propeller dust hung over the field, giving it softness. It was time for the planes to start coming back from their mission, and one by one they did come—big Flying Fortresses and fiery little Lightnings. Nobody paid a great deal of attention, for this returning was a daily routine thing.

Finally they were all in—all, that is, except one. Operations reported a Fortress missing. Returning pilots said it had lagged behind and lost altitude just after leaving the target. The last report said the Fortress couldn't stay in the air more than five minutes. Hours had passed since then. So it was gone.

Ten men were in that plane. The day's accomplishments had been great, but the thought of ten lost friends cast a pall over us. We had already seen death that afternoon. One of the returning Fortresses had released a red flare over the field, and I had stood with others beneath the great plane as they handed its dead pilot, head downward, through the escape hatch onto a stretcher.

The faces of his crew were grave, and nobody talked very loud. One man clutched a leather cap with blood on it. The pilot's hands were very white. Everybody knew the pilot. He was so young, a couple of hours before. The war came inside us then, and we felt it deeply.

After the last report, half a dozen of us went to the high control tower. We went there every evening, for two things—to watch the sunset, and to get word on the progress of the German bombers that frequently came just after dusk to blast our airdrome.

The sunsets in the deserts are truly things with souls. The violence of their color is incredible. They splatter the sky and the clouds with a surging beauty. The mountains stand dark against the horizon, and palm trees silhouette themselves dramatically against the fiery west.

As we stood on the tower looking down over this scene, the day began folding itself up. Fighter planes, which had patrolled the field all day, were coming in. All the soldiers in the tent camps had finished supper. That noiseless peace that sometimes comes just before dusk hung over the airdrome. Men talked in low tones about the dead pilot and the lost Fortress. We thought we would wait a few minutes more to see if the Germans were coming over.

And then an electric thing happened. Far off in the dusk a red flare shot into the sky. It made an arc against the dark background of the mountains and fell to the earth. It couldn't be anything else. It had to be. The ten dead men were coming home!

"Where's the flare gun? Gimme a green flare!" yelled an officer.

He ran to the edge of the tower, shouted, "Look out below!" and fired a green rocket into the air. Then we saw the plane—just a tiny black speck. It seemed almost on the ground, it was so low, and in the first glance we could sense that it was barely moving, barely staying in the air. Crippled and alone, two hours behind all the rest, it was dragging itself home.

I was a layman, and no longer of the fraternity that flies, but I could feel. And at that moment I felt something close to human love for that faithful, battered machine, that far dark speck struggling toward us with such pathetic slowness.

All of us stood tense, hardly remembering anyone else was there. With all our nerves we seemed to pull the plane toward us. I suspect a photograph would have shown us leaning slightly to the left. Not one of us thought the plane would ever make the field, but on it came—so slowly that it was cruel to watch.

It reached the far end of the airdrome, still holding its pathetic altitude. It skimmed over the tops of parked planes, and kept on, actually reaching out—it seemed to us—for the runway. A few hundred yards more now. Could it? Would it? Was it truly possible?

They cleared the last plane, they were over the runway. They settled slowly. The wheels touched softly. And as the plane rolled on down the runway, the thousands of men around that vast field suddenly realized that they were weak and that they could hear their hearts pounding.

The last of the sunset died, and the sky turned into blackness, which would help the Germans if they came on schedule with their bombs. But nobody cared. Our ten dead men were miraculously back from the grave.

And what a story they had to tell! Nothing quite like it had happened before in this war.

The Tripoli airdrome, which was their target, was heavily defended, by both fighter planes and anti-aircraft guns. Flying into that hailstorm, as one pilot said, was like a mouse attacking a dozen cats.

The Thunderbird—for that was the name of their Fortress—was first hit just as it dropped its bomb load. One engine went out. Then a few minutes later the other engine on the same side went. When both engines went out on the same side it was usually fatal. And therein lay the difference of that feat from other instances of bringing damaged bombers home.

The Thunderbird was forced to drop below the other Fortresses. And the moment a Fortress dropped down or lagged behind, German fighters were on it like vultures. The boys didn't know how many Germans were in the air, but they thought there must have have been thirty.

Our Lightning fighters, escorting the Fortresses, stuck by the Thunderbird and fought as long as they could, but finally they had to leave or they wouldn't have had enough fuel to make it home.

The last fighter left the crippled Fortress about forty miles from Tripoli. Fortunately, the swarm of German fighters started home at the same time, for their gas was low, too.

The Thunderbird flew on for another twenty miles. Then a single German fighter appeared, and dived at them. Its guns did great damage to the already crippled plane, but simply couldn't knock it out of the air.

Finally the fighter ran out of ammunition, and left. Our boys were alone with their grave troubles. Two engines were gone, most of the guns were out of commission, and they were still more than four hundred miles from home. The radio was out. They were losing altitude, five hundred feet a minute—and then they were down to two thousand.

The pilot called up his crew and held a consultation. Did they want to jump? They all said they would ride the plane as long as it was in the air. He decided to keep going.

The ship was completely out of trim, cocked over at a terrible angle. But they gradually got it trimmed so that it stopped losing altitude.

By then they were down to nine hundred feet, and a solid wall of mountains ahead barred the way homeward. They flew along parallel to those mountains for a long time, but they were then miraculously gaining some altitude. Finally they got the thing to fifteen hundred feet.

The lowest pass was sixteen hundred feet, but they came across at fifteen hundred. Explain that if you can! Maybe it was as the pilot said: "We didn't come over the mountains, we came through them."

The co-pilot said, "I was blowing on the windshield trying to push her along. Once I almost wanted to reach a foot down and sort of walk us along over the pass."

And the navigator said, "If I had been on the wingtip, I could have touched the ground with my hand when we went through the pass."

The air currents were bad. One wing was cocked away down. It was hard to hold. The pilots had a terrible fear that the low wing would drop clear down and they'd roll over and go into a spin. But they didn't.

The navigator came into the cockpit, and he and the pilots navigated the plane home. Never for a second could they feel any real assurance of making it. They were practically rigid, but they talked a blue streak all the time, and cussed—as airmen do.

Everything seemed against them. The gas consumption doubled, squandering their precious supply. To top off their misery, they had a bad headwind. The gas gauge went down and down.

At last the navigator said they were only forty miles from home, but those forty miles passed as though they were driving a horse and buggy. Dusk, coming down on the sandy haze, made the vast desert an infinite thing. One oasis looked exactly like another. But they knew they were near home. Then they shot their red flare and waited for the green flare from our control tower. A minute later it came—the most beautiful sight that crew had ever seen.

When the plane touched the ground they cut the switches and let it roll. For it had no brakes. At the end of the roll the big Fortress veered off the side of the runway. It climaxed its historic homecoming by spinning madly around five times and then running backwards for fifty yards before it stopped. When they checked the gas gauges, they found one tank dry and the other down to twenty gallons.

Deep dusk enveloped the field. Five more minutes and they never would have found it. The weary, crippled Fortress had flown for the incredible time of four and one-half hours on one pair of motors. Any pilot will tell you it's impossible.

MacARTHUR SCORES AGAIN

By JOHN J. FLOHERTY

Illustration by Tom Hall

IN THE army barracks at Fort Smith, Arkansas, a son was born to a soldier. That was in 1880. Among the first sounds to enter the infant's ears were the tramp, tramp of marching men, the shrill notes of a bugle and the bark of military commands.

During the first four years of his life the child lived in a world that revolved around duty and discipline, with little to relieve the monotony of the daily routine of an army post. Shortly before his fourth birthday his father, General Arthur MacArthur, was ordered to a new and active post in New Mexico. The journey was made by army train through a territory infested by hostile Indians. It was then that Douglas MacArthur began his life of adventure.

Several times during the journey marauding redskins harassed the troops and finally launched a major attack. The noise and confusion of battle did not disturb the soldier's son. The rattle of the escorting cavalry's carbines, the twanging flutter of the Indians' arrows, the shouts of fighting men and the screams of wounded horses were accepted by him as a part of life in the army. In spite of his mother's efforts to keep him in the shelter of the army wagon in which they rode, he insisted on peeping under the tarpaulin cover to see the fun. An Indian's bullet ripped through the canvas and shattered a hickory bow a foot from the boy and his mother. When the Indians had been driven off and the boy's father rode up to the wagon to see if his little family were safe, Douglas saw in him a battle-stained hero. Then and there Destiny placed a finger on the child and branded him forever as a soldier.

As the boy grew up the example of his hero father played an important part in his future career. The elder MacArthur was given the task of quelling the Philippine uprising of 1899. A family man as well as a fighter, he took his wife and son, then in his teens, with him. So successful was he in this undertaking, he was made military governor. It was during this period that young MacArthur, now almost nineteen, developed his great love for the Islands.

The administrative and military atmosphere in which the boy lived, and his eagerness to follow in his father's footsteps made his entrance to West Point in 1899 inevitable.

He was now officially embarked on his career as a soldier. At the "Point" he soon outdistanced the other cadets. First in his class, he became first senior captain. On the athletic field sportsmanship was paramount to him. "Know how to lose as well as how to win" was one of his creeds. Years after he had been graduated, while president of the American Olympic team at Amsterdam, several questionable decisions had so discouraged the boxing team that they were seriously considering withdrawing. When the manager informed MacArthur of the possible intentions of the team, the soldier-president snapped back, "Americans don't quit!" There was no further talk of withdrawing.

MacArthur was graduated from West Point in 1903 at the head of his class and with the highest average ever attained there. Commissioned as a second lieutenant, he was assigned to duty in the Philippines, the one place in all the world he would have chosen had the choice been his. There he saw plenty of action. The insurrectos were carrying on a guerrilla warfare in the hills and in the jungles of Luzon. Although they were his enemies he admired the zest and sheer bravery with which the natives fought and often wished he could have the training of a division of such splendid fighting material.

From his first day of command he literally led his men, sharing their dangers and hardships. "Fighting" to him was no abstract word. It meant personal combat whether with fists or firearms. The old campaign hat he wore had two holes in it made by an enemy bullet. During the Russo-Japanese war he served as aide to his father, who was sent on a mission to Japan. His selection was based on his fitness for the post rather than because his name was MacArthur. Later he served as aide to the commander-in-chief, President Theodore Roosevelt.

In 1914 while he was serving with General Funston at Vera Cruz, reconnaissance by a technician skilled in the art of war was of major importance. MacArthur, disguising himself as a Mexican peon, penetrated several miles behind the enemy lines. So authentic was his make-up and superb his acting, he passed by challenging sentries without creating suspicion. He returned loaded with invaluable information but in a state of almost complete exhaustion.

When the United States entered World War I, Major MacArthur saw a chance to realize one of his most cherished dreams, the formation of a division in which every state in the union would be represented. He even had the name, "Rainbow Division," all thought out. By order of the Secretary of War this fighting division was formed with MacArthur as the chief of staff. On the battlefields of France "Mac" was known far and wide as a two-fisted fighter who went into the thick of it with his men. On two occasions he was taken protestingly to the rear after having been seriously wounded. On another occasion he was caught in a trench during a severe gas attack and suffered for years from the results of it. Machine gun nests were his pet hate. When one of them was reported in his vicinity he could not rest until he had destroyed it. For one of these raids he was awarded the Distinguished Service Cross, to which the coveted oak leaf cluster was added for good measure in recognition of his personal courage.

It was this personal disregard of danger, more perhaps than any other of his soldierly traits, that endeared him to the men of his command and set him apart from other high ranking officers as a soldiers' soldier.

On one occasion he accompanied a detachment of his men on a raid far out in No Man's Land. Although insisting that every man be equipped with gas mask and helmet, he went without them. He did not even carry a pistol. The party returned with nine prisoners, after which MacArthur went to headquarters and resumed his administrative duties.

When at the end of the war the warrior returned, he was loaded with decorations which he valued less highly than the comradeship and devotion of his men. The "war to end all wars" had been fought and won. The job for which he had prepared so diligently had been finished. The world, sick of conflict, resumed the paths of peace. The trade of the soldier was looked upon as obsolescent. With the American Expeditionary Force demobilized, and more generals than jobs, MacArthur was assigned to the post of Commandant of West Point. There, instead of condoning the decadence of the profession of arms, he set about modernizing the army. He argued in high places that the armistice was only a temporary cessation of the conflict. Someday the slaughter would break out again in catastrophic proportions. His pleadings and logic were looked upon as the ravings of a man carried away by his military zeal.

When a decade of peace had passed, MacArthur was made chief of staff and given an army of pitiful proportions to administer. Again he pleaded for the strengthening of American arms and described in detail the awfulness of the war-to-come, but those in power, few of whom knew the muzzle of a gun from the bolt, were more interested in the then current depression, and were not impressed by MacArthur's pleadings for a strong air force, an enlarged navy and a motorized army commensurate with our standing as a world power. The man who had devoted his life to the study of war and to its contributing causes was pooh-poohed.

The apathy of the politicians and the people living in a fool's paradise alarmed MacArthur. He saw the war clouds piling up in the east and warned the country of its unpreparedness for the approaching storm. The Philippines that he knew so well were the key if not the door to the Orient.

When he was approached by President Quezon in 1935 with the proposition of becoming military adviser to the Philippine Government, he accepted without delay. He knew from hard experience the fighting heart under those mahogany skins. He visualized an army of 400,000 natives, trained, equipped and armed for modern warfare, all within a decade.

From the beginning his efforts in establishing a military consciousness in the Philippines were successful. He founded a military academy at Baguio and conducted it on the same standards of proficiency he had known at West Point. With the meager funds at his

Tom Hall

Portrait of General Douglas MacArthur

disposal he secured a few planes and a small fleet of torpedo-carrying motor boats. One hundred and fifty native pilots were trained by the same methods as used at Kelly and Randolph Fields.

When the war caldron began to boil over in the Orient and the Japs invaded Thailand, the President, late in 1941, sent a hurry call to MacArthur to return to the United States Army and appointed him commanding general of our forces in the Far East.

For sixteen months previously General MacArthur had worked day and night in the almost hopeless task of making adequate preparation for the invasion that he knew might come at any moment. He knew he would be outnumbered ten to one in men and planes, but he was familiar with every foot of the ground he was to hold and he was determined to make any advance of the Japs expensive out of all proportion to whatever ground they might gain.

Then came the attack on Pearl Harbor, dissipating all his hopes for the protection he believed would come eventually.

For ninety-four terrifying days MacArthur fought fiercely and resisted brilliantly. He established a pattern of defense that claimed the admiration of the world and brought confusion to the enemy. During the attack on Manila when a part of the city was already in ruins, an officer approached MacArthur and suggested that the American flag that flew over staff headquarters might be an aid to the Jap bombers in identifying the target. The general looked up at the Stars and Stripes defiantly whipping out from the flagstaff, his face lighted by an ecstatic smile. *"Let's keep the flag flying,"* he said curtly.

One day orders came from the President of the United States, instructing MacArthur to break through the Japanese lines and proceed from Corregidor to Australia. The purpose of the order was to expedite an American offensive against Japan. This involved a longer and more hazardous journey than any ever attempted by a commanding general in the direction of a campaign. Between the point of departure and the coast of Australia lay the far flung archipelagos now dominated by the enemy and harboring their air, naval and land forces. Stark danger lay in every mile.

The general and his staff, well aware of the risks involved, spent days in discussing and preparing plans so secret that many of those actually participating in the expedition were ignorant of them. The venture was in no sense an escape; it was rather a move on a chess board larger than the United States, that would place MacArthur in a position to conduct a comprehensive campaign.

Some of the general's advisers recommended that the first leg of the journey to a distant island be made by submarine; others insisted on a destroyer or cruiser. MacArthur listened patiently but none offered the certainty of success contained in the plan he had already worked out.

Ever since his arrival in the Philippines he had pinned his faith in speedy torpedo-carrying motor boats. He saw in them many advantages not possessed by the larger types of vessels when used in the shallow water adjacent to the Islands. Half a dozen of them could deliver as many torpedoes as the largest destroyer and attack from several points simultaneously. Their high speed and hare-like maneuvering made them difficult targets and besides, a fleet of them could be built at a fraction of the cost of the larger vessels. It was on MacArthur's advice that a fleet of the speedy P. T. boats were sent to the Philippines under command of Lieutenant John D. Bulkeley, United States Navy, who made the historic dash into Subic Bay sinking a 5,000-ton Jap cargo transport vessel.

When General MacArthur announced that he had decided to use four motor torpedo boats for the hazardous trip, his advisers warned him that the attempt was too desperate; some called it a "fantastic venture." The general was not thinking of his personal safety; he was concerned with the safety of his large and invaluable staff who must accompany him. He considered it folly to risk the loss of his trained and skilled assistants through the possible sinking of a single vessel by a superior force.

A unified plan was agreed upon and secret arrangements made for transportation over the four thousand mile route by boat, plane, railroad and automobile.

The evening of March eleventh came with streams of gold and purple that soon faded into tropical night. The air vibrated with the chittering of a million insects and the swishing of palm-fronds in the cooling breeze.

In the deep shadows close to the water's edge MacArthur and a number of his staff officers stood waiting. Besides the general were his wife and four-year-old son and the boy's Chinese nurse, Ah Ju.

Before long a low rumble as of very distant thunder could be heard coming across the bay. MacArthur's quick ears were the first to catch the low-pitched sound. "The boats are coming," he said quietly, and moved toward a nearby dock. In a few minutes the low gray hulls of two P. T. boats nosed close to where the general and his party were standing. Each boat quickly and silently took on its complement of passengers and a quantity of personal luggage, files of documents, arms and ammunition. MacArthur and his family stepped aboard the leading boat and were followed by several of the staff. In command of the flotilla was Lieutenant Bulkeley. The second boat took on the remainder of the party with their baggage and other equipment.

The boats crept away into the darkness of Manila Bay and were soon stealthily moving through the mine fields across its entrance under the guns of Corregidor. Then they headed for the broad reaches of the China Sea.

At the very moment that MacArthur boarded his boat, Major General Hugh Casey of the Engineers was leading the remainder of the departing staff aboard two more P. T. boats hidden in a deep inlet on the Bataan coastline. The plan was that the four boats meet at a predetermined point before dawn and seek cover during daylight in a certain crevice on the coast that was concealed by heavy foliage.

The boats carrying Casey's party were delayed by Jap vessels and did not reach the rendezvous until noon. It was decided to push on, keeping the boats spread out over a large area. Speed was now of importance. The boats opened their throttles wide and tore the ocean in their wakes to shreds. A stiff wind came up from the southward kicking up a nasty sea. The boats smashed bodily through the mounting waves. Only the crew, by virtue of their familiarity with the wild plunging, could keep on their feet and then only by holding on grimly to the handholds. In the tiny cabins the passengers were packed like sardines and were frequently thrown in a mass from one side of the vessel to the other. At intervals as the boats dived into deep troughs the battered groups were left almost suspended in air for an instant, only to crash on the transoms or decks as the craft leaped upward on the next sea. One officer reported that each succeeding jolt almost snapped his head from his shoulders. The women and the boy were secured to the transoms and so were saved from serious injury. Practically all the passenger personnel were violently seasick; some were in a state of near-collapse.

At sundown the wind died out as quickly as it had come up and while traveling was still rough, it lost its shocking violence. Spirits rose and all were thankful for a respite. It did not last long, however. The boat on the left of the line shut off its engines. Its example was followed simultaneously by the other three. On the horizon directly ahead was the faint silhouette of a warship. The surface mist made it difficult to determine whether she was a destroyer or a small cruiser; her hull was hidden under the horizon. As long as the P. T. boats were hove to, they were safe from detection. Under way, their high clouds of spray could be seen for many miles. Unfortunately they were within an area of Jap air reconnaissance and might be spotted from the air at any moment. In case of air attack they would fight it out with the fifty-caliber guns mounted on deck. However, no plane was sighted and darkness settled on the sea.

The boats got under way again and kept together during the night. Shortly before daybreak each boat, following orders, steered a course that led it some fifteen miles away from the others and later in the morning converged toward a certain island-rendezvous. MacArthur's boat on the right of the line had a much longer course to steer than those nearer the center. When in mid-morning Lieutenant Bulkeley steered for the island he was not surprised to discover that one of the boats had already arrived. A heavy morning mist hung over the sea that made it difficult to identify a craft at any considerable distance. As the general's boat approached the island the skipper of the boat already arrived became convinced that the approaching craft was an enemy and ordered his crew to clear for action. In telling of the near-tragedy the general's spokesman said later, "Only the merest chance identified the general's boat in time to avoid opening fire."

Three of the boats arrived safely at the rendezvous; the fourth developed engine trouble. Her passengers were transferred to another boat that luckily saw her plight. The crew of the disabled craft succeeded in doing a quick repair job and rejoined the fleet later.

A submarine had met the little fleet according to plan and a conference was held on the crowded deck of the general's boat. Several of those present urged a transfer to the underwater craft but General MacArthur held out for the speed boats. He considered the possibility of sinking or capture too great to risk putting all his people on one vessel.

The boats, lightly moored, hugged the shore ready to escape should an enemy craft sight them. The submarine submerged some distance off shore and waited for nightfall.

The cloudless sky was scanned continuously for enemy aircraft. As the day dragged by slowly there was no escape from the insufferable heat. The sun beating down on the boats made the interior of the cabins unbearable while everything on deck was blistering to the touch.

Toward evening the nineteen officers were redistributed among the three sound boats while the fourth continued repairs in the hope of rejoining the fleet at the next rendezvous.

Shortly after dark two of the boats, one of which was General MacArthur's, began their night-long journey to their next stopping place. The third, bearing General Casey, did not leave until two hours later. As soon as the boats cleared the island, throttles were opened and a night of thrills began. They had been under way scarcely an hour when both boats sighted several Japanese destroyers. They altered their course so as to fall far astern of the Japs. Immediately after this maneuver the two boats separated. About midnight a strong wind sprang up, bringing with it violent rain squalls and a rough sea.

Under other circumstances the general's boat would have been at reduced speed as she was taking tons of salt water over her bow and kicking up fifty-foot clouds of spray with every sea. MacArthur, although not a sailor, remained on the bridge and took it as it came. Dressed only in water-soaked shirt and trousers he held on doggedly to a bridge handhold, taking up the shocks with bent knees after the manner of a circus rider. Occasionally he went below to where his wife and son were being violently shaken up in the complete blackness and oil-impregnated atmosphere of the little cabin. Although miserably seasick they had no word of complaint or fear. Ah Ju, believing her end had come, accepted it all with the silent stoicism of her race.

Shortly after midnight the boat lurched heavily and lay almost on her beam end. MacArthur gripped the handrail with all his strength to save himself from being flung from his feet. The sudden change in direction while at high speed caused the stern of the boat to skid in a wide arc and flatten out the sea like a hot iron on wrinkled cloth. Boat and personnel were smothered in a house-high cloud of blasted water. A trifle bewildered but calm, the general waited for an explanation of the unexpected maneuver. Lieutenant Bulkeley shouted in his ear, "Jap vessel was directly in our course."

"Good work, Lieutenant!" MacArthur replied. That is all that was said.

Heavy clouds made the darkness almost impenetrable. Every man in the deck force was on lookout. Bulkeley himself was at the wheel. Split seconds might prove too valuable to waste in giving orders to a wheelsman. They were in an area known to be infested by Japanese craft.

An hour or so before dawn the sea grew heavier and more confused. Bulkeley had to cut the throttles a few notches to prevent the boat from swamping. Even at the reduced speed she rolled and pitched as she leaped for half her length from the water and threw her racing propellers high in the air.

The general, concerned for the safety of his family, went below to reassure them. He found them uninjured, bravely enduring the discomfort with the rest.

It was with mingled feelings of satisfaction and anxiety that

MacArthur saw the first flush of dawn creep up from the rim of the sea. It meant that they were nearing the rendezvous but it also meant that the protecting shield of darkness would soon be withdrawn. Before long a blue-gray silhouette stretched along the horizon. When they got under the lee of the distant island the sea lost much of its violence. As they ran to cover Bulkeley opened the throttles, making the boat step along with every ounce of power she had in her. They were playing a gigantic game of "I Spy" in which the Jap was "It."

In spite of navigation that was mostly dead reckoning, they made an almost perfect landfall. A bay with a narrow opening lay ahead. Here they were to await the arrival of the planes that would take them on the next leg of their journey.

Soon after the arrival of the general's boat, while luggage, supplies and arms were being taken ashore, the second boat slid into the bay and came to anchor close by. After several hours had passed without a sign of the third boat carrying General Casey and his group, MacArthur became deeply concerned. A period of anxious waiting began. Once the drone of motors came from far in the distance. Hopes rose only to give way to disappointment as the low rumble was gradually swallowed in silence. It was a Jap plane on early morning reconnaissance.

At noon the missing boat came roaring into the bay and reported that they had had to take a circuitous course to avoid several enemy vessels.

So far the score was in MacArthur's favor. Three of his boats and their passengers were present and accounted for. The fourth boat, temporarily disabled, was safe from detection where it lay.

The secret spot at which they were to meet the planes lay some distance inland. Only to MacArthur and Casey was its exact location known. After a hurried lunch under cover of the thick foliage, the general, his family and staff set out for the undisclosed point of take-off, carrying with them the luggage and material they had taken along. The crews remained with the boats, standing by in case a retreat by water became necessary.

It was dusk when they arrived at the appointed spot. Before them lay a broad plateau with a covering of knee-high grass. There was not a plane in sight.

MacArthur, the realist, knew too well that, in all-out war, secrets are short-lived no matter how many precautions are taken to keep knowledge of what is going on from the enemy.

The night was spent in watchfulness. Surprise attack might occur at any moment. Guns and ammunition were kept in readiness. As befitted American soldiers, they would uphold American traditions and fight it out to a finish. The general could handle a tommy gun with the best of them.

Another dawn came, filled with anxieties. MacArthur, who had lived for several years in domestic comfort in a Manila hotel, enjoying the fruits and glamor of his well-earned rank, now found himself the prototype of his father, a frontier fighter ready to defend with his life the wife and son who were sharing the fortunes of war with him. The impeccable uniform, the breastful of decorations topped by four glittering stars that his son had known since birth, had been replaced by salt-soaked khaki without so much as a glint of gold. The dapper, and for his years, youthful officer, was now a "tough guy," unkempt and unshaven. The next day dragged slowly by with every member of the party scanning the skies for the three B-17's expected from Australia, but night came with nothing but an occasional sea bird sighted against the darkening sky. To the unbearable heat was added the torture of thirst and the torment of night raiding insects.

Three hideous nights and anxious days spent at the secret rendezvous were filled with dread that information of the desperate voyage would reach the enemy. Less than half an hour's flight away was an important Japanese air base.

On the evening of the third day just as the general and his party were reconciling themselves to another night of torture, the drumming of planes was heard in the southern sky. Whether they were friendly or enemy aircraft none could tell. To have signaled or even shown themselves might have invited machine-gun attack or worse.

Despite the great altitude at which the planes were flying, they were soon recognized as two B-17's. This was disconcerting since it had been determined that three flying fortresses would be needed to take the party and their impedimenta over the second leg of the journey.

As he watched the giant winged forts spiral down for a landing, General MacArthur was deep in thought. How to make two planes do safely the work of three was the disturbing problem.

Before the wheels of the planes touched ground he turned to his staff and said decisively, "Sorry, gentlemen! There are, as you see, only two planes where we had planned on three. That means that each of us must get rid of every unnnecessary ounce of weight. Baggage, equipment and supplies must be abandoned. We must dispense with unnecessary clothing as well as pistols, belts and binoculars or anything else that has weight." The general's wardrobe was a shirt, trousers and water-soaked shoes.

When the planes had landed, MacArthur, Casey and the two pilots conferred on the problem of distributing the weight of twenty-three people evenly in the two planes that must play the double role of transport and fighting craft.

The planes took off about midnight and began an eleven-hour flight to northern Australia. This was as perilous an undertaking as any ever attempted by a general and his staff. The heavily laden planes, it must be remembered, had just made an eleven-hour flight from Australia and without adequate maintenance service began their return journey over the islands held by the enemy.

Added to the sheer danger of the trip was the utter discomfort of it for the passengers. A plane-of-war is neither equipped nor intended for comfort or convenience. Its metal interior is as bleak as the inside of a locomotive boiler. Without sound insulation it transmits to the ears of those within it the full impact of the hurricane of noise liberated by its engines and propellers. Conversation except over the interphone system is almost impossible.

After the planes had taken off and squared away on their course, they began a steady climb to an altitude that would give them comparative safety, particularly during the hours of darkness. The islands below, giving off their heat accumulated during the day, sent up billows of turbulent air that tossed the planes as if they were on a heavy sea. Several of the passengers who had only recently recovered from seasickness, were now violently airsick.

As the planes reached a fifteen-thousand-foot altitude the temperature dropped rapidly, chilling the lightly clad passengers to the bone. Nothing could be done to relieve their suffering; they could only sit in the total blackness and wait.

The general, seated near the control room with his wife and son beside him, spoke occasionally through the interphone to the pilot and to the navigator who informed him of the progress of the journey high over the Indies. At times they were only minutes by air flight from the Jap airfields on several of the islands.

Although the planes were being pressed at better than cruising speed, less than half the journey could be made in darkness. Dawn would bring new perils. With the giant planes naked against the cloudless sky, they were fair prey for enemy aircraft.

Luck rode with MacArthur on that nerve-shattering flight. Although the planes were always within the sphere of enemy activity, they got through unobserved.

The big bombers finally landed at Darwin shortly after an air raid alarm had sounded.

MacArthur's journey was by no means ended. There still lay ahead of him a two-thousand-mile journey to Melbourne. He could have made this trip by air and in comparative comfort and safety. He chose instead to take a more difficult route for along it lay the most important military supply route in the area of which he had command.

Sending fourteen of his officers by air to Melbourne, after giving his family a full day's rest, he took his party by narrow gauge, single-track railroad southward to Berdum in the Australian desert. From there he proceeded over a five-hundred-mile military highway through one of the most desolate stretches of country in the world. At Alice Springs he and his party entrained for Melbourne. MacArthur, fighter and family man, had come through.

A SAGA OF WORLD WAR II

FROM "THE RAFT"

By ROBERT TRUMBULL

Illustration by Tom Hall

Early in 1942, three American Navy fliers, Harold Dixon, Gene Aldrich and Tony Pastula, took off on a mission from a carrier in the South Seas. They became hopelessly lost, made a forced landing in the water, and drifted, without food or instruments, for 34 days in a rubber raft 4 feet by 8 feet. This is the account of their last three days on the raft, and their final rescue, as told by Harold Dixon to Robert Trumbull.

EVENING of the thirty-second day we got a shift of wind to the north. Night fell ominously. The sky was dark and threatening; the sea turned from gray to black. As we tumbled along uneasily, our way was lit by long, jagged streaks of lightning, each flash followed by a rolling thunder clap like cannon fire. The air was heavy and stirred sluggishly in the fitful breeze. The waves lost their frenzy, but still rose high in powerful surges of slowly expanding force.

In the weird twilight, the sky was an awesome spectacle foreboding ill. I called it to the attention of the boys.

There were several layers of clouds, and each layer seemed to be traveling in a different direction. This was beyond the experience of any of us, and we could not imagine what it portended.

"Whatever it means," Tony said, speaking for us all, "it don't mean nothing good."

In my twenty-two years in the navy I had never seen a sky or sea like this, and I didn't like the look of things a bit.

"Better rest while we can," I advised the boys. "Any minute we'll have to bail."

We lay down in the bottom of the raft. The spray that broke on us was cold, and we squeezed ourselves together to keep the warmth of our bodies.

359

It rained often during the night. Each time we got up to bail and wring out our clothes again.

Tonight we talked more than usual, trying to cheer each other. We all realized, I think, that our spirits occasionally dropped near the danger point of lowness, and it became a game to see who could do the most to lift us out of our despondency. We made little jokes, forced and desperate.

We didn't mind the bailing. Our hips and shoulders were so numb and sore from lying wedged in the bottom of the raft that we actually welcomed the opportunity to get up and move our stiffened muscles. We suffered from lack of circulation. We had so little flesh that our veins were drawn across our bones. When we sat up, our blood would move, but this exposed us to the wind and spray. We chilled easily, so that after a moment we would be forced to lie down again in search of warmth.

Thus we passed the night. It seemed a long time until daylight.

With morning, we saw that the sky was almost solidly overcast. We waited in vain for the sun to come out and warm us. Everything was gray, except our yellow raft. Its giddy color on the muttering, gloomy sea accentuated its incongruity.

The wind now had shifted to the northeast again, and was driving us along at a lively clip. This was more to our desire, but we couldn't be sure where we were, and couldn't have done anything about it if we had known. The only chart we had was in my head.

About eleven o'clock in the morning we hit a shower, heavy and as cold as ice water. The raft held water over our ankles when it ended.

We had lost the last of our rags in the last tip-over, so we took off all our clothes, mopped the bottom of the boat and wrung over the side, repeating until the raft was dry.

As we finished this tiresome chore the sun appeared, for the first time that day. In our chilled condition the rays felt good.

"Let's take a sun bath before we put our clothes on," I suggested.

The boys assented readily, and we lay against the sides to rest, for we were tired as well as cold. We stretched our clothes across the thwarts to dry.

After a while Tony spoke up nervously.

"Don't you think we'd better put on our clothes?"

I wasn't looking forward to it. They were damp.

"Well, it's pretty rough, you know," Tony argued. "The boat's liable to go over on us again."

The wind had risen and the waves were coming to a boil. The raft was bobbling like an orange rind.

I hesitated for a few seconds, and was just about to agree with Tony when a big comber caught us.

We were lifted high, the raft on such a slant that we had to grab the sides and thwarts to keep from falling out. As we started to slide down the long, sheer trough of the wave, the breaking crest gave us an extra push upward on one side. The wind caught beneath the rounded air chamber. There was a wild scramble of arms and legs, mad grasping, and a confusion of shouts.

"The clothes! The clothes!" I yelled frantically as I went through the air. The scornful wind snatched the words, and a great wave engulfed me.

My head was out of the water again, and somehow my hand was on the raft. Gene, it appeared, had never let go, and was hanging on desperately. Tony had fallen almost on us. I grabbed him by an arm.

The waves were flinging us about, pulling at our legs as if with hands. The raft was upside down.

Never letting go our handholds, we grouped ourselves together and at an unspoken signal heaved the raft upward, trying to keep our grasp on the upended gunwale at the same time. A comber thundered down and almost tore it from our grip.

Quickly, before the next wave came, we pushed upward again. The light raft went over this time, and I worked my way to the opposite side to hold it down while the boys climbed in.

For a few minutes we rested, panting, each with an arm locked across a thwart in case we tipped again. The blood was pounding in my temples. I couldn't breathe without pain.

My chest and torso ached, and, as I have explained before, I was perpetually half numb from the hips down. With a supreme effort of will I raised my head and rolled my body over so that I faced upward across the raft. The boys were lying still, heads down, twisted, inert, like dead men except for their loud and broken gasps for air.

I noted automatically that our weight was not all on one side, which seemed to be our greatest peril. The raft was riding evenly; although it pitched and swerved in continual jerky motion, the bottom was holding to the water. So I sank my head upon my breast and rested.

How long we lay this way I don't remember. I know that we were not in full possession of our minds. When I myself began to think again, it frightened me to realize how easily I slipped away.

I found myself as if awakened by a noise I half remembered from a dream. The boys were sitting up, revived but not disposed to talk. I tried to straighten on my haunches, and then the situation struck me like a blow.

All our clothes were lost—every thread and stitch, except, ridiculously, a police whistle that hung by a cord around my neck.

Now on this day, our thirty-third in the raft, our position was desperate. Since we had lost even my last inadequate makeshift sea anchor, we had no means whatever of controlling our progress. From now on we would go where the wind sent us, and that might mean that we would float until the rubber boat finally rotted and burst. We had lost all our rags, so had no way of catching drinking water beyond what might lie in the bottom of the raft. We had nothing for bailing except our hands. We had one shoe-paddle* left, two wallets which had somehow become wedged in the front of the raft, and my police whistle. I did not see how we could make any use of these.

The worst blow of all was the loss of all our clothes, and the piece of fabric we had been using to shade our heads. From now on we were entirely unprotected against the equatorial sun, and it was midsummer. We knew, too well, what the sun was going to do to us.

We thought we were in the vicinity of islands, but with no charts

*Made earlier by cutting down Dixon's shoes.

and no navigation instruments we could not be positive as to our position. As far as we could be sure, we might still be a thousand miles from land. Now we would never know where we were unless we actually sighted an island.

This was the one time during the entire trip that I was truly disheartened. In fact, I was just about ready to give up. I knew that the end of our voyage was very near; we must make an island in a day or two, or die.

Sitting glumly about the boat, discouraged, the three of us considered all the possibilities.

Loss of our clothes, our only shelter, seemed like a mighty hard blow for us to take at this stage of the game, after we had worked and schemed for so long to save ourselves.

The thought of what we had already gone through—that clinched the argument. We all agreed that neither this nor any other disaster which could overtake us now was sufficient reason for giving up the fight we had been making. We shook hands all around, and vowed we'd go on.

It was another night of chilling showers. We huddled together in the bottom of the raft, and talked a great deal to keep up our spirits, pursuing any subject that came into our minds.

After every shower we scooped out most of the water with our hands, and lay down again to keep warm. It took just about all our courage to stay cheerful. We knew that the end of our voyage was coming soon, one way or the other.

We were glad to see daylight in the morning. Although we knew we were going to be badly burned when the sun came overhead, we were anxious to warm ourselves. I tried to keep from thinking about what the sun was going to do to us later in the day. I preferred to let that worry come when it must.

The sun did not emerge from behind the clouds until about 8:30 o'clock in the morning. When it did, I stretched out on the forward thwart to warm myself and rest. Tony lay in the bottom, while Aldrich sat up, watching.

By this time, I thought, the navy must have given us up for dead. I learned later that this was true. I would have preferred another end, but this morning I let the sailor's fatalism have its play. I got to thinking over my past life. I had left home at the age of seventeen, worked my way around the country for a year at various jobs, then joined the navy. My older brother had been in the navy during the First World War, as they call it now.

I envied my older brother. I had been reared in a typical midwestern farm family, and the adventure of going to far places in uniform appealed to me. I tried several times to enlist, but first I was too young, then too thin, to make the grade. As I grew I put on weight, and finally got in at nineteen. I had no idea then of making the navy my career; I just wanted to serve a "hitch" for the experience.

That was twenty-two years ago. The navy had been good to me, and I was glad to die in the service, the warsman's way, if die I must.

I scooped up a bit of the indigo sea in my palm, and drank it. Toward the end I could stand a bit of sea water; my system seemed to be in need of salt. I blamed the sun for this.

I had shed two sets of skin prior to the time we lost our clothes. I was in the process of building a new set now, and the tender underskin was still exposed. Lying there entirely unprotected, I began to smart all over my body. My loins and midriff, which had never been sunburned before in all my life, turned scarlet in a half hour. Before the day was over this part of me looked as if it had been seared with a red-hot iron. The rest of my body, which had been protected somewhat by my rotting clothes, burned almost as severely.

The boys were in the same state. The scalding torture we had felt on our faces, hands, and arms now covered our bodies, every inch. The clouds had rolled away and the sea threw back the glare, so that everywhere we turned there was solid heat. I shifted my position frequently to take all advantage I could of the shade of my own body, and to try to keep from exposing the same area too long, but this did little good. The sun hit us practically all over, all of the time. I felt as if I were on fire. My body will always bear the scars of that cooking.

The sun began to hit Tony.

He was lying in the bottom of the raft, the back of his hand lying across his eyes. Suddenly he took his hand away, and sat up, listening. He seemed to be looking far off. He smiled slightly.

"Hey, chief," he said softly. "I hear music."

Humor him, and maybe he'll snap out of it, I thought.

"What kind of music, Tony?" I asked casually.

"Beautiful—like a choir of angels!"

He slid back into the bottom of the raft and closed his eyes again, still smiling.

Although we had divided our days into two-hour watches, I was up and vigilant myself most of the time until my eyes began to fail. Now, because of that and my general physical condition, I was forced to let the man on watch take full responsibility for the boat while I conserved my dwindling energy for my own two-hour shift. Thus I lay on the forward thwart this thirty-fourth morning, turning uneasily under the sun so that my body would burn evenly and I would not suffer unnecessarily from overexposure of any one area more than another. Gene was on watch; Tony was lying in the bottom trying to shade his face—his delirium when he heard the music seemed to have passed.

It was about ten o'clock. The sky was hot and clear as a blue flame. The wind was steady, and the boat was rising and falling slowly on long, gentle swells. The sun was just now approaching the fullness of its anger.

We topped a wave, and in that brief instant while we seemed to hang suspended before the long downward slide began, Gene spoke for the first time since taking the watch.

"Chief," he said, "I see a beautiful field of corn."

I didn't even look up. I thought sadly that the boy's mind had finally gone, and I wished he had taken my advice to cover his head when we first went into the raft.

Without moving, I cast my eyes about the sea, but we were in the trough and I saw only the rumpled carpet of waves. It was possible, I said to myself, that Gene was seeing a mirage: the sun does play tricks on you sometimes. At any rate I was not surprised that

Gene was affected. There was nothing I could do for him, so I paid no more attention.

After a few minutes, when we had risen to the next crest, he spoke again insistently: "Sure enough, chief!—I see something green in the distance!"

With this statement, so rationally put in his Missouri drawl, it dawned upon me suddenly that perhaps he did see something. I looked hard, but could still see nothing in the tumbling sea. Tony was looking, too, but had not spoken. I tried to stand up, and found I couldn't balance on my cramped and crooked legs. I asked the boys to hold me upright.

We stood, the three of us, in the center of the boat, the boys each with one hand against the side and an arm around my waist, holding me erect with their shoulders while I steadied myself with arms around their necks.

We came to the summit of the next large swell. Sure enough, in the distance I could see something green. As Gene had said, it was beautiful. I instantly recognized it as an island, one of the low, verdant atolls of the far South Sea. I let out a hoarse whoop.

Tony took a deep breath, and let it go out noisily, trying to repress his joy.

"Well," he said, "thank God—and it's about time."

We were still far off. The island appeared as a low shelf of green—coconut trees, I guessed, and I was right. Chartless, we had no idea what the island was, whether it was inhabited, or whether it was in friend's or enemy's hands.

The wind had risen strongly, making long and prominent streaks on the water, which gave me an excellent gauge of the exact wind direction. I took a bearing on the island, compared it with the wind direction, and found that our course of drift was carrying us about ten degrees to the right of the island.

We realized, of course, that this was our God-given chance for refuge, so, weak as we were, we saw nothing for it but to row. I took the port side of the raft, using our one remaining shoe-paddle. Gene and Tony paddled together on the starboard, using their hands only.

We turned to with a will, rowing across the wind to make up

Tom Hall

"Sure enough, chief! — I see something green in the distance!"

for the distance by which the wind would cause us to miss the island if we simply drifted. In this manner we were able to make about one knot across the wind while we were being driven about five knots downwind.

It was fortunate indeed that we were able to see the island from such a distance. If we had been much closer when we began to row, the wind would have taken us past it because we would not have been able, by our feeble paddling, to compensate sufficiently for the drift.

We rowed all day, exactly across wind at 90 degrees to our sailing direction. I kept watching the island at intervals. We found it better to row facing the stern of the raft, pushing the water behind the boat with a forward sweep of our arms, so I had to stop rowing occasionally and turn to keep my bearing.

At first we thought there was only one island, but as we approached we saw that there were two, with a wide gap of water between. It was easy to make a choice. We took the nearer island.

By one o'clock our progress was visible. The waves were longer and crested in knifelike ridges that curled and broke in a thunder-our gush of white foam. There was danger of our tipping over any time one of these breakers got behind us, but, while they were in front, the spray blowing backward enabled me to judge the wind exactly.

As we came up on the island, I thought it couldn't possibly be anything but a desert atoll, although it was a lovely green and apparently stuck up pretty well out of the water. When we came within six or eight miles I saw what I thought was a ledge of rocks above the white beach. I figured then that it must be a volcanic island, and we might find shelter in a cavern. This would also mean that the island was marked on the map, and might be visited—by our own or friendly forces, I hoped. There was still the uncertainty that this might be in the Japanese mandate, and if that was so I could see our doom. However, as long as we were determined to get there, I preferred to think that it was uninhabited.

The closer we approached, the better the island looked to me. I could see two or three especially tall trees that towered above the others. We wondered if they might be coconut trees, but that seemed too much to hope. Until I was close enough to identify them honestly as palms, I didn't dare believe they were.

I was sure, at any rate, that there would be lots of birds on the island, which meant eggs and possibly young birds that we could capture. I thought, too, that there might be mussels, and possibly fish in abundance that we could rig spears to catch.

Aldrich's eyes were still in good condition. As we came in closer, perhaps within three miles of the curving beach, he turned and took a long look. We had seen by this time that the island was not so high as we had thought at first.

"Chief," Gene said, "those aren't rocks on the beach. They're shacks."

I looked again, and again I decided they were rocks.

"Wishful thinking, Gene," I said. "If they were shacks it would mean that the island is inhabited. They still look like rocks to me."

The waves were very high, and we could see the island only when we came to a crest; when we dipped to the valley of the waves, the island sank from sight. The buoyant raft rode the roughening sea so easily that it appeared as if the island and not we were rising and falling steeply in an even rhythm, while the raft lay perfectly still.

When we were about a mile from the island I saw from the wind streaks and blowing foam that we were directly upwind, and that the stiff breeze would land us at the center of the beach without assistance.

"Okay, boys," I said. "We can knock off the rowing."

We stopped and turned about, to watch our progress. We were completely exhausted, I know now. We had been rowing all day on will power alone, but we were so intent on reaching this island that we didn't realize our terrible weakness, and rose above it.

"Well," Gene said joyfully, "are they shacks or rocks?"

He was right. They were shacks.

From now on it was just a matter of drifting in the wind. I kept a close eye on the bearings by the wind streaks, to be sure that we hit the beach.

We became conscious of a steady, sullen thunder that seemed to grow in volume. I realized after a moment that it was surf breaking over a barrier reef, and I feared we were in for a little trouble. As we drifted closer I was able to see, and immediately gave the order to square away for a possible tip-over.

I had seen natives bring outrigger canoes over heavy surf in Hawaii, but those breakers were not nearly so murderous as these appeared. The nearer we approached the reef, the larger the breakers looked. I soon saw that our eyes were not deceiving us. These waves were building up characteristically in rows one behind the other, each coming to its turn as leader of the irresistible flow to shore.

The leading wave gained swiftly in height and speed as the wall of coral dammed the powerful tide that pushed against it, and the rushing tons of water found their only outlet upward. When the wave reached the reef it was about thirty feet high. The crest began to curl dangerously, seemed to hesitate the merest fraction of a second, then fell forward over the natural dam. There was a roar like a cannon shot as the mass of water smashed, and a great burst of foam spewed forward in a straight line of boiling white which diminished in size but held its form until it washed high on the beach, far ahead.

These rows of waves were building behind us now. Our only hope was to paddle over the reef ahead of the breaker—that is, in the interval between two waves.

We were fortunate enough to pass over the reef at the one instant when the surf was not breaking. We could have been dashed against the rocky bottom, or the ledge itself, if we had been caught in that wild churning of forces when the breaker crashed from its great height. As it was, we did not come out unscathed.

The breaker caught the raft behind. The heavy blow of the rushing foam against the stern sped us up the sloping rear of the smaller, shoreward-speeding wave ahead. Instead of sliding down its front, we shot straight out into the air.

The raft turned a complete flip-flop. When we saw it next it was speeding landward like a chip before the surf. The three of us were in the water.

I can remember spinning head over heels three or four times, and raking along the floor of the sea. Whether it was sand or rock I don't know, but afterward I discovered that a patch of skin about six inches in diameter had been scraped from the center of my back. Gene and Tony, I learned, were going through exactly the same thing. Tony said this was the first time he had ever had his eyes open underwater. "Everything was green and pretty," he said.

After a threshing by the water that left me only half conscious, I found myself sitting on the flat ledge of coral rock. The raft, I saw, was upside down again and was heading for the beach about a hundred yards away from me. Gene and I were close together, and we still had about three hundred yards to go to reach solid ground. Tony was about fifty yards behind us.

None of us was able to stand. I tried to raise myself on my feet, but couldn't get my balance. Then I found that the current was skidding me along on my bottom. Gene, even with me and to my right, also let himself drift and we kept abreast.

I heard a call for help, and looked back. It was Tony. Being unable to swim, he thought he was going to drown. When I waved and yelled, he realized he was out of danger, and thenceforth scooted along like Gene and me. I imagine things had happened so fast that when Tony got into shallow water he didn't realize it, and possibly he was hollering as a nervous reaction from the terrific beating his shrunken body had taken in the surf.

We caught the boat at the very edge of the beach, and grabbed the anchor line. Crawling on all fours, we dragged ourselves from the last persistent clutch of the sea, and somehow hauled the raft behind us.

We tried to stand upon our feet, but couldn't. We were terribly dizzy from exhaustion; the whole world seemed to be spinning around us. We lay on the beach together, faintly conscious of the broken coral that was cutting our flaming, sunburned flesh as our bodies jerked in the effort to breathe.

When I was able to look about, the sun was low.

A short distance away several rotting piles had been driven into the sand, evidently placed there by someone for tying up boats. The three of us took hold of the anchor line, dragging the raft with one hand while with the other we pulled ourselves painfully, inch by inch, over the jagged coral to the row of wooden stakes. I felt each of these ancient poles, selecting the one that was most solid. We tied the boat to that.

There were several thatched huts a few yards from where we lay.

Grasping one of the pilings with both hands, I pulled myself to my knees.

"Boys," I said, "you know there may be Japs here waiting for us."

They raised their heads and nodded.

I looked at each one closely. They were gazing steadily into my eyes. Tony gestured toward the police whistle, still on a cord about my neck.

"If we have to scatter," he suggested calmly, "two blasts on the whistle will be the signal to meet wherever you are."

It was agreed.

We were too weak to try to find food, so we decided to rest for the night in one of the shacks.

I chose three long pieces of driftwood lying about that were best suited to my purpose, and handed one to each.

"If there are Japs on this island," I said, "they'll not see an American sailor crawl. We'll stand, and march, and make them shoot us down, like men-o'-warsmen."

Using the sticks of driftwood as canes to support us, we got on our feet. Three abreast then, myself in the middle, we walked to the nearest hut and went in.

Right outside our shelter there was a dense grove of coconut trees, and Gene decided to gather some nuts. When he got outside the wind was so strong that he couldn't stand against it, even by using his stick to lean on, and the coral hurt his feet, so he had to give up and come back to the shack. It was with reluctance that we gave up the idea of food that night, but we thought the wind would die down by morning.

I spied a couple of chickens in the jungle, but of course they frightened easily, and we were in no condition to attempt chasing them down.

About a half hour later Gene saw two men approaching up the beach, perhaps three hundred yards away. He thought they saw us, but they turned and went in the other direction.

By now the rising wind was blowing gusts of rain into our shelter, so we rigged one of the coconut mats to protect us. We didn't know it at the time, but this heavy wind from offshore was to develop into a hurricane the next day.

The wind rose gradually, and it rained steadily. We spent a miserable night. The wind kept blowing the mats with which we tried to cover ourselves, and the rough, woven fiber scratched painfully against our sunburn. We were unable to sleep at all.

The next morning early, the first thing I did was to look around the shack and try to patch it where the wind, during the night, had blown off the siding. In casting about for materials for this repair, we found several fishlines in the rafters, with poles, but I refused to use them. I knew how the natives would feel about our breaking their lines, which were probably not easy to obtain in these parts. Instead, we gathered up some coconut leaves. Using the fiber from these, we patched the mat walls pretty well. The shack was well made, but seemed to be very old. It was rotting in places. I thought it must have stood there a long while. While looking about in the rafters I found a thick book in a strange language. It developed that this was a native Bible.

While we were still working on the patching job, we saw a native coming toward us from the beach. It had stopped raining. I grabbed my police whistle, which I had laid on the ground the night before, and blew a loud blast. The native stopped and looked at us, evidently aghast. It was obvious that he couldn't understand our being there.

After I blew my whistle two or three more times, he finally gathered his wits and ran up to see what was going on. We were sitting on the floor, leaning against the wall where we had been patching the mats. The native stared, fascinated. We all pointed to our mouths, trying to signify that we were hungry. He could see from our emaciated condition that we were in a bad state, so it didn't take him long to get the idea. He held up his hand reassuringly, and dashed off into the coconut jungle.

In a few minutes he was back, with several coconut kernels. I have never seen this particular cultivation of coconut anywhere but on this island. As I learned later, the baby coconut tree sprouts from a nut. When it has grown to a height of perhaps two and a half feet, the little plant is broken off. Then the natives crack open the nut, and it is filled entirely with a white, fibrous, vegetablelike substance. The coconut meat as we know it has entirely disappeared and has been replaced by this new growth, which is very easy to digest.

The native broke open the kernels and handed them to us. We snatched them and began munching immediately. I have never tasted anything more appetizing than those coconut kernels were that morning.

As we ate, the native made signs to us that he was going for help. He pointed to my police whistle, and held out his hand, smiling encouragingly. I gave him the whistle, and immediately he turned and ran off among the coconut trees, tooting the whistle vigorously. We looked at each other in great relief. At least the natives were friendly.

Our visitor was gone for perhaps a half hour. He returned with a party of several natives and a man who seemed to be the leader. This was the resident commissioner. Not knowing who we were, he had brought assistance in case we might turn out to be enemies.

The first native recognized from our eyes that we were white men; by our burned skins he could not tell whether we were white, brown, yellow, red or black. He was quite sure, however, that we were not Japanese. He told the commissioner that he thought we were New Zealanders or Australians, so of course the commissioner expected us to be from allies of his country, as of course we were. He was taking no chances, though, and brought some man power along. There are no weapons on the island except knives.

The commissioner's first question was as to our nationality. Upon learning that we were American sailors, he showed his delight immediately. He explained, then, several peculiar aspects of our experience with the shack. In the first place, we had got into the only "tabu shack" on that section of the island. The various sheds we saw were for the storing of copra—in fact, there were about four tons of copra in the shacks at this time—but the one we had staggered into was the only shack that had a tabu: it was reserved for the higher ranking men of the island people. The natives were not only afraid to enter, they hesitated even to come near. The two natives of the night before, who Gene thought had seen us, did see us indeed, but they were afraid to say so for fear they would incur the wrath of their chief for venturing so near the forbidden.

The commissioner was curious as to how we had reached this particular part of the island. Had we walked there? We merely turned and pointed seaward. He was astounded. That, he said, was impossible! He could not believe we had come upon this beach from the sea. No one had ever come over that reef and lived to tell the tale!

It was our turn to be astonished. But after a surprised glance at each other, we pointed to our little raft, tied to the piling near the shack.

The commissioner walked out excitedly and took a look at the raft. He examined it carefully, feeling it all over with his hands, the natives chattering among themselves and looking back at us wonderingly. Then he came slowly back into the shack, put his hands on his hips and grinned down at us—he just grinned, speechless, shaking his head from side to side. We were now beginning to feel like curiosities for fair.

The commissioner explained that it was considered impossible for any man to come over that reef. There was a lookout tower on this beach, he said, and it was constantly manned by sharp-eyed natives on the watch for enemy craft, but as a rule they didn't consider it necessary to pay any attention to the impassable reef. For this reason, and also, perhaps, because our boat was so small, our fight against the waves and our last faltering march across the beach had gone unnoticed by the practiced watchers only a few yards off.

Our dialogue meant nothing to the natives, who spoke no English, but they knew that something unusual was afoot. When the commissioner explained to them who we were and what we had done, when they were told that we had actually come in over this reef in such a craft, they just stood around with their mouths open, staring at us as if we were supermen, or gods.

I was becoming a little embarrassed by their awe-stricken regard, so I tried to explain to the commissioner that our flat-bottomed, air-borne raft drew no water, and thus enabled us to cross the giant breakers where the heavy, native-built canoes might fail. The commissioner just shook his head again, his admiring grin spreading until I thought it would cut his face in two. The natives were still staring at us, saying nothing but "Oh" and "Ah."

At length the commissioner gave an order in the island language, and the husky, handsome brown natives gathered us into their arms like babies and set off with us at a swift pace.

We went toward the leeward side of the island, passing through beautiful groves of coconut trees and other tropical growth. I still was able to take some interest in what I saw as we went along, and I noted numerous taro beds.

The natives carried us a mile or more until we arrived at the commissioner's residence on the leeward side. The house stood on the highest point on the island, about forty feet above sea level. I learned that we were on one of the tiny atolls that dot the South Seas. The particular group to which this one belonged is one of the most isolated in all the South Pacific. There is more than one island in the group, but the others are deserted, and are visited only for the gathering of coconuts for the copra trade. Yesterday, in choosing one of the two visible islands as our objective, we had the fortune to pick the only inhabited one within many hundreds of miles.

We learned, when we were able to check our reckonings later, that we had completely circled the entire small group of islets before sighting our first land on the thirty-fourth day. In all, we covered approximately one thousand miles in the raft, but actually, from the point at which we landed our plane to this island the distance was about 750 miles.

We received a warm welcome from the commissioner's wife. She put us to bed at once in a large room at one end of the beautiful wide tropical-style building, and set about preparing us our first real meal since we left the ship.

There were lots of mosquitoes, of course, but over our three beds there was a huge net that kept out the buzzing pests. Each evening servants would come in and lower the nets for us, then with fanlike brushes would drive out all the mosquitoes that had collected in the room.

The meals were prepared in two huts in the yard, one for cooking and the other for baking. Our gracious hostess had her kitchens going like beehives a few minutes after our arrival.

The commissioner's wife had just enough coffee left in her supply to make us one pot, which she gave us immediately. When I tasted my first sip of coffee I was able to believe, at last, that it was all true and not one of those nightmares I used to have when I dozed in the raft. We were really safe—it seemed impossible to believe, but that welcome cup of coffee was the convincer.

Lying there in civilized beds, we realized for the first time what an ordeal we had come through, as evidenced by the physical conditions and reactions which now pressed themselves upon our consciousness. Our skinned backs and cooked hips kept us in constant torment for many days, and we found ourselves still unable to sleep at first.

Our legs had been so long doubled up in the raft, with little room to stand and none to walk, that as we abandoned our tired bodies to complete relaxation now they froze into the sitting position. We were able to straighten them after a week, but until then I lay most of the time on my back with my knees in the air.

The commissioner was gone a great deal that day. We soon learned that he was very much concerned over the fact that the barometer was dropping rapidly while the wind seemed to be increasing. The tall, slim palms were threshing back and forth like whips. The roar almost drowned the excited voices of the natives, who were running about securing their possessions, for it was plain that this was to be a disastrous storm.

By evening the gale had built to a hurricane. The surf was crashing like a series of small tidal waves against the tiny coral island.

The thunderous boom of the sea, and the wind howling through thousands of palm trees, combined in an overpowering din that dominated all else and seemed to make the whole island shake. Then the rain was hurled against our house like tremendous buckets of marbles.

The commissioner's house was substantial and stood the ruthless beating without injury, but the natives' little homes were lifted from the ground and tumbled about like toys. Many of them ended as mere heaps of sticks and straw tangled among hundreds of fallen coconut palms.

The trees fell like jackstraws. Many of those that did not blow over were stripped of their fronds, leaving them grotesquely high waving stumps. All the nuts that were on the trees dropped, of course, whether they were ripe or not.

The hurricane lasted three days, and the damage that it did in that time was enormous. On the fourth morning, when the tumult of wind and rain had left the battered and bedraggled little island behind, the commissioner made a tour of inspection and came back with a grave face.

He estimated that a third of the coconut trees on the island had been blown down. Those left standing were so badly punished that it would be two years, he estimated, before they would be in condition to bear again. All the island's taro was killed except his own home garden, and all the banana trees were destroyed beyond repair. The commissioner explained, very worried, that the island was low on provisions of all sorts, because there had not been a supply ship along in some time, owing to the war.

Under the kind and skillful care of the commissioner's wife we recuperated amazingly. Strength began to flow back into our muscles, and in a few days we were able to straighten our legs, then to walk with only a barely perceptible unsteadiness. We were still weak, of course, and were to remain so for some time, but mentally we seemed quite normal, all of us, and that relieved a worry I had had.

When it no longer tired me too much to talk, I had long conversations with the commissioner about the island, and the serious food shortage he and his people faced because of the hurricane. With war conditions as they were in the Southwest Pacific, he didn't know when he could expect relief. I was becoming a bit anxious, too, about getting back home to the Pacific Fleet where I belonged. The commissioner then said that he had radioed an urgent plea for help, but had no answering word that he could take as assurance of immediate help.

Radioed? What! I had been almost a week on the island and didn't know there was a radio!

I went into action without delay. It seemed that the government had installed a small radio transmitter on the island, and had sent a trained native of one of the larger islands in that area to man it for the duration of the war.

Straightway I met this operator. He had some real cigarette tobacco and we discussed matters over my first honest-to-goodness civilized smoke. The languid South Sea air got a message to carry in a hurry. I made my report to my commanding officer, and went back to rest and recuperate, confident that we'd get some action now. We did.

Seven days from the date of our arrival on the island, there was an American warship offshore, and pretty soon we were shaking hands with the commander.

The ship that rescued us also saved the island. The vessel left a badly needed supply of food, and the natives' troubles were over. The commissioner's gratitude was unbounded. We were warm friends by now. When we shook hands and said good-by, I resolved that someday I would go back to that lovely, generous place, and if God is willing I will.

SOURCES OF STORIES IN VOLUME VIII

Leonidas, from Men of Old Greece, by Jennie Hall. Little, Brown & Company.

The Greek Slave and the Little Roman Boy, from Buried Cities, by Jennie Hall. The Macmillan Company.

The Lance of Kanana, by Harry W. French. Lothrop, Lee & Shepard Company.

The Boy Viking, Olaf II of Norway, from Historic Boys, by Elbridge S. Brooks. G. P. Putnam's Sons.

Knighted by King Henry IV, from Men of Iron, by Howard Pyle. Harper & Brothers.

Joan the Maid, from The Red True Story Book. Longmans, Green & Company.

The Great Discoveries, from The Story of Mankind, by Hendrik Willem Van Loon. Horace Liveright, Inc.

Christmas with Queen Bess, from Master Skylark, by John Bennett. The Century Company.

The Mountain Man, from Silent Scot, by Constance Lindsay Skinner. The Macmillan Company.

Salt-Water Tea, from Johnny Tremain, by Esther Forbes. Houghton Mifflin Company.

The Story of Molly Pitcher, by Agnes Repplier, from The Red True Story Book. Longmans, Green & Company.

Daniel Boone's Rifle, from The Long Rifle, by Stewart Edward White. Doubleday, Doran & Company, Inc.

Davy Crockett Legends, from Davy Crockett, by Constance Rourke. Harcourt, Brace & Company, Inc.

Napoleon, from The Story of Mankind, by Hendrik Willem Van Loon. Liveright Publishing Corporation.

The Tree of Jade, from The Pool of Stars, by Cornelia Meigs. The Macmillan Company.

Emmeline, by Elsie Singmaster. Houghton Mifflin Company.

Abe Lincoln's Books, from Abe Lincoln Grows Up, by Carl Sandburg. Harcourt, Brace & Company, Inc.

Louisa Alcott, War Nurse, from Invincible Louisa, by Cornelia Meigs. Little, Brown & Company.

The Devil and Daniel Webster, by Stephen Vincent Benét. Farrar & Rinehart, Inc.

Thunderbird Limps Home, from Here Is Your War, by Ernie Pyle. Henry Holt and Company, Inc.

MacArthur Scores Again, from The Courage and the Glory, by John J. Floherty. J. B. Lippincott Company.

A Saga of World War II, chapters from The Raft, by Robert Trumbull. Henry Holt and Company, Inc.